Grade 2

Complete Canadian Math

- Addition
- Subtraction
- Multiplication
- Measurement
- Graphing
- Fractions
- Time and Money
- Geometry
- Answer Key

Follows curriculum taught in Canadian schools 

A Note to Parents:

Your child will enjoy these colourful learning activities designed to reinforce the curriculum taught in Canadian schools. You can help your child make the most of each learning session by:

- Reading the directions aloud and moving your finger under each word while your child watches;
- Doing one or two questions together to ensure your child understands what to do, then letting him or her work independently;
- Praising your child's efforts and working at a pace that is comfortable for him or her;
- Maintaining your child's enthusiasm by making each session short, pleasant, and part of your routine.

Activities marked "Challenge" are designed to stretch children's thinking beyond expectations. If your child doesn't seem ready for them, just skip them for now and come back to them later. Most children will need a little more parental support to work through the Challenge activities. Since all children develop at their own pace, it is important to let your child's interest guide you in providing just the right amount of challenge.

Completing the activities in this Complete Canadian workbook will help your child build a solid foundation of skills—and confidence—for success at school and beyond!

Sincerely,

Elaine J. Kenny, B.Ed.

For special bulk purchases please contact: sales@canadiancurriculumpress.ca.

For other inquiries please contact: inquiries@canadiancurriculumpress.ca.

ISBN 978-1-77062-904-2

Canadian co-author: Elaine J. Kenny, B.Ed.

Senior Series Editor: Lisa Penttilä
Layout and Cover Design: Michael P. Brodey
Selected illustrations: Andrea Scobie

We acknowledge the financial support of the Government of Canada through the Canada Book Fund (CBF) for our publishing activities.

Canadian Heritage
Patrimoine canadien

Printed in Canada.

Table of Contents

Sorting and Classifying 4
Number Recognition and Counting 13
Counting by 2s, 5s, and 10s 33
Hundred Chart 42
Less Than, Greater Than 43
Ordinal Numbers 49
Addition to 20 54
Addition Story Problems 75
Subtraction From 20 78
Subtraction Story Problems 98
Addition and Subtraction Review 101
Place Value 116
Two-Digit Addition (no regrouping) 130
Two-Digit Subtraction (no regrouping) 140
Two-Digit Addition (with regrouping) 148
Problem Solving With Addition 152
Two-Digit Subtraction (with regrouping) 153
Problem Solving With Subtraction 160
Review Two-Digit Addition and Subtraction 161
Three-Digit Addition 172
Three-Digit Subtraction 177
Review Three-Digit Addition and Subtraction 182
Multiplication 185
Problem Solving: Add, Subtract, or Multiply 191
Shapes 193
Measurement 203
Graphing 214
Fractions 223
Telling Time 234
Money 245
Money Problems 256
Geometry 262
Glossary of Math Terms 266
Answer Key 268
Suggestions for Parents 311
Test Practice 316
Test Practice Answer Key 340
Tangram Activities 343

Name Luke

Dapper Dog's Campout

Directions: Dapper Dog is going on a camping trip. Draw an **X** on the word in each row that does not belong.

1.	flashlight	candle	radio	fire
2.	shirt	pants	coat	bat
3.	cow	car	bus	train
4.	beans	hot dog	ball	bread
5.	gloves	hat	book	boots
6.	fork	butter	cup	plate
7.	book	ball	bat	milk
8.	dogs	bees	flies	ants

Name ____________________

Classification Fun

Directions: Write each word in the correct row at the bottom of the page.

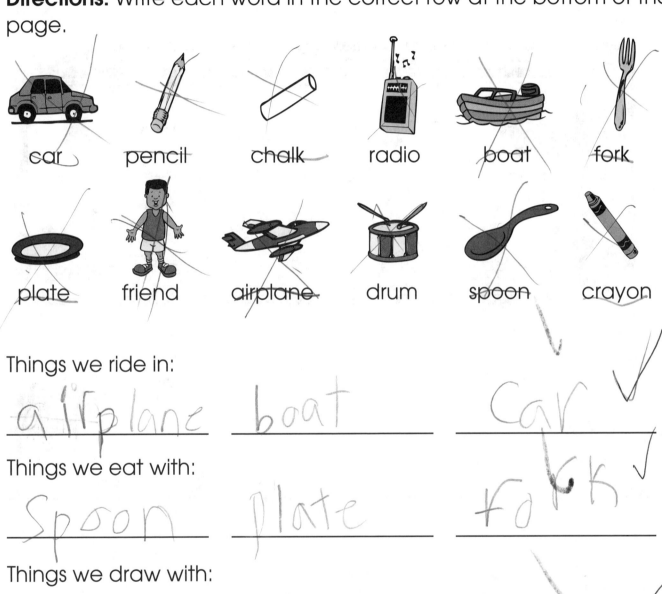

Things we ride in:

______________ ______________ ______________

Things we eat with:

______________ ______________ ______________

Things we draw with:

______________ ______________ ______________

Things we listen to:

______________ ______________ ______________

Name luke

Where Does It Belong?

Directions: Read the words in the fish tank. Write each word in its place.

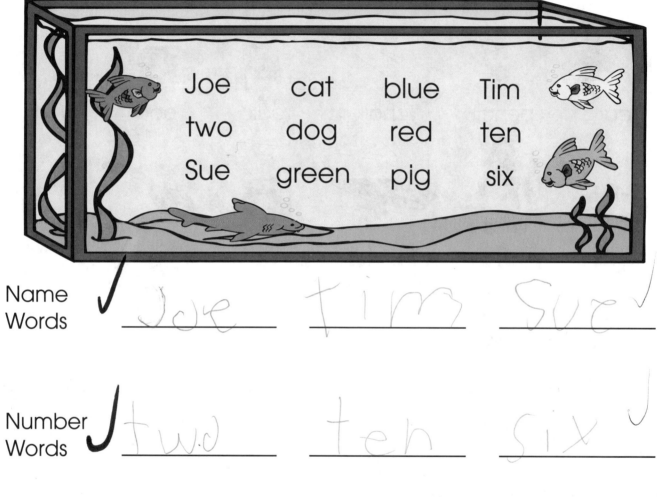

Joe	cat	blue	Tim
two	dog	red	ten
Sue	green	pig	six

Name Words: Joe, tim, Sue

Number Words: two, ten, six

Animal Words: Cat, dog, pig

Colour Words: blue, red, green

Name ____________________

Classifying

Directions: The words in each list form a group. Choose the word from the box that describes each group and write it on the line.

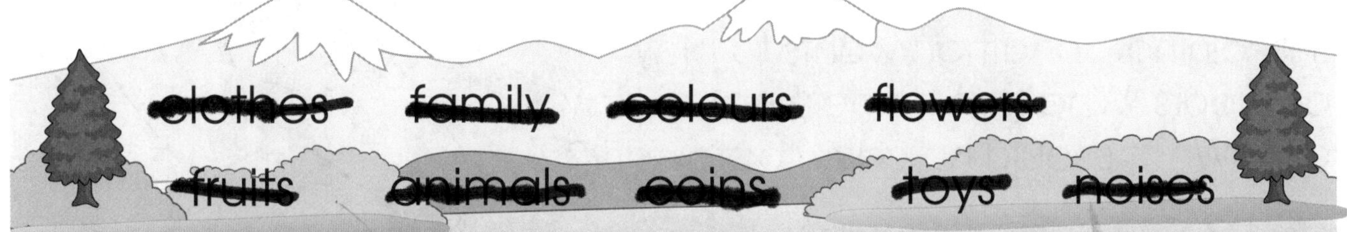

rose buttercup tulip daisy	crash bang ring pop	mother father sister brother
____________	____________	____________
puzzle wagon blocks doll	green purple blue red	grapes orange apple plum
____________	____________	____________
shirt socks dress coat	dime penny nickel quarter	dog horse elephant moose
____________	____________	____________

Name Luke

Classifying: A Rainy Day

Directions: Read the story. Then, circle the objects Jonathan needs to stay dry.

It is raining. Jonathan wants to play outdoors. What should he wear to stay dry? What should he carry to stay dry?

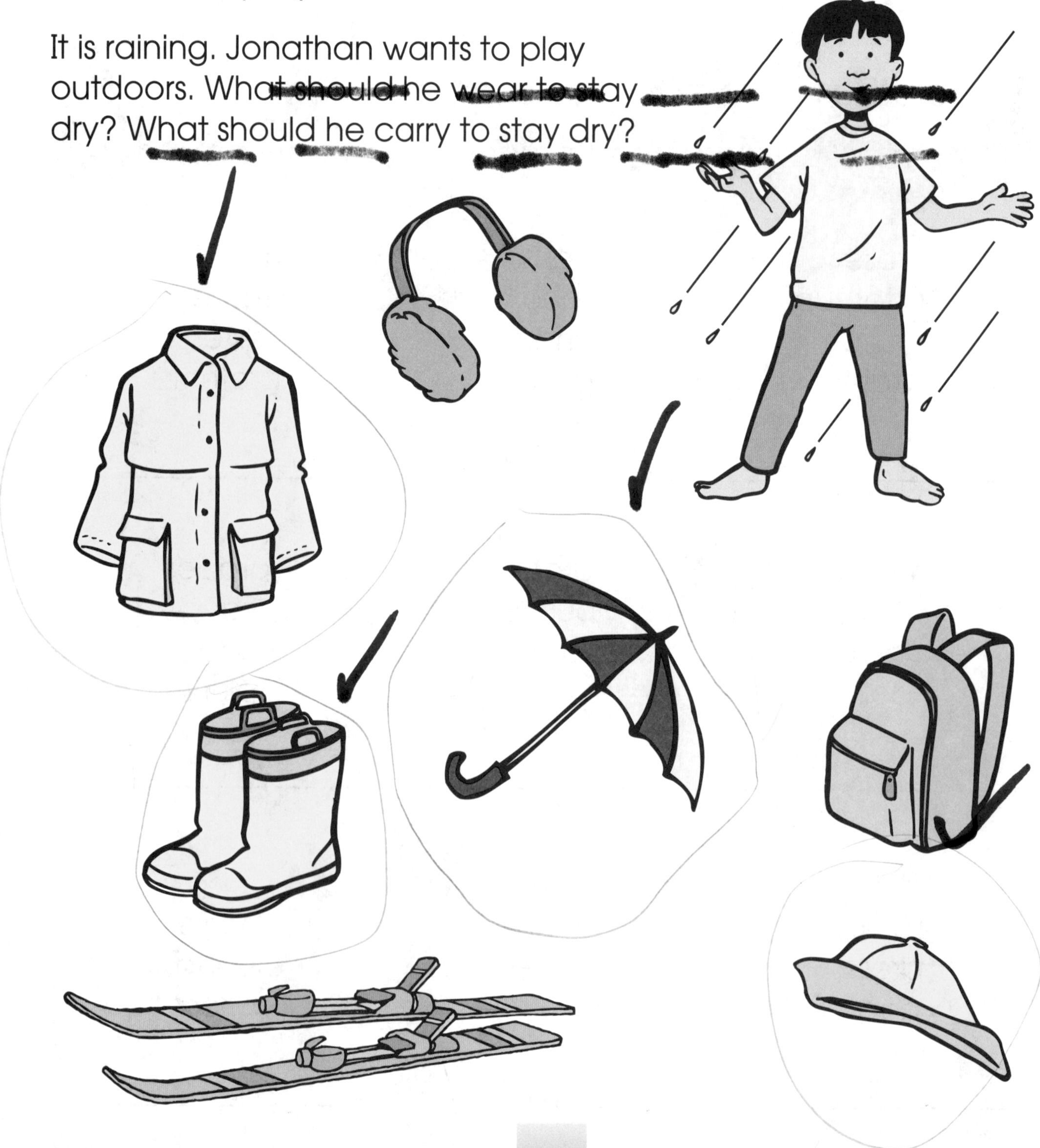

Name Luke

Classifying: Outdoor/Indoor Games

Classifying is putting things that are alike into groups.

Directions: Read about games. Draw an **X** on the games you can play indoors. Circle the objects used for outdoor games.

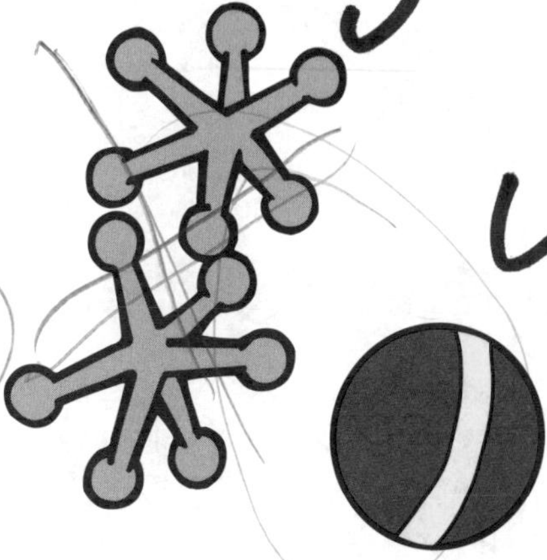

OLD MAID

Some games are outdoor games. Some games are indoor games. Outdoor games are active. Indoor games are quiet.

Which do you like best? Outdoor

Name ______________________

Classifying: Art Tools

Directions: Read about art tools. Then, colour only the art tools.

Andrea uses different art tools to help her design her masterpieces. To cut, she needs scissors. To draw, she needs a pencil. To colour, she needs crayons. To paint, she needs a brush.

Write which tools are needed to:

draw	colour	cut
____________	____________	____________

Name ______________________

Classifying: Foods

Darcy likes fruit and things made from fruit. She also likes bread.

Directions: Circle the things on the menu that Darcy will eat.

MENU	
apple pie	corn
peas	rolls
beans	banana bread
oranges	grape juice
chicken	

Name ______________________

Classifying: Animal Habitats

Directions: Read the story. Then, write each animal's name under **WATER** or **LAND** to tell where it lives.

Animals live in different habitats. A **habitat** is the place of an animal's natural home. Many animals live on land and others live in water. Most animals that live in water breathe with gills. Animals that live on land breathe with lungs.

fish	shrimp	moose	dog
cat	eel	whale	horse
bear	deer	shark	jellyfish

WATER

1. fish
2. shrimp
3. Whale
4. Shark
5. jelly finh
6. ______

LAND

1. cat
2. bear
3. moose
4. dog
5. horse
6. ______

Name ______________________

Dot-to-Dot Fun

Directions: Connect the dots. Colour the creature.

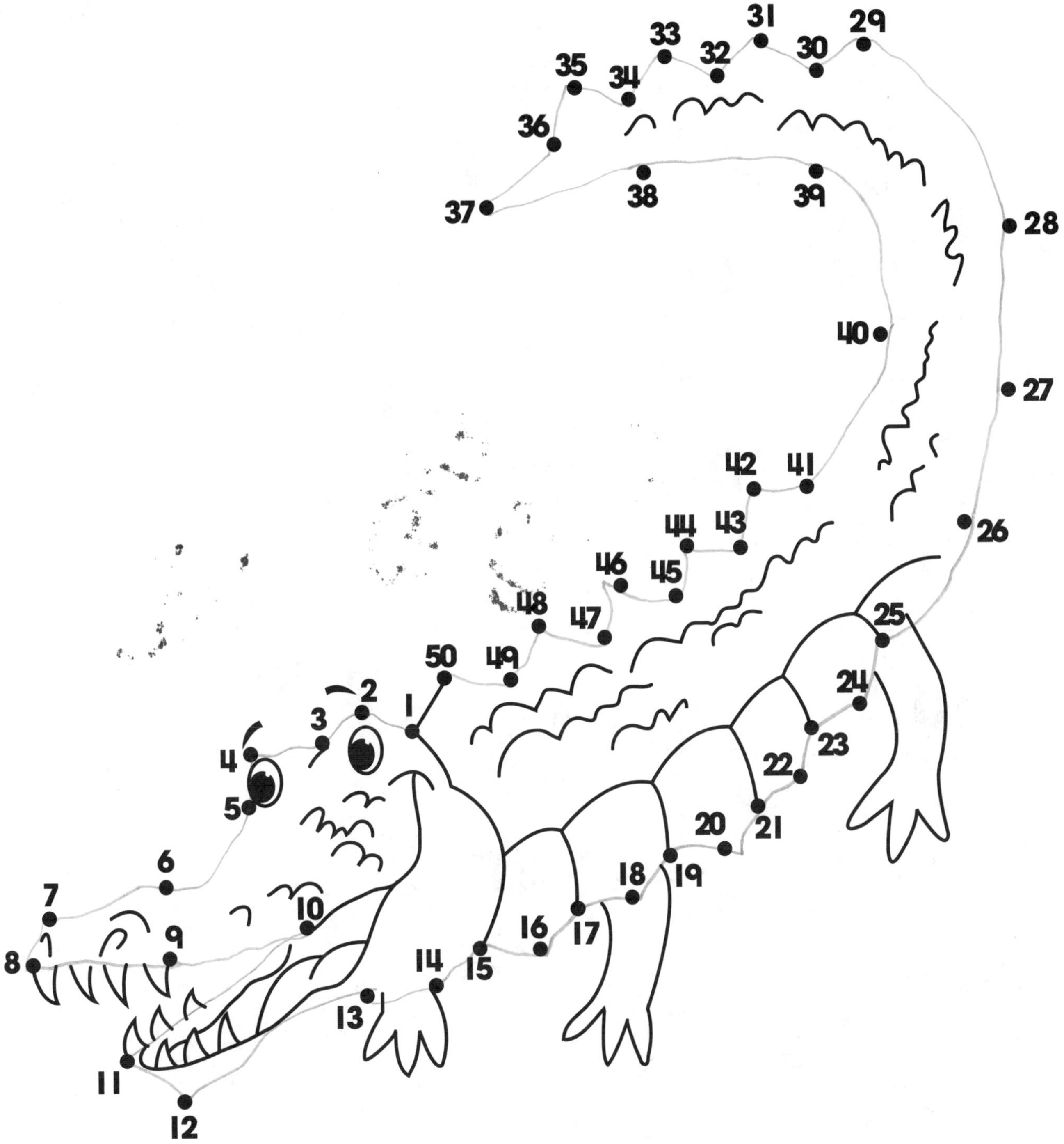

1 2 3 4 5 6 7 8 9 10 11 12 13 14 15 16 17 18 19 20 21 22 23 24 25 26 27 28 29 30 31 32 33 34 35 36 37 38 39 40 41 42 43 44 45 46 47 48 49 50

Name ____________________

Happy Hikers

Directions: Trace a path through the maze by counting by 10s from **1** to **100** in the correct order. Colour the picture.

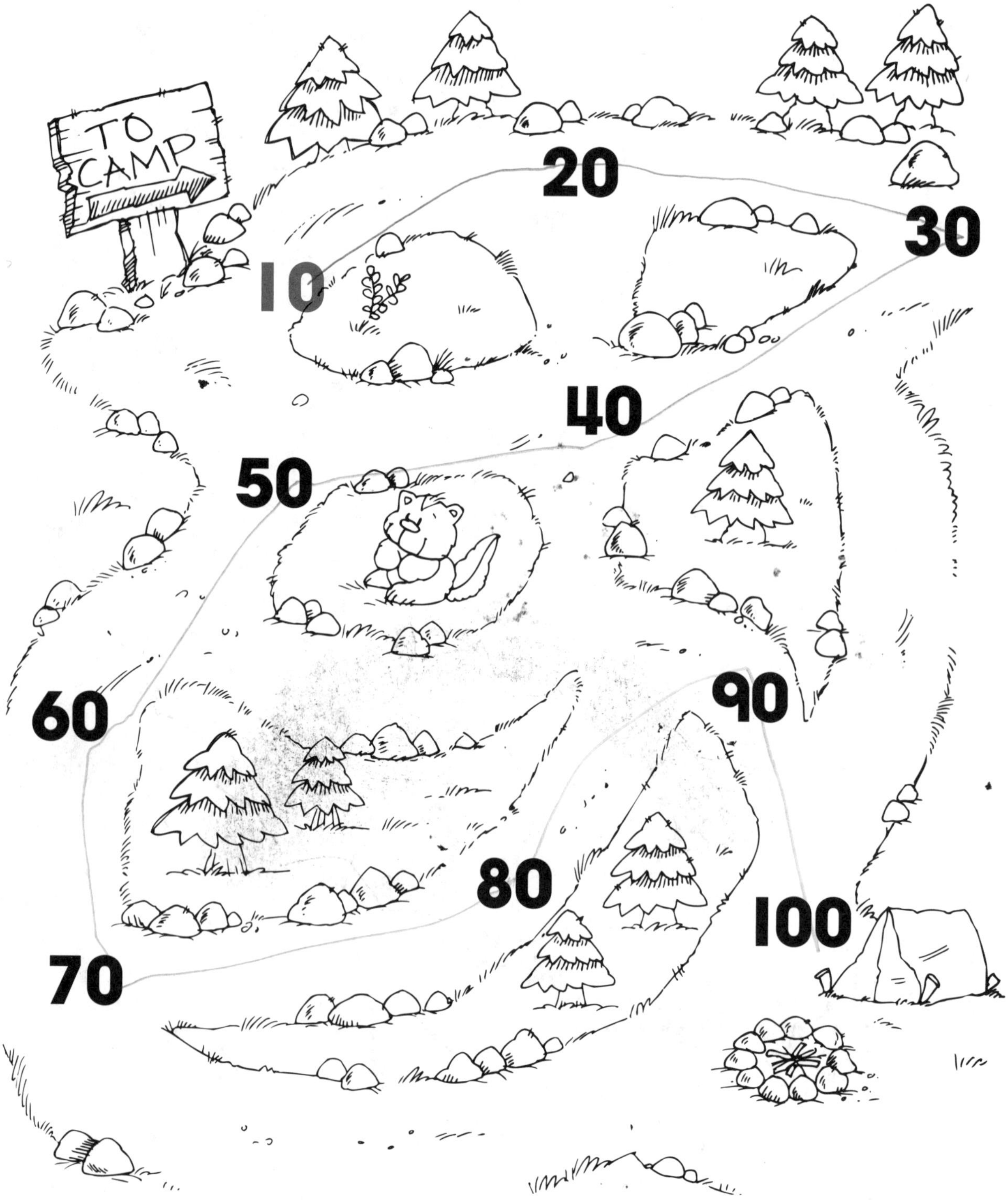

TO CAMP

10

20

30

40

50

60

70

80

90

100

Rainbow-Coloured Numbers

Directions: Colour the spaces: **1 = red**, **2 = blue**, **3 = yellow**, **4 = green**, and **5 = orange**

Name ____________________

Food Favourites

Directions: Count the pictures in each group. Circle the number.

18 31 24

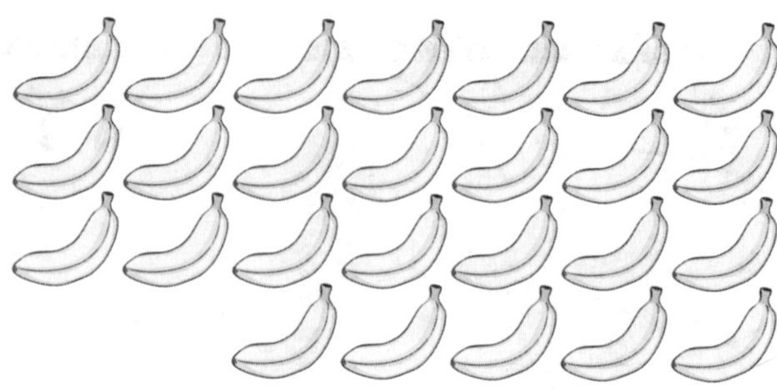

12 26 31

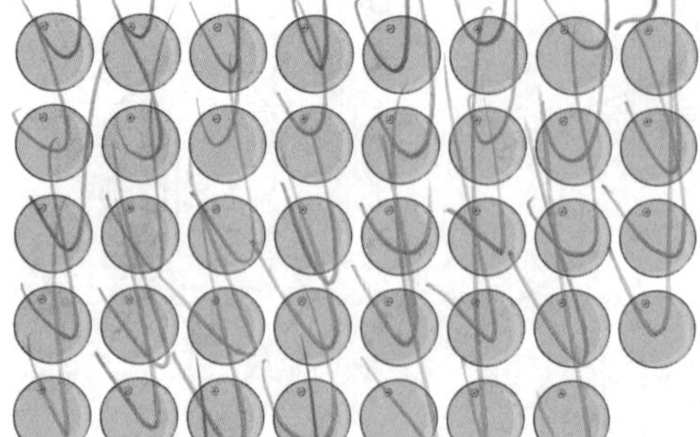

13 27 39

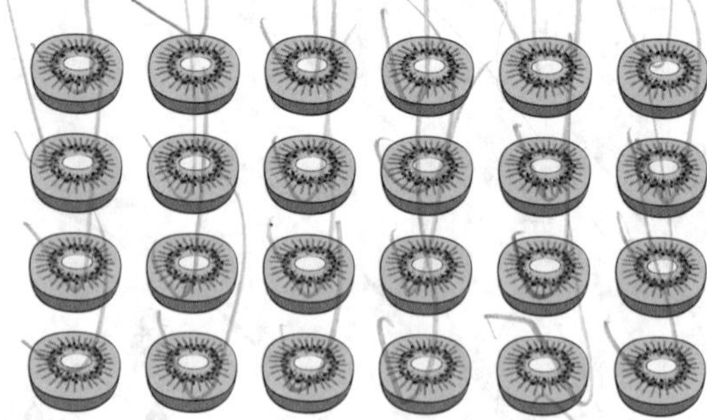

16 28 24

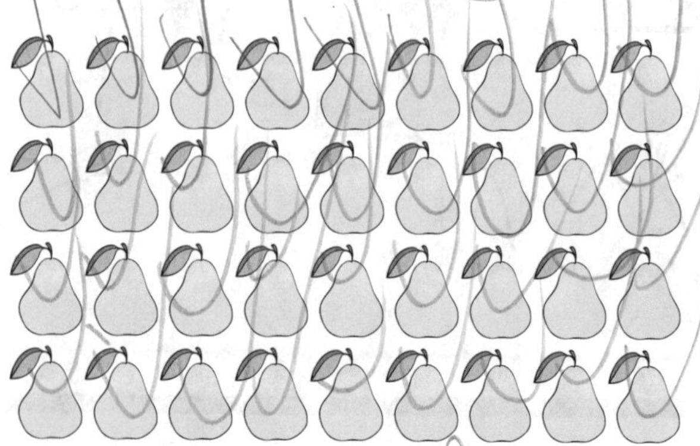

5 10 36

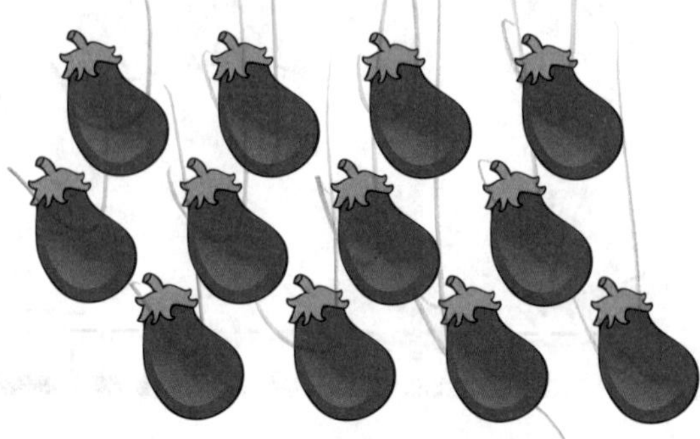

13 18 12

Name ________________________________

Silly Shapes

Directions: Count and colour each group of shapes. Cut out the numbers and glue them in the correct boxes.

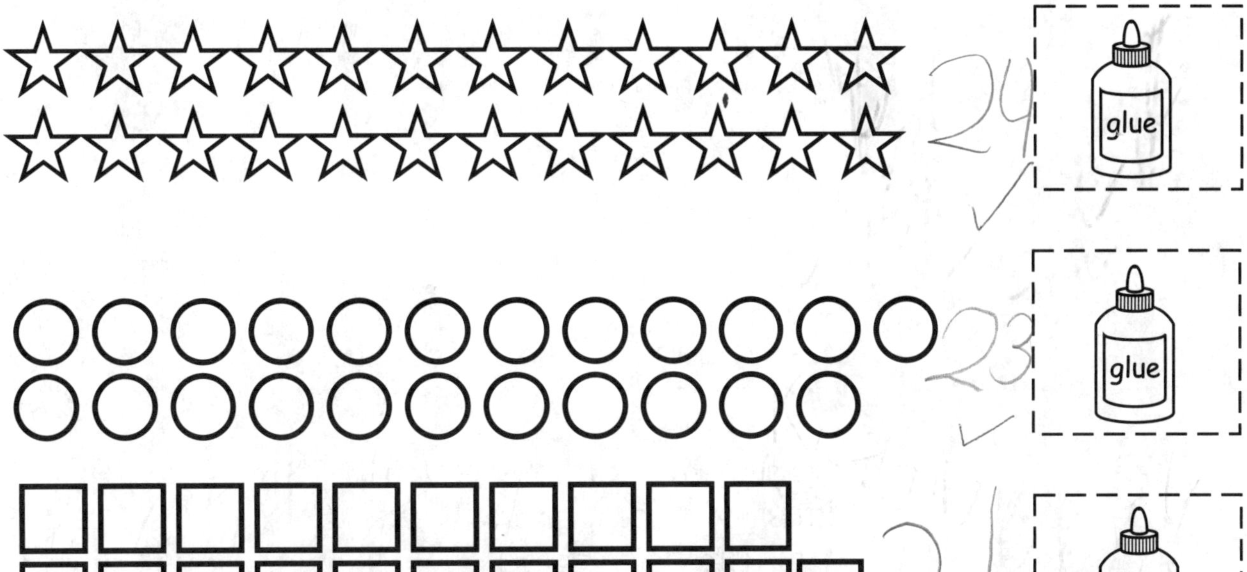

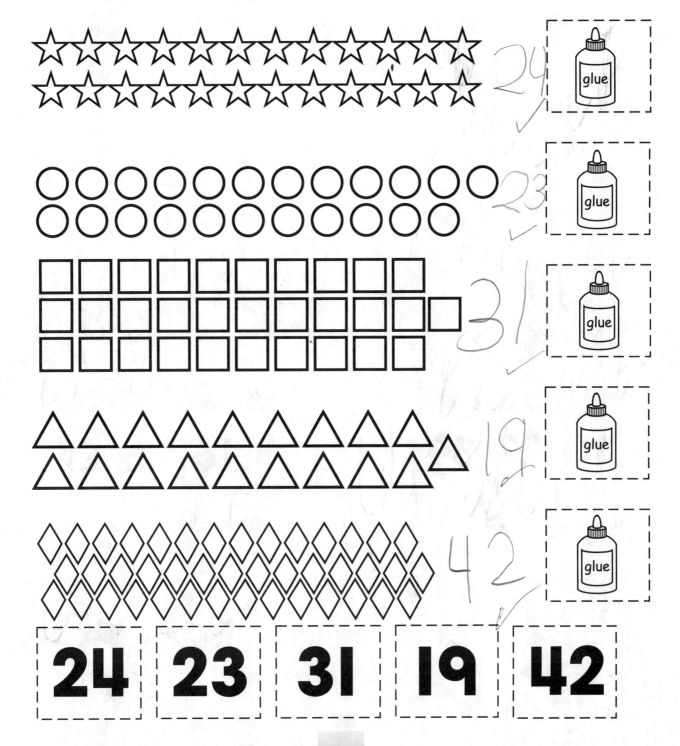

24	23	31	19	42

This page was left intentionally blank for cutting activity on previous page.

Name Luke

Clown Capers

Directions: Count the number of each thing in the picture. Write the number on the line.

1 ____

2 ____

3 ____

4 ____

5 ____

6 ____

1 ____

8 ____

P ____

10 ____

Name ______________________

Take an Animal Count!

Directions: Count each group of zoo animals. Draw a line from the number to the correct number word. The first one shows you what to do.

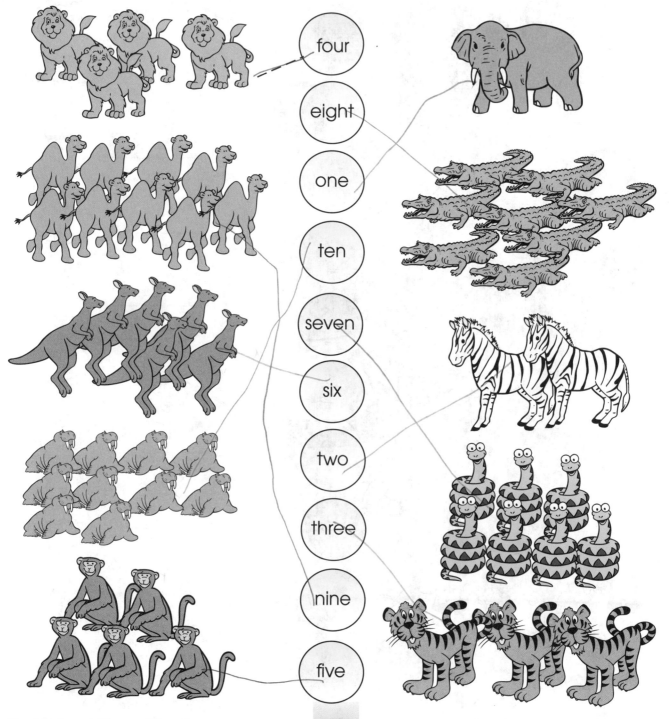

four

eight

one

ten

seven

six

two

three

nine

five

Name ____________________

Sheepish Shepherd

Directions: Count the sheep on the hill. Then, write that number on each tree.

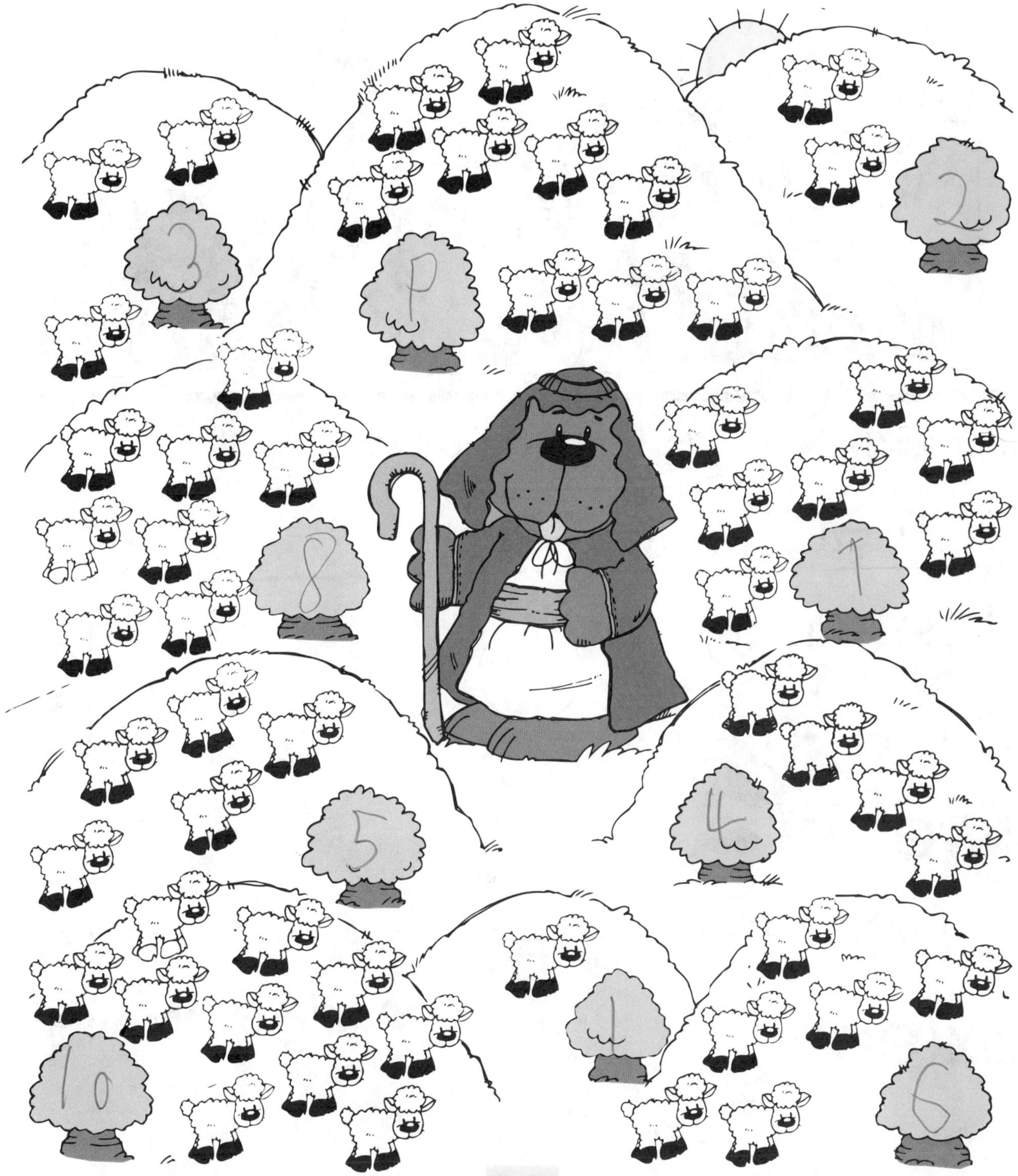

Name ______________________________

Number Words

Directions: Number the buildings from eleven to sixteen.

Directions: Draw a line from the word to the number.

eleven	14
fifteen	12
thirteen	15
twelve	13
fourteen	16
sixteen	11

Name ____________________

Number Words

Directions: Number the buildings from fifteen to twenty.

Directions: Draw a line from the word to the number.

fifteen	20
eighteen	16
sixteen	18
twenty	19
nineteen	17
seventeen	15

Name ______________________

Number Words

Directions: Write each number beside the correct picture. Then, write it again.

one	two	three	four	five	six	seven	eight	nine	ten

Example:

six six six six

Name LUKE BROUWERS

Sequencing Numbers

Sequencing is putting numbers in the correct order.

Directions: Write the missing numbers.

Example: 14, **15**, 16

23, 24, 25

17, 18, 19

18, 19, 20

16, 17, 18

32, 33, 34

34, 35, 36

35, 36, 37

45, 46, 47

42, 43, 44

28, 29, 30

26, 27, 28

22, 23, 24

42, 43, 44

11, 12, 13

47, 48, 49

32, 33, 34

36, 37, 38

34, 35, 36

16, 17, 18

42, 43, 44

21, 22, 23

47, 48, 49

22, 23, 24

28, 29, 30

Name ____________________

Counting

Directions: Write the numbers that are:

next in order	one less	one greater
22, 23, ____, ____	____, 16	6, ____
674, ____, ____	____, 247	125, ____
227, ____, ____	____, 550	499, ____
199, ____, ____	____, 333	750, ____
329, ____, ____	____, 862	933, ____

Directions: Write the missing numbers.

Name ____________________

Too Much for Mo

Directions: Count the number of each vegetable in the picture. Write the number in the correct box.

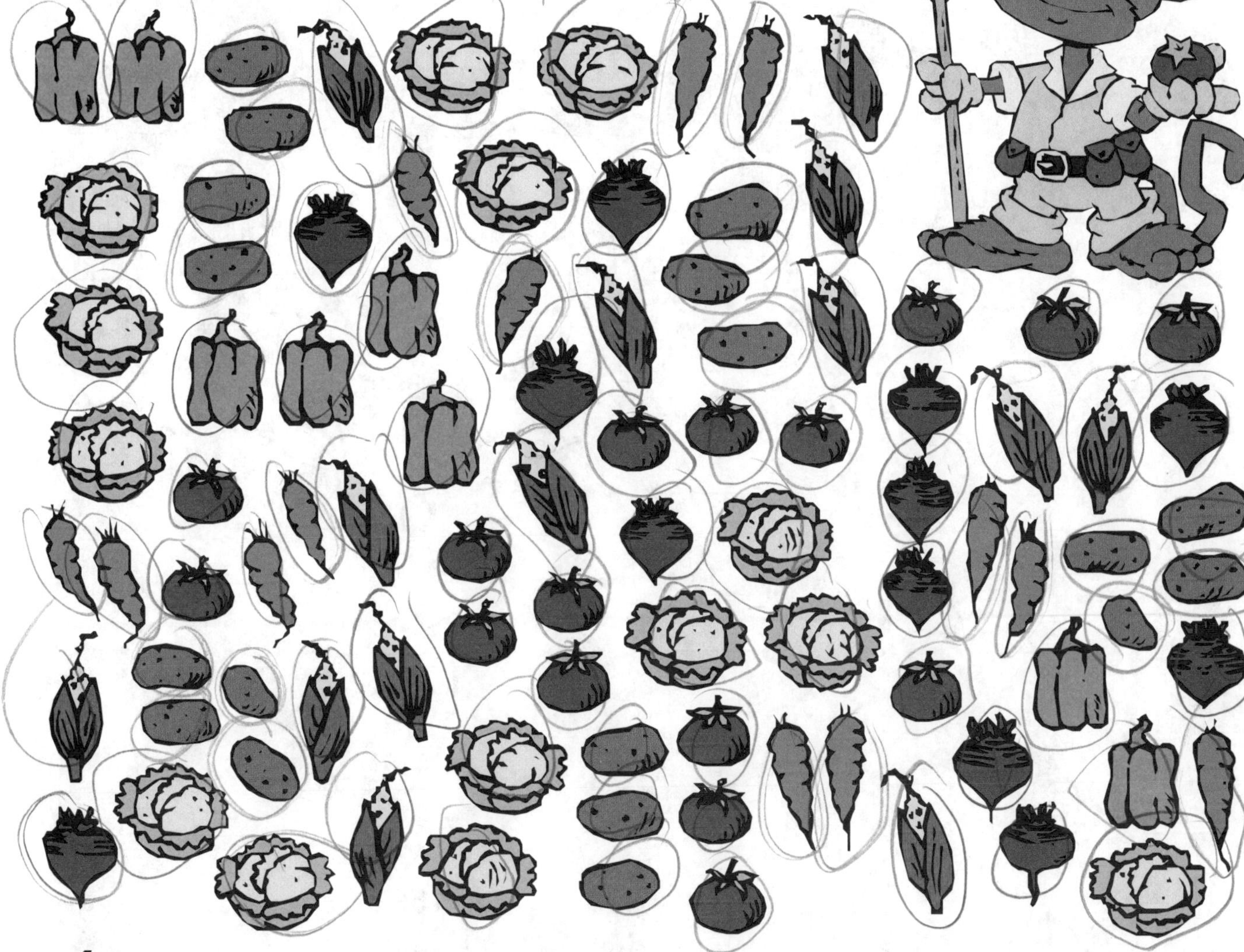

Name ____________________

Canadian Animal Mystery

Directions: Connect the dots from **1** to **75**. Colour the animal.

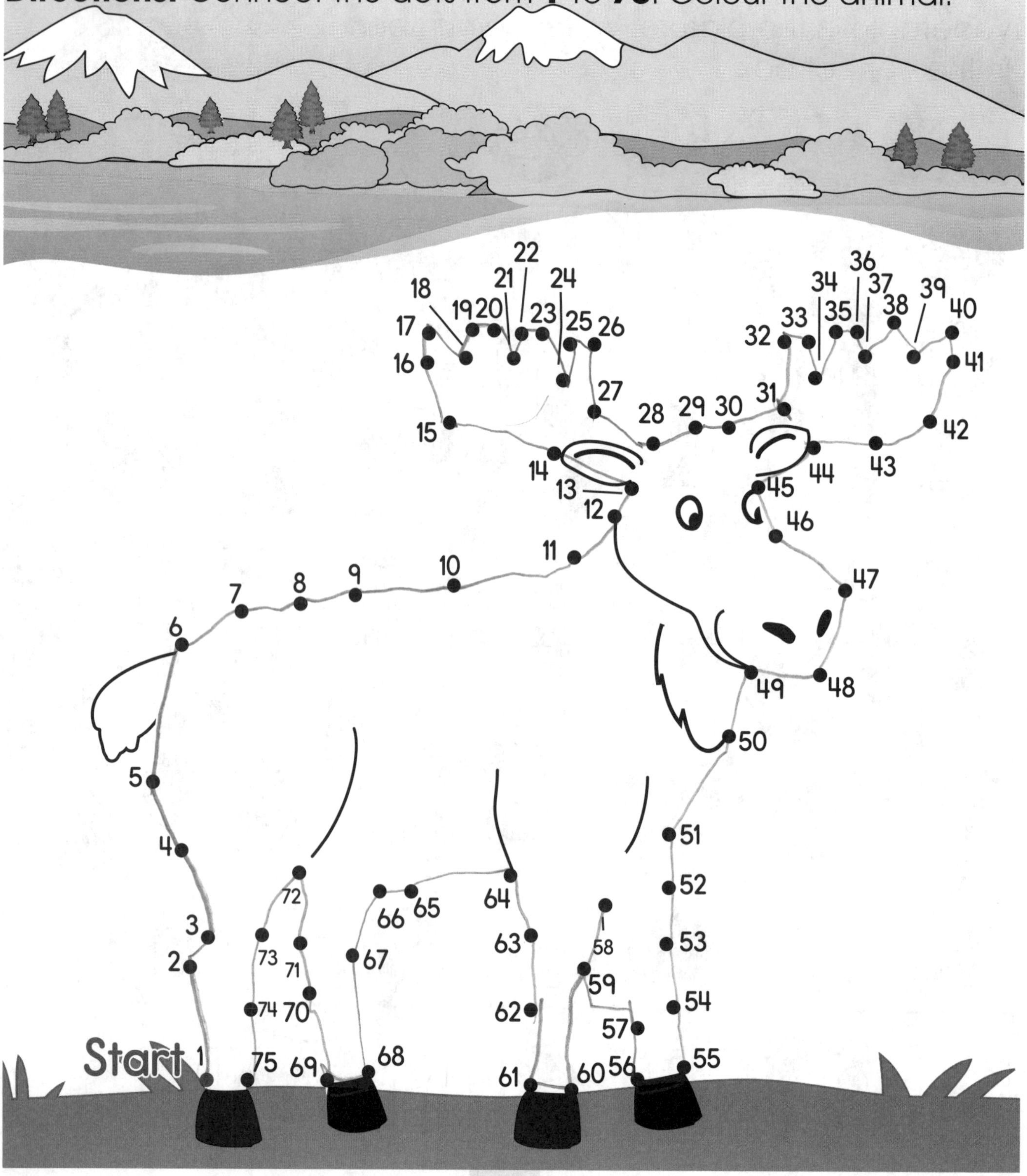

Start

1 2 3 4 5 6 7 8 9 10 11 12 13 14 15 16 17 18 19 20 21 22 23 24 25 26 27 28 29 30 31 32 33 34 35 36 37 38 39 40 41 42 43 44 45 46 47 48 49 50 51 52 53 54 55 56 57 58 59 60 61 62 63 64 65 66 67 68 69 70 71 72 73 74 75

Name ____________________

Note the Count

Directions: Count the number of notes on each page of music. Write the number on the line below it. In each box, circle the greater number of notes.

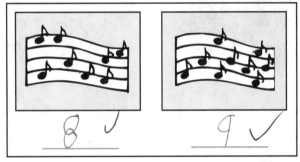

Directions: Colour the note in each box that is greater.

Name Sydney

Plump Piglets

Directions: Read the clues to find out how many ears of corn each pig ate. Write the number on the line below each pig.

I ate the number that comes before **26**.
Patsy
25
I ate the number that comes between **87** and **89**.
Horace
29
I ate the number that comes after **92**.
Pinky
93
I ate the number that comes before **57**.
Hilda
56
I ate the number that comes between **39** and **41**.
Porky
40

Who ate the most? Pinky Who ate the least? Patsy

Name ____________________

Teddy Bears in a Row

Directions: Cut out the bears at the bottom of the page. Glue them where they belong in number order.

	40	
10		12
	85	

29		31
	79	
64		66

This page was left intentionally blank for cutting activity on previous page.

Name Luke

Counting by Twos

Directions: Count by **2**s to draw the path to the store.

4 2 6

10 8

8 12 10

10 14

16 16

18

20

Name ______________________

Two for the Pool

Directions: Count by **2**s. Write the numbers to **30** in the water drops. Begin at the top of the slide and go down.

Name Luke

Cookie Clues

Directions: Find out what holds something good! Count by **5**s to connect the dots. Colour the picture.

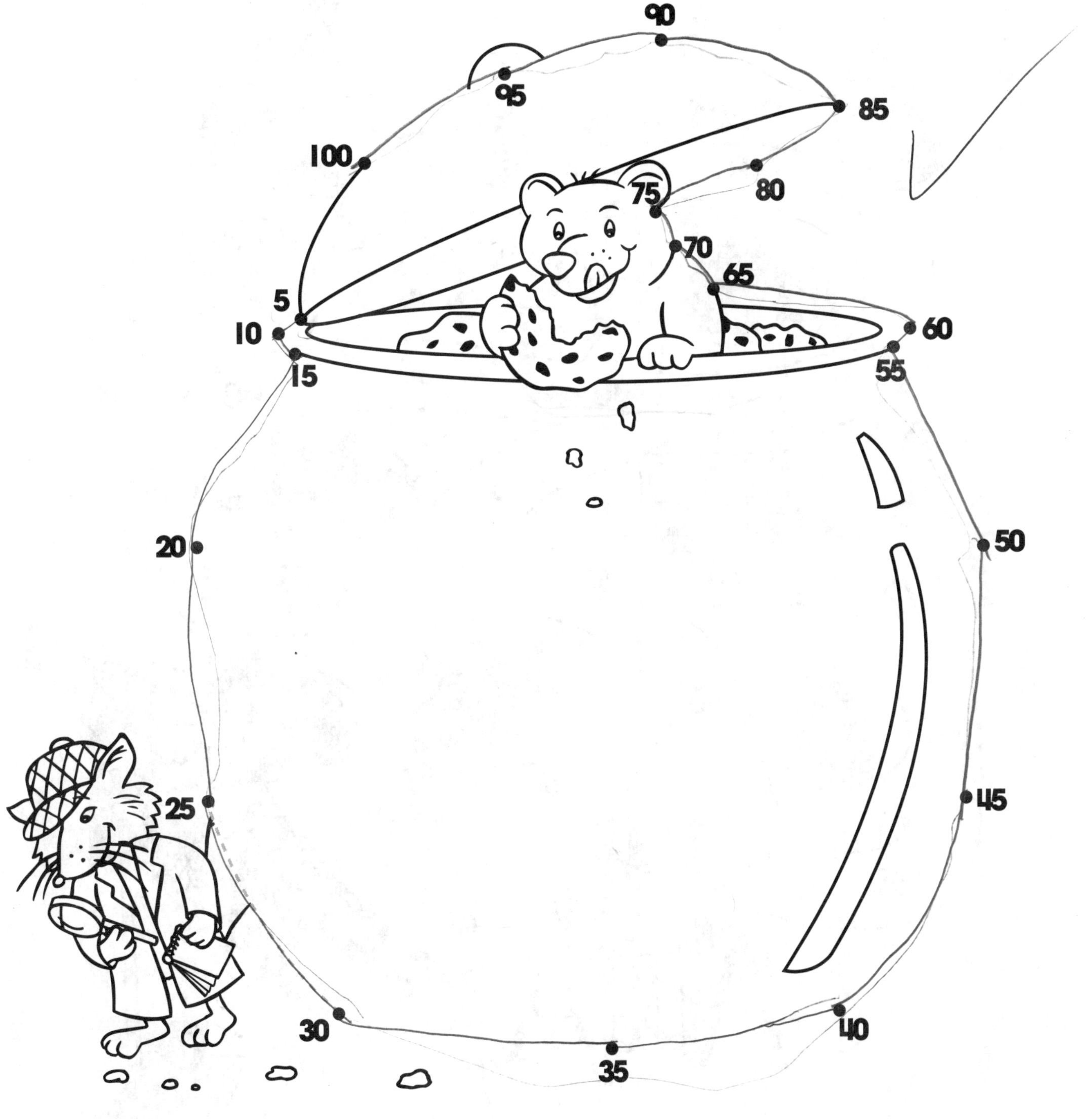

5 10 15 20 25 30 35 40 45 50 55 60 65 70 75 80 85 90 95 100

Name Luke

Counting by Fives

Directions: Count by **5**s to draw the path to the playground.

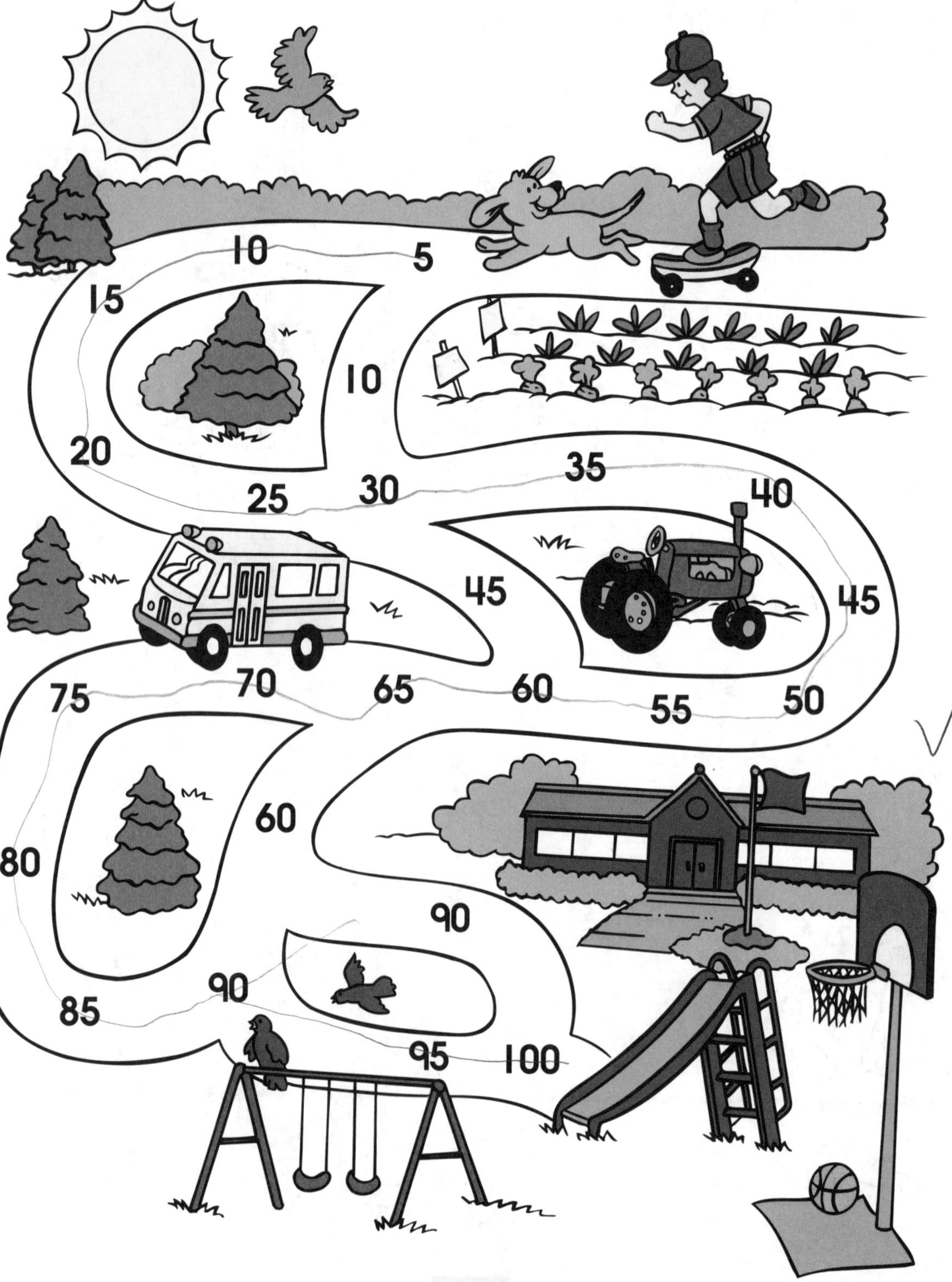

5 10 15 20 10 25 30 35 40 45 45 50 55 60 65 70 75 60 80 85 90 90 95 100

Name Luke

I'm Counting on You

Directions: Count by **2**s. Trace and write the numbers below.

2	4	6	8	10	12	14	16	18	20

Directions: Count by **5**s. Trace and write the numbers below.

5	10	15	20	25	30	35	40	45	50

Directions: Count by **2**s.
Connect the dots.
Colour the picture.

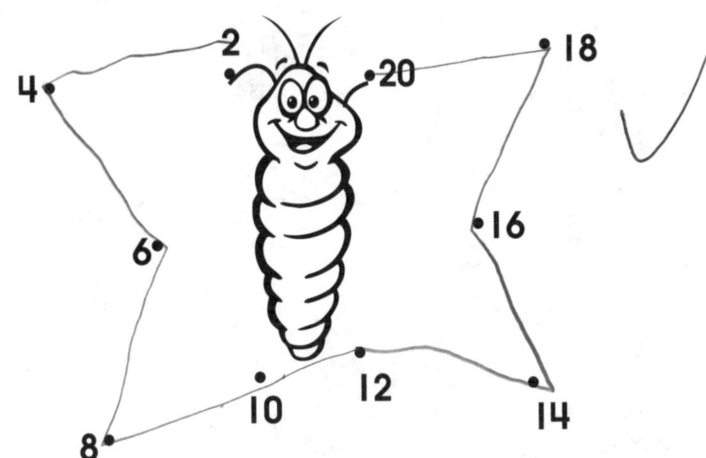

Directions: Count by **5**s.
Connect the dots.
Colour the picture.

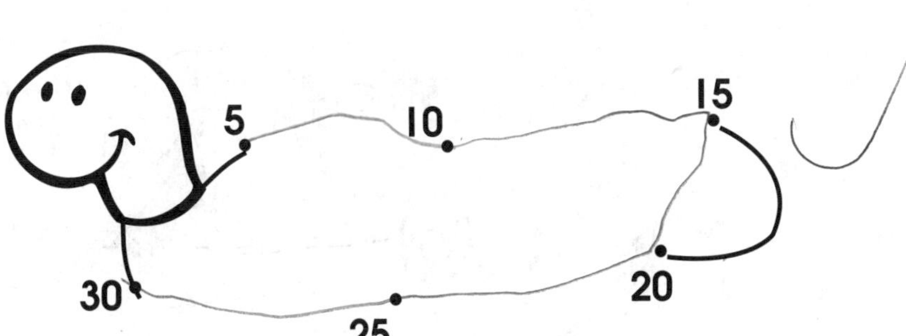

Name Luke/Sydney

Desert Trek

Directions: Count by **10**s. Colour each canteen with a **10** to lead the camel to the watering hole.

Name ____________________

Frog Count

Directions: Count by **5**s.
Draw a triangle around each number as you count by **5**s.

1	2	3	4	5	6	7	8	9	10
11	12	13	14	15	16	17	18	19	20
21	22	23	24	25	26	27	28	29	30
31	32	33	34	35	36	37	38	39	40
41	42	43	44	45	46	47	48	49	50

Directions: Count by **5**s.

5 ___ 10 ___ ___ ___ ___ ___ ___ ___ ___ ___

Directions: Count by **10**s.
Draw a box around each number as you count by **10**s.

1	2	3	4	5	6	7	8	9	10
11	12	13	14	15	16	17	18	19	20
21	22	23	24	25	26	27	28	29	30
31	32	33	34	35	36	37	38	39	40
41	42	43	44	45	46	47	48	49	50

Directions: Count by **10**s. 10 ___ ___ ___ ___ ___

Name ______________________________

Counting by Twos, Fives, and Tens

Directions: Write the missing numbers.

Count by **2**s.

Count by **5**s.

Count by **10**s.

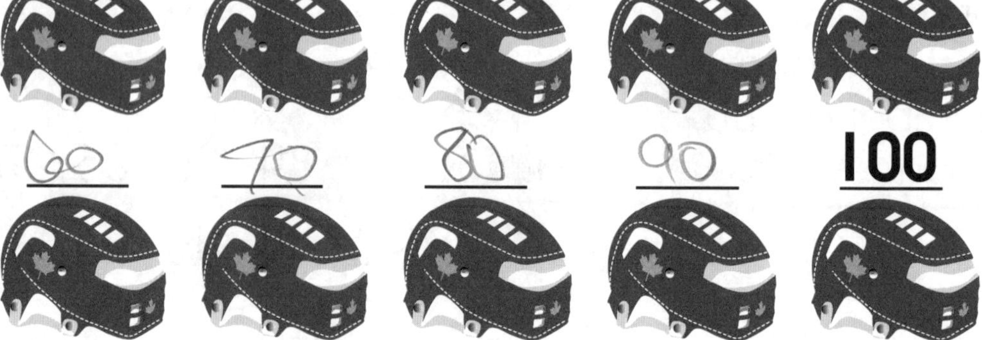

Name ____________________

Critter Count

Directions: Count by **2**s, **5**s, and **10**s to find the "critter count."

Each worm = 2. Count by **2**s to find the total.

= 10

= 16

Each turtle = 5. Count by **5**s to find the total.

= 20

= 35

Each ladybug = 10. Count by **10**s to find the total.

= 50

= 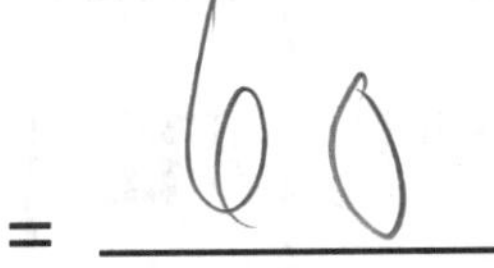

60

Name ______________________

Hundred Chart

Directions: Count aloud to 100, by 1s, 2s, 5s and 10s. Point to each number as you count.

1	2	3	4	5	6	7	8	9	10
11	12	13	14	15	16	17	18	19	20
21	22	23	24	25	26	27	28	29	30
31	32	33	34	35	36	37	38	39	40
41	42	43	44	45	46	47	48	49	50
51	52	53	54	55	56	57	58	59	60
61	62	63	64	65	66	67	68	69	70
71	72	73	74	75	76	77	78	79	80
81	82	83	84	85	86	87	88	89	90
91	92	93	94	95	96	97	98	99	100

Name ______________________

Largest and Smallest

Directions: In each shape, circle the smallest number. Draw a square around the largest number.

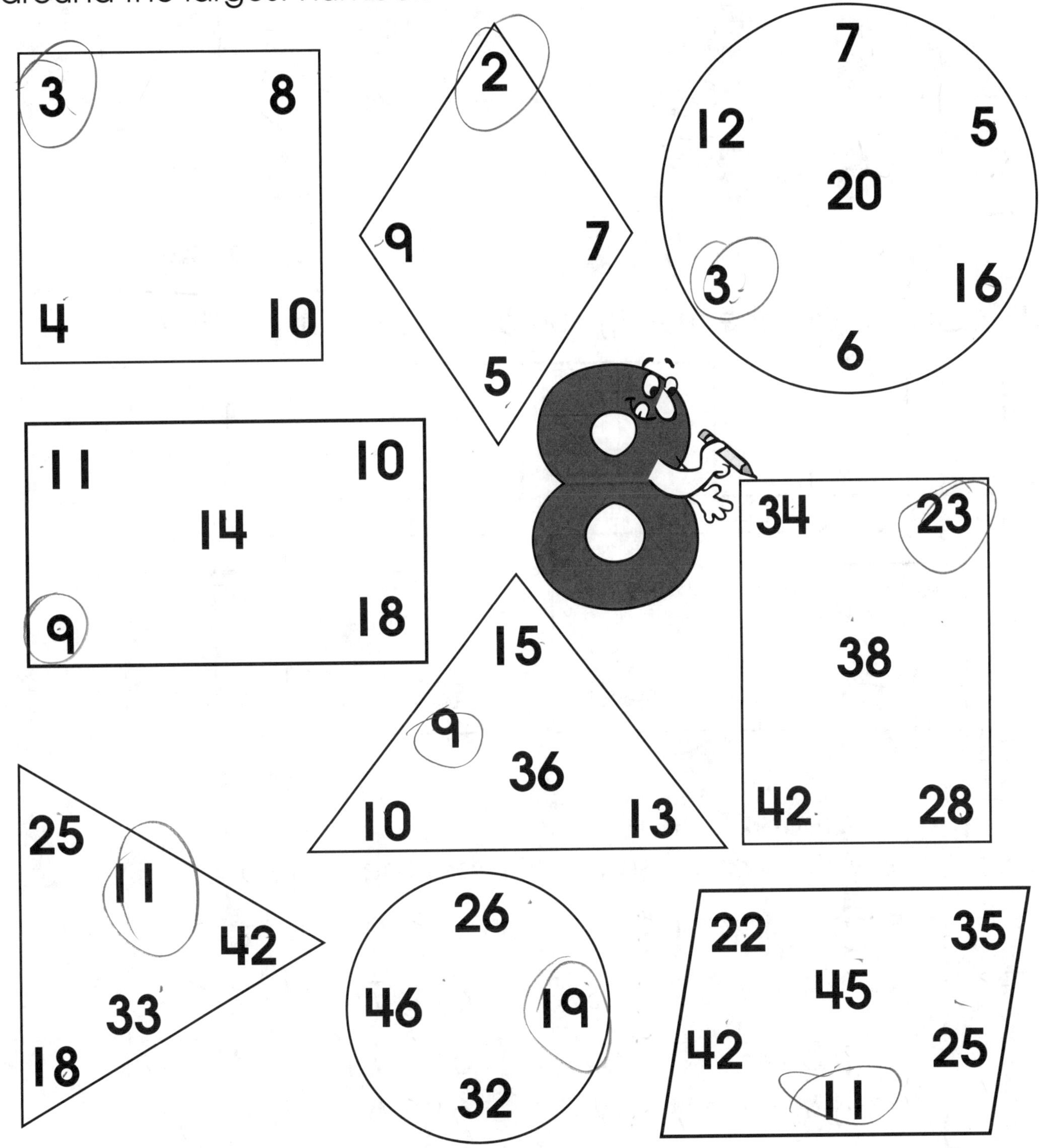

3 8 4 10

2 9 7 5

7 12 5 20 3 16 6

11 10 14 9 18

15 9 36 10 13

34 23 38 42 28

25 11 42 33 18

26 46 19 32

22 35 45 42 25 11

Name ______________________

Fishing for Answers

5 > 3

5 is **greater than** 3

3 < 5

3 is **less than** 5

Directions: Write the missing numbers in the number line.

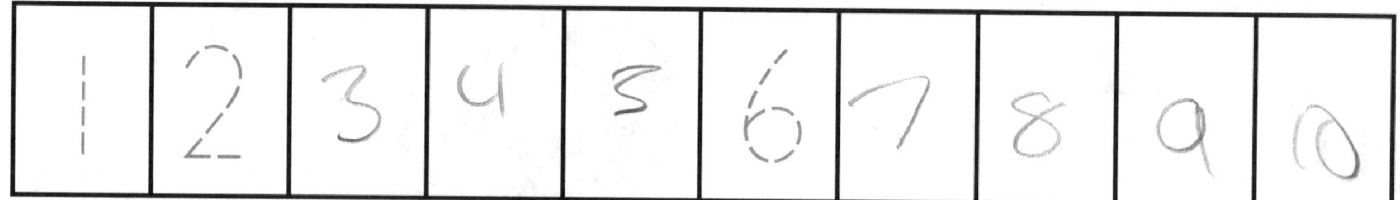

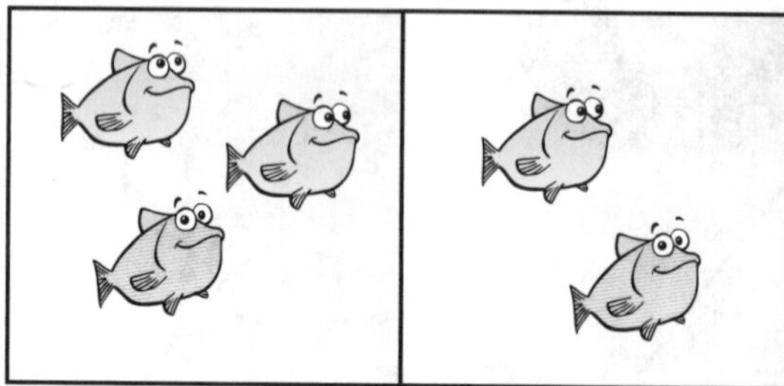

3 > 2

greater than

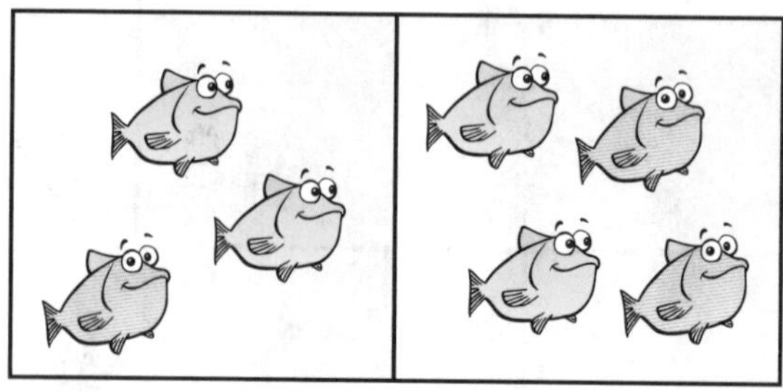

3 < 4

less than

Directions: Write **>** or **<**. Use the number line to help you.

5 ◯ 2	1 ◯ 7	1 ◯ 9	8 ◯ 5
3 ◯ 4	9 ◯ 3	8 ◯ 7	2 ◯ 4
6 ◯ 5	5 ◯ 3	5 ◯ 7	3 ◯ 5
7 ◯ 3	7 ◯ 6	2 ◯ 8	4 ◯ 2

Name ______________________________

"Mouth" Math

Directions: Write less than (**<**) or greater than (**>**) in each circle. Make sure the "mouth" is open toward the greater number!

36  49

35 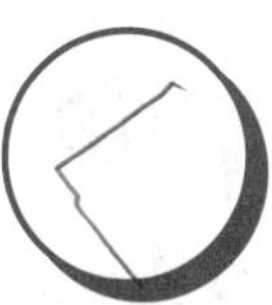 53

20  18

74 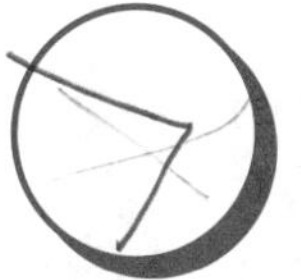 21

53  76

68  80

29  26

45  19

90  89

70 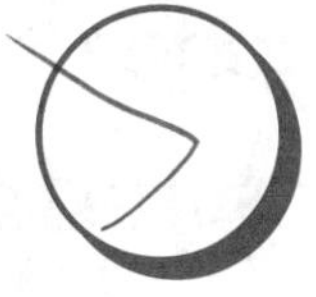 67

Name ____________________

Who Has the Most?

Directions: Circle the correct answer.

1. Traci has 3 s.
   Bob has 4 s.
   Bill has 5 s.
   Who has the most s?
   Traci Bob Bill

2. Pam has 7 s.
   Joe has 5 s.
   Jane has 6 s.
   Who has the most  s?
   Pam Joe Jane

3. Jennifer has 23 s.
   Sandy has 19 s.
   Jack has 25 s.
   Who has the most s?
   Jennifer Sandy Jack

4. Ali has 19 s.
   Burt has 18 s.
   Brent has 17 s.
   Who has the most  s?
   Ali Burt Brent

5. The boys have 14 s.
   The girls have 16 s.
   The teachers have 17 s.
   Who has the most s?
   boys girls teachers

6. Rose has 12 s.
   Betsy has 11 s.

   Leslie has 13 s.

   Who has the most s?

   Rose Betsy Leslie

Name ____________________

Who Has the Fewest?

Directions: Circle the correct answer.

1. Pat had 4 s.
   Charles had 3 s.
   Andrea had 5 s.
   Who had the fewest number of s?
   Pat Charles Andrea

2. Jeff has 5 s.
   John has 4 s.
   Bill has 6 s.
   Who has the fewest number of s?
   Jeff John Bill

3. Jane has 7 s.
   Susan has 9 s.
   Fred has 8 s.
   Who has the fewest number of s?
   Jane Susan Fred

4. Charles bought 12 s.
   Rose bought 6 s.
   Dawn bought 24 s.
   Who bought the fewest number of 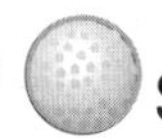 s?
   Charles Rose Dawn

5. John had 9 s.
   Jack had 8 s.
   Mark had 7 s.
   Who had the fewest number of s?
   John  Jack Mark

6. Edith bought 12 s.
   Michelle bought 16 s.
   Marty bought 13 s.
   Who bought the fewest number of s?
   Edith Michelle Marty

Name ______________________

Less Than, Greater Than

< >

Directions: The open mouth points to the larger number. The small point goes to the smaller number. Draw the symbol **<** or **>** to the correct number.

Example: **5** (>) **3** — This means that 5 is greater than 3, and 3 is less than 5.

greater than

12 ◯ **2** **16** ◯ **6**

16 ◯ **15** **1** ◯ **2**

7 ◯ **1** **19** ◯ **5**

9 ◯ **6** **11** ◯ **13**

Name ____________________

Have a Ball!

Directions: Colour the second ball **brown.**

Colour the sixth ball **yellow.**

Colour the fourth ball **orange.**

Colour the first ball **black.**

Colour the fifth ball **green.**

    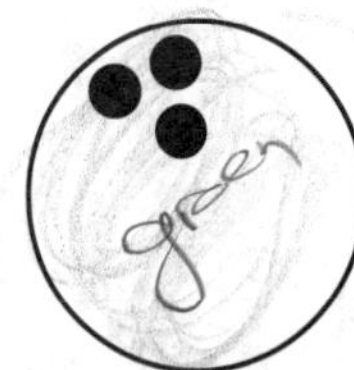 

Colour the seventh ball **purple.**

Name ______________________

Swimming in Style!

Directions: Colour the swimsuits. The first person is wearing a yellow mask.

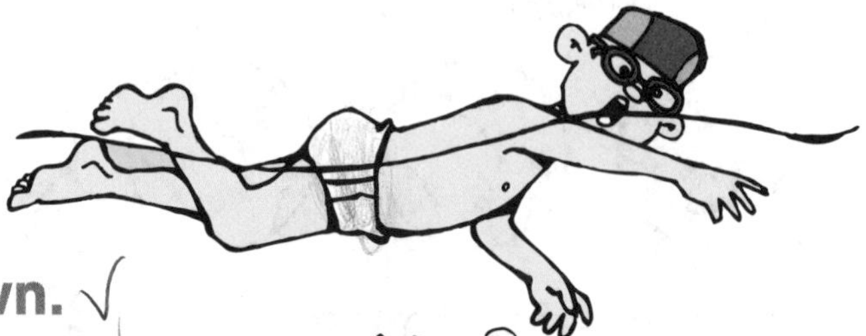

Colour the fourth suit **brown.**

Colour the second suit **purple.**

Colour the first suit **red.**

Colour the seventh suit **pink.**

Colour the third suit **blue.**

Colour the eighth suit **green.**

Colour the fifth suit **orange.**

Colour the sixth suit **yellow.**

Name ____________________

Orderly Ordinals

Directions: Write each word on the correct line to put the words in order.

second	fifth	seventh	first	tenth
third	eighth	sixth	fourth	ninth

1. ____________________
2. ____________________
3. ____________________
4. ____________________
5. ____________________
6. ____________________
7. ____________________
8. ____________________
9. ____________________
10. ____________________

Directions: Which picture is circled in each row? Underline the word that tells the correct number.

third fourth

fourth sixth

first ninth

third fifth

fifth sixth

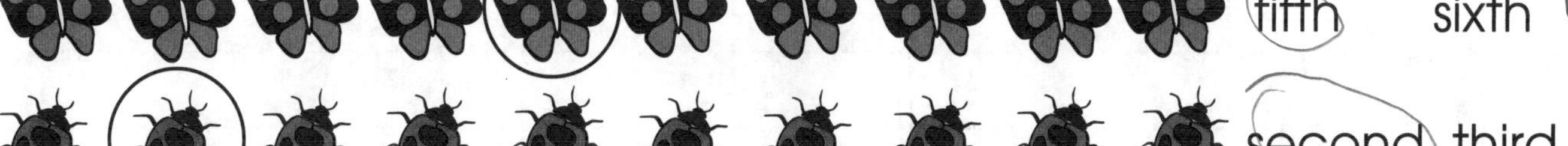

second third

Name ______________________

Which Place in the Race?

Directions: Write the correct word to tell each runner's place in the race.

first second third fourth fifth sixth seventh

fifth

first

fourth

third

seventh

second

sixth

Name ______________________________

Flags First

Directions: Start at the bottom right of the page.

Colour the ninth flag **red.**
Write **O** on the second flag.
Colour the eighth flag **blue.**
Write **D** on the first flag.
Colour the sixth flag **yellow.**
Write **G** on the fourth flag.
Colour the tenth flag **purple.**
Write **O** on the third flag.
Colour the seventh flag **green.**
Colour the fifth flag **orange.**
What word did you spell? ____________________

Name ____________________

How Many Robots in All?

Directions: Look at the pictures. Complete the addition sentences.

Example:

How many s are there in all?

2 + 4 = 6

How many s are there in all?

3 + 5 = 8

How many s are there in all?

4 + 3 = 7

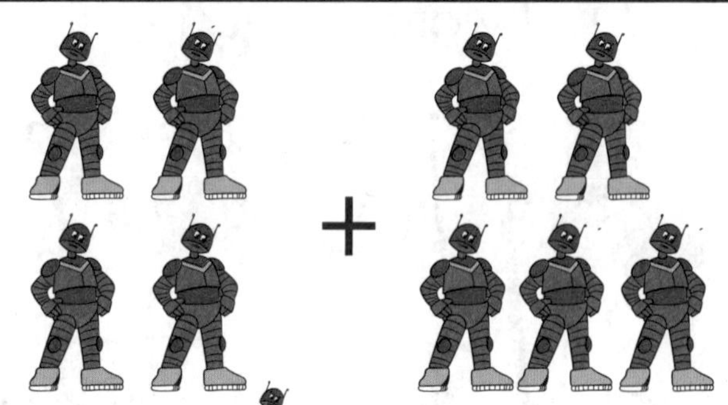

How many s are there in all?

4 + 5 = 9

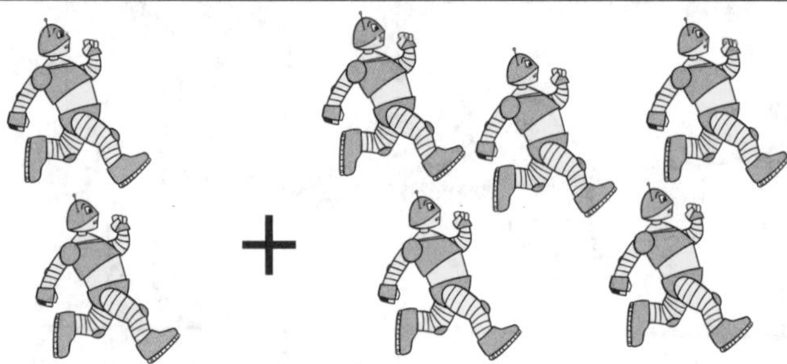

How many s are there in all?

2 + 5 = 7

How many s are there in all?

4 + 4 = 8

Name ___________________________

How Many Rabbits?

Directions: Look at the pictures. Complete the addition sentences.

Example:

How many s are there in all?

4 + 3 = 7

How many s are there in all?

3 + 6 = 9

How many s are there in all?

6 + 1 = 7

How many s are there in all?

3 + 4 = 7

How many s are there in all?

4 + 5 = 9

How many s are there in all?

8 + 3 = 11

Name ______________________

Alien Problems

Directions: Look at the pictures. Complete the addition sentences.

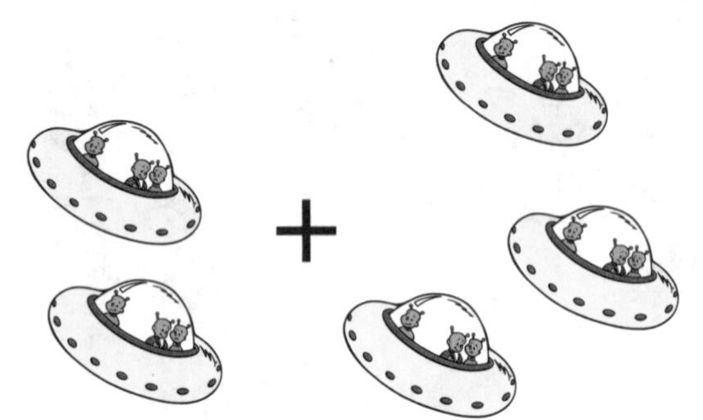

Example:

2 + 3 = 5

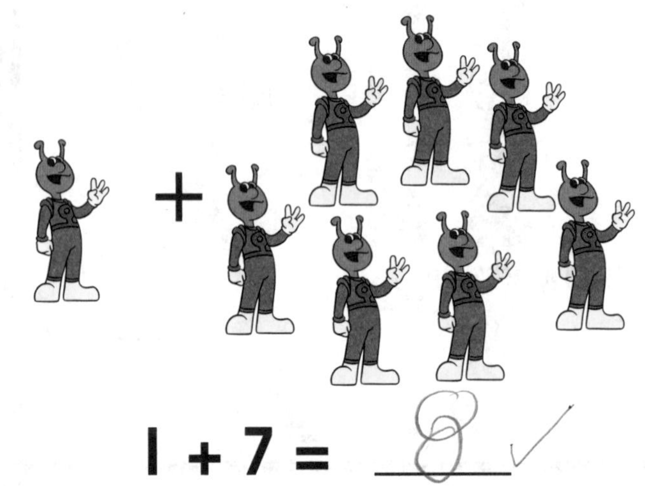

1 + 7 = 8

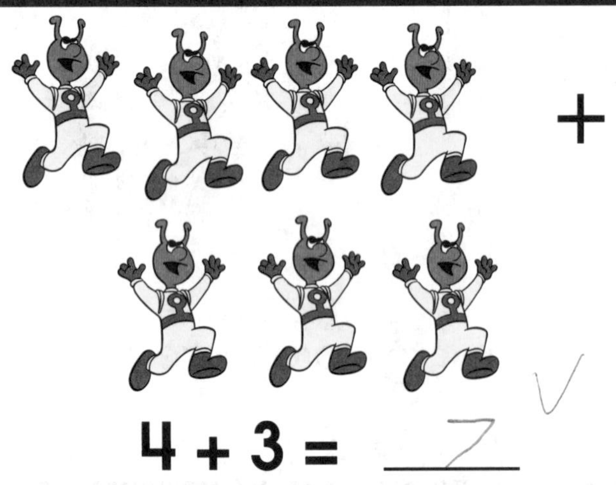

4 + 3 = 7

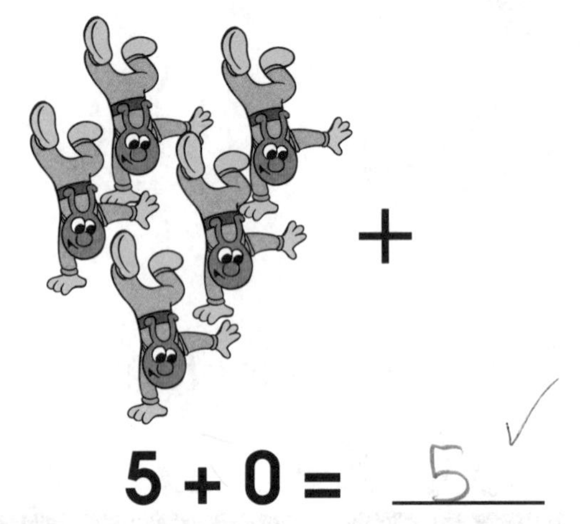

5 + 0 = 5

3 + 3 = 6

4 + 5 = 9

Name ____________________

The Missing Chickens

Directions: Draw the missing pictures. Complete the addition sentences.

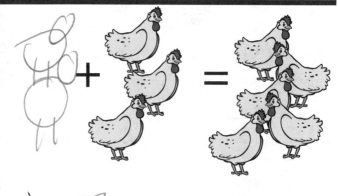

Example:

1 + 2 = 3

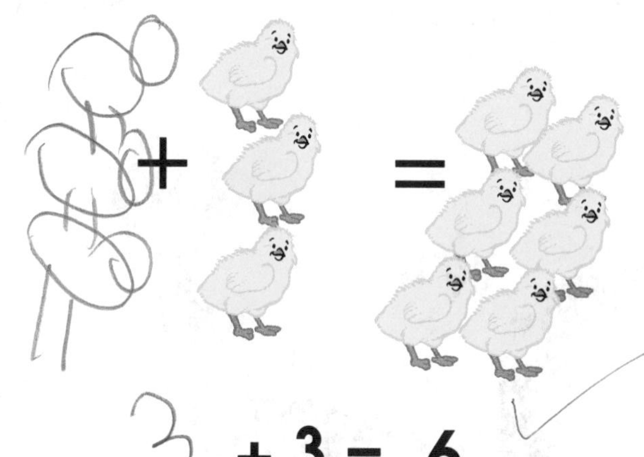

3 + 3 = 6

5 + 2 = 7

2 + 3 = 5

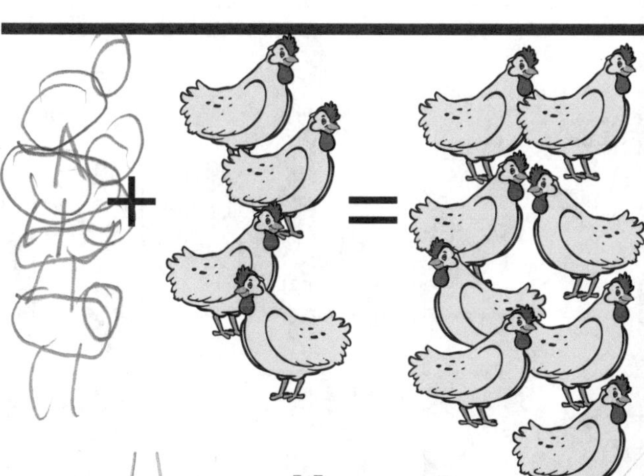

4 + 4 = 8

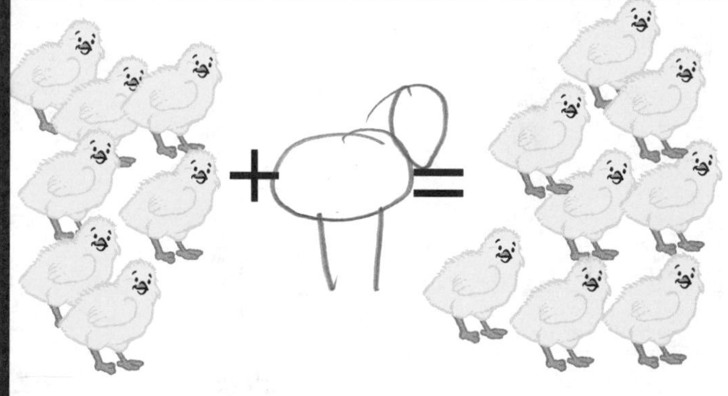

7 + 1 = 8

Name ____________________

Signs of Gain

Directions: Roll a die. Write the addend from the die in the top box. Add to find the sum. Roll again to make each sentence different.

5 + 1 = 6	6 + 1 = 7	3 + 1 = 4

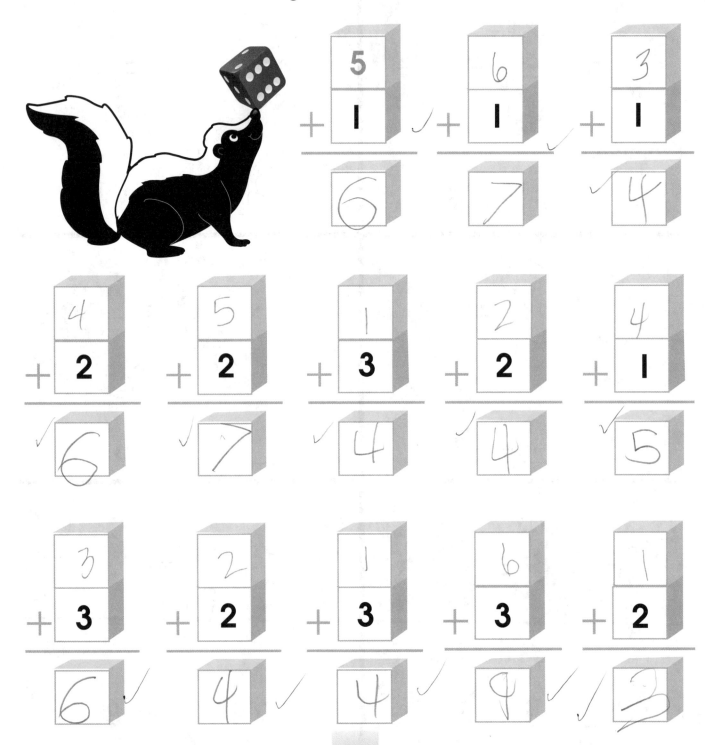

4 + 2 = 6	5 + 2 = 7	1 + 3 = 4	2 + 2 = 4	4 + 1 = 5
3 + 3 = 6	2 + 2 = 4	1 + 3 = 4	6 + 3 = 9	1 + 2 = 3

Name ______________________

How Many in All?

Directions: Count the number in each group and write the number on the line. Then, add the groups together and write the sum.

__8__ strawberries

__5__ strawberries

How many in all? __13__

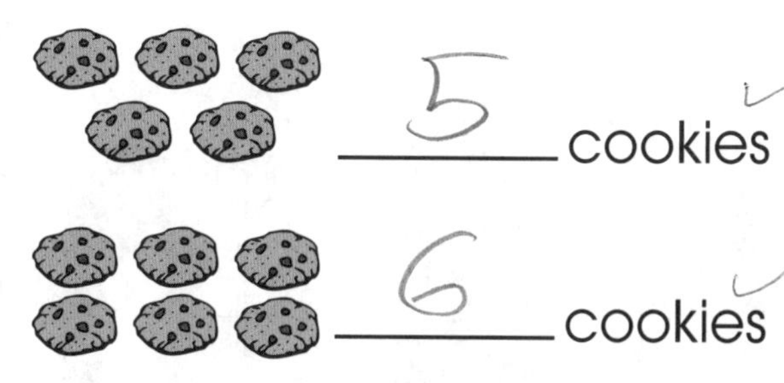

__5__ cookies

__6__ cookies

How many in all? __11__

__7__ shoes

__6__ shoes

How many in all? __13__

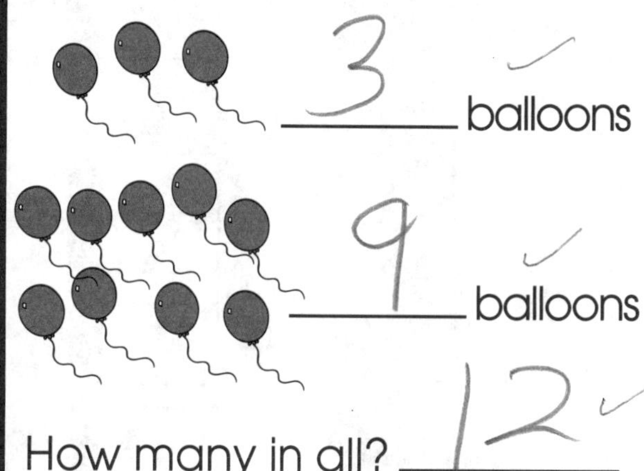

__3__ balloons

__9__ balloons

How many in all? __12__

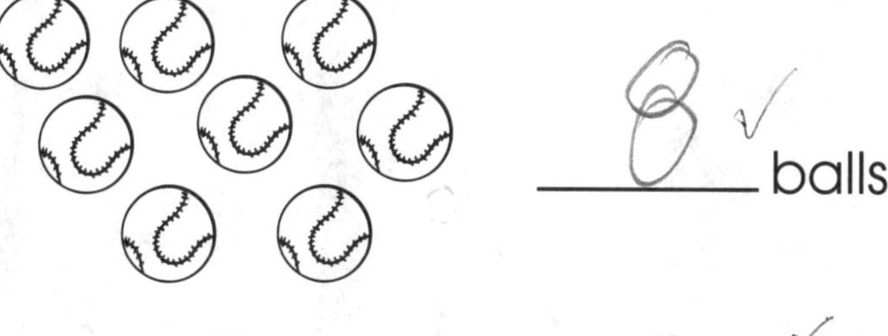

__8__ balls

__3__ balls

How many in all? __11__

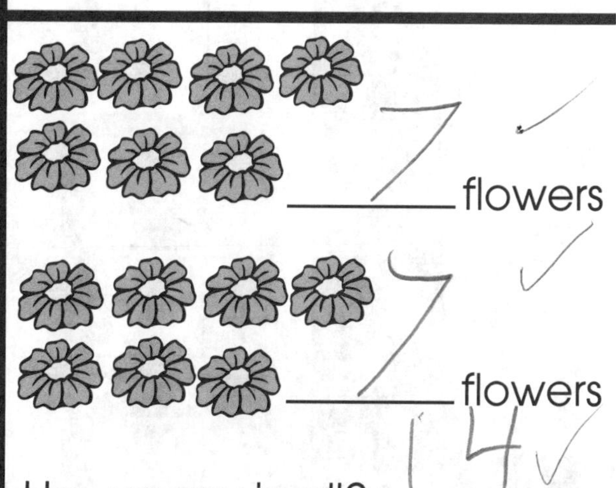

__7__ flowers

__7__ flowers

How many in all? __14__

Name ________________________

Adding 1

Directions: Write a number in the top box of each problem. Complete the problem. Make each problem different.

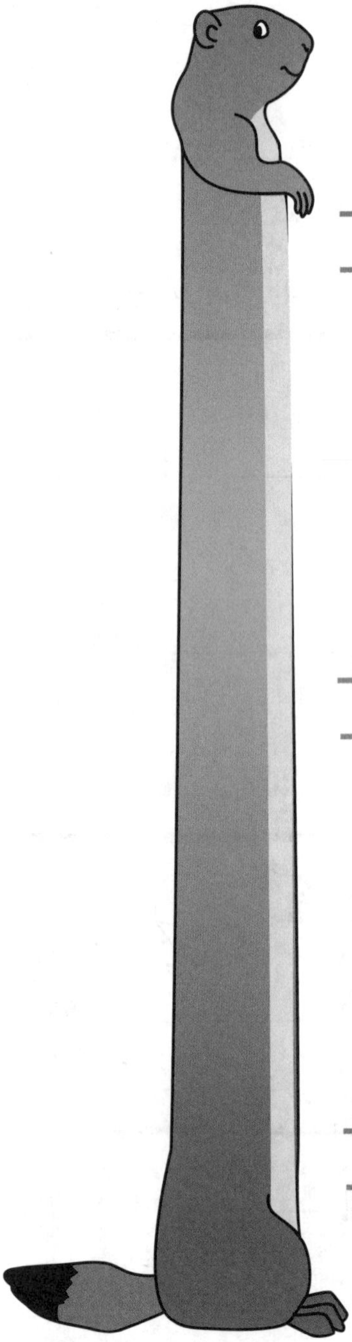

10	14		
+ 1	+ 1	+ 1	+ 1
11			

+ 1	+ 1	+ 1	+ 1

+ 1	+ 1	+ 1	+ 1

Name ______________________

Counting Up

Directions: Count up to get the sum. Write the missing addend in each blank.

3 + ___ = 6

4 + ___ = 5

7 + ___ = 9

2 + ___ = 4

3 + ___ = 8

5 + ___ = 5

8 + ___ = 10

7 + ___ = 8

6 + ___ = 9

8 + ___ = 9

4 + ___ = 6

6 + ___ = 6

5 + ___ = 7

4 + ___ = 7

9 + ___ = 10

5 + ___ = 8

7 + ___ = 10

6 + ___ = 8

Name ________________________________

Animal Addition

Directions: Add to find the sum. **Example:**

4 + 7 = 11

3 + 9 = ____

6 + 7 = ____

6 + 5 = ____

5 + 7 = ____

4 + 9 = ____

9 + 6 = ____

7 + 7 = ____

9 + 6 = ____

6 + 8 = ____

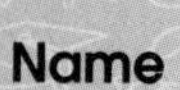

Name ______________________

It's All the Same

Directions: Count the objects and fill in the blanks. Then, switch the addends and write another addition sentence.

Example:

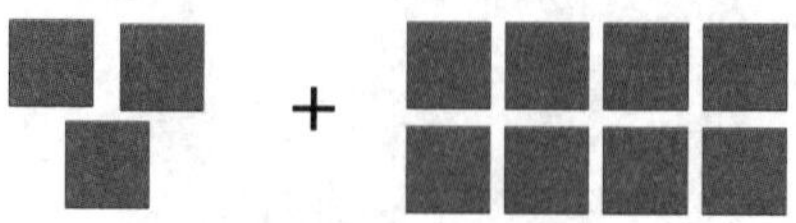

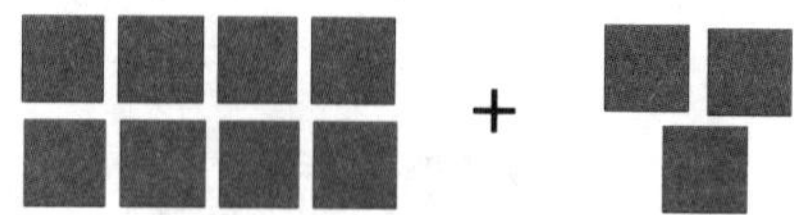

If **3** + **8** = **11**, so does **8** + **3**.

If 8 + 9 = 17, so does 9 + 8.

If 7 + 8 = 15, so does 8 + 7.

If 4 + 6 = 10, so does 6 + 4.

If 6 + 7 = 12, so does 7 + 6.

Name ______________________________

Add the Apples

Directions: Match the addition sentences with their sums.

3 + 2 10
6 + 8 14
5 + 5 5

8 + 2 15
9 + 6 4
2 + 2 10

1 + 2 11
6 + 7 3
5 + 6 13

6 + 6 12
6 + 3 9
3 + 4 7

6 + 2 8
1 + 1 6
1 + 5 2

7 + 2 15
6 + 9 9
12 + 1 13

10 + 1 14
9 + 5 8
7 + 1 11

Name ____________________

Target Practice

Directions: Add the numbers from the inside out. The first one has been done for you.

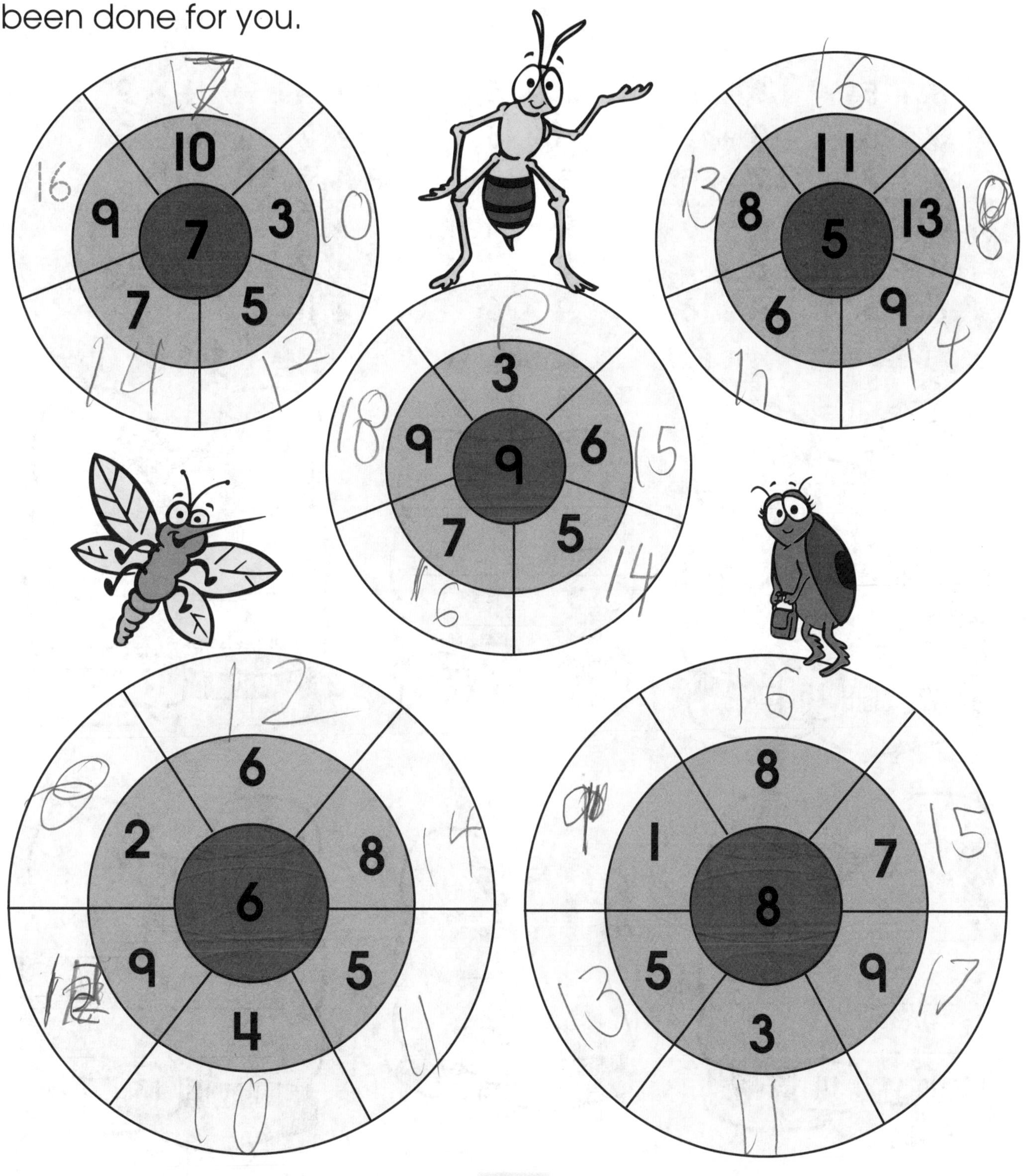

Centre 7: 10, 3, 5, 7, 9

Centre 5: 11, 13, 9, 6, 8

Centre 9: 3, 6, 5, 7, 9

Centre 6: 6, 8, 5, 4, 9, 2

Centre 8: 8, 7, 9, 3, 5, 1

Name ____________________

Ride the Rapids

Directions: Write each problem on the life jacket with the correct answer.

8 + 5	8 + 6	7 + 5	8 + 4	4 + 9
6 + 6	9 + 7	9 + 5	6 + 7	5 + 9
7 + 8	7 + 9	8 + 9	8 + 8	
6 + 9	7 + 6	5 + 8	3 + 9	
9 + 3	5 + 7	8 + 7	7 + 7	
6 + 8	9 + 8	9 + 6	9 + 4	

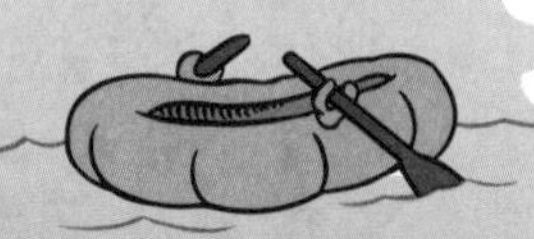

14

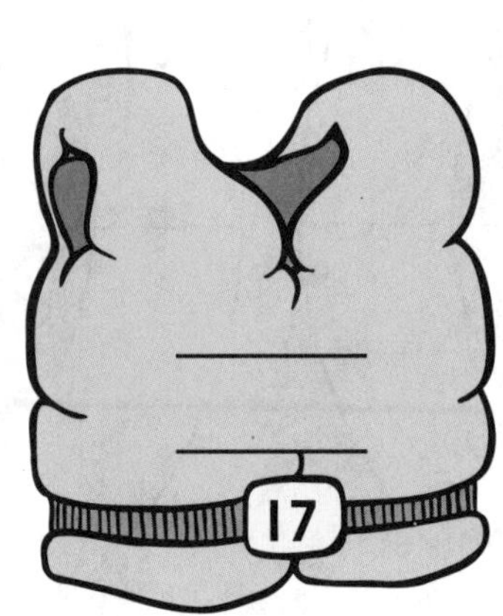

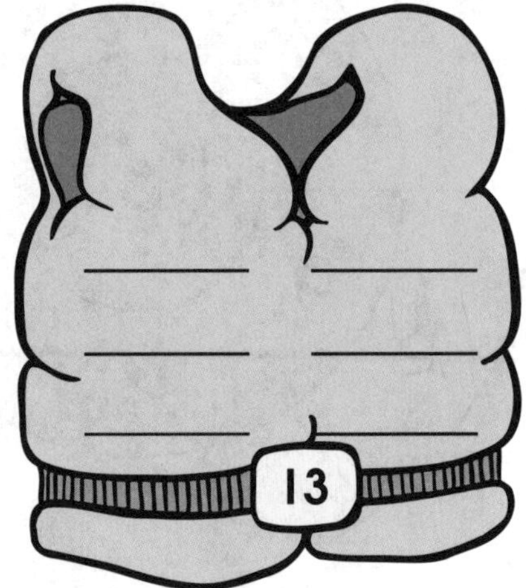

Name ________________________

Math-Minded Farming

Directions: Look at each number. Then, look in each side. Circle each pair of numbers that can be added together to equal that number.

Name ______________________________

Ancient Adding

Directions: Roll a pair of dice. Write the addend from each die on the lines below. Add to find the sum. Roll again to make each sentence different.

___ + ___ = ___

___ + ___ = ___

___ + ___ = ___

___ + ___ = ___

___ + ___ = ___

___ + ___ = ___

___ + ___ = ___

___ + ___ = ___

___ + ___ = ___

___ + ___ = ___

___ + ___ = ___

___ + ___ = ___

___ + ___ = ___

___ + ___ = ___

Name ____________________

Lots of Number Partners

Directions: Connect as many pairs as you can to make each sum.

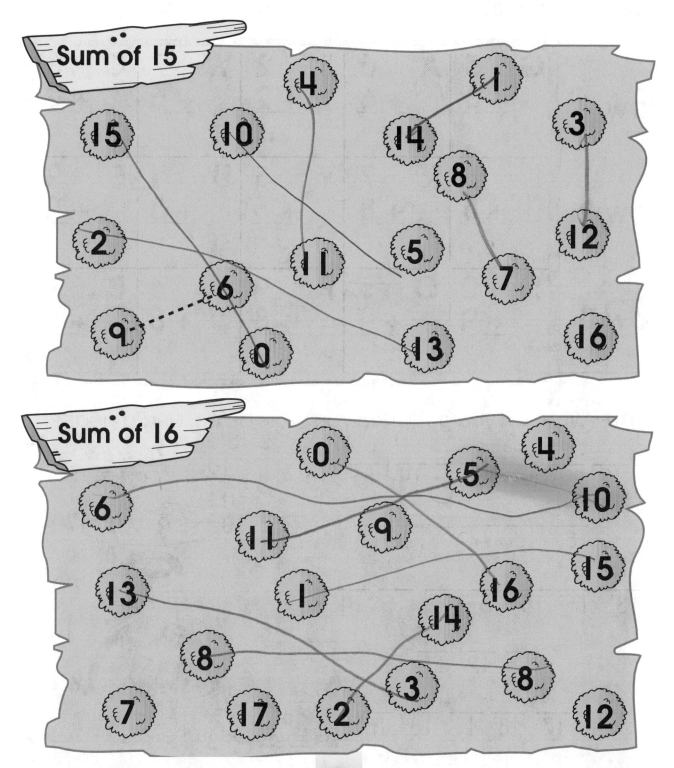

Sum of 15

4, 1, 15, 10, 14, 3, 8, 2, 5, 12, 11, 7, 6, 9, 0, 13, 16

Sum of 16

0, 4, 5, 6, 10, 11, 9, 15, 13, 1, 16, 14, 8, 8, 3, 7, 17, 2, 12

Name ____________________

Solve the Riddle

Directions: Add to find the sums. Connect the dots in order. Use the sums and letters from the boxes to answer the riddle.

Row 1	G $5 + 3$	A $6 + 6$	T $2 + 2$	W $7 + 6$	C $3 + 2$
Row 2	L $8 + 8$	R $7 + 8$	Y $5 + 5$	U $4 + 3$	E $9 + 9$
Row 3	N $2 + 9$	O $5 + 4$	P $9 + 8$	I $6 + 8$	E $1 + 2$

RIDDLE: What will you get when you cross an eel and a goat?

___ ___ ___   ___ ___ ___ ___
10 9 7   13 14 16 16

___ ___ ___   ___ ___
8 18 4   12 11

___ ___ ___ ___ ___ ___ ___ ___
3 16 18 5 4 15 14 5

___ ___ ___
5 12 11

___ ___ ___ ___ ___ ___
9 17 18 11 18 15

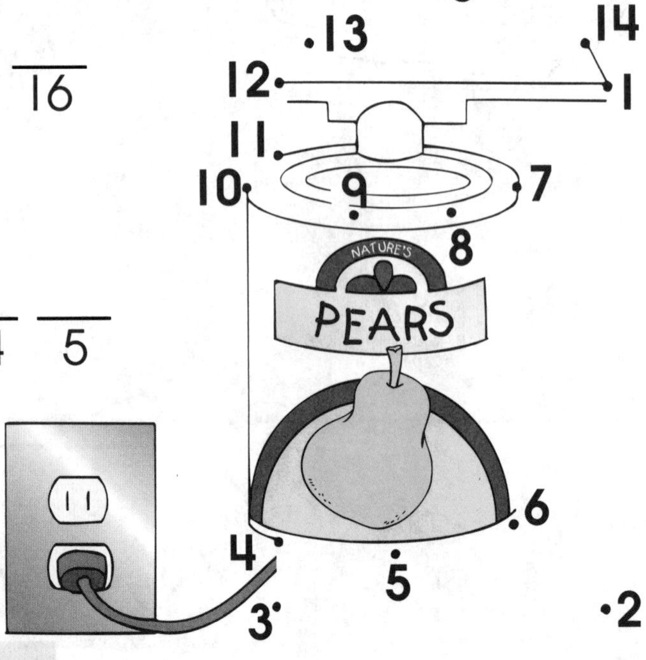

Name ______________________________

Snorkeling Solutions

Directions: Add the numbers in each mask. Write the sums in the bubbles. Colour the bubbles of the four largest sums.

Name ________________________

Colouring by Number

Directions: Find each sum.
If the sum is **13**, colour the space **brown.**
If the sum is **14**, colour the space **yellow.**
If the sum is **16**, colour the space **red.**
If the sum is **17**, colour the space **blue.**

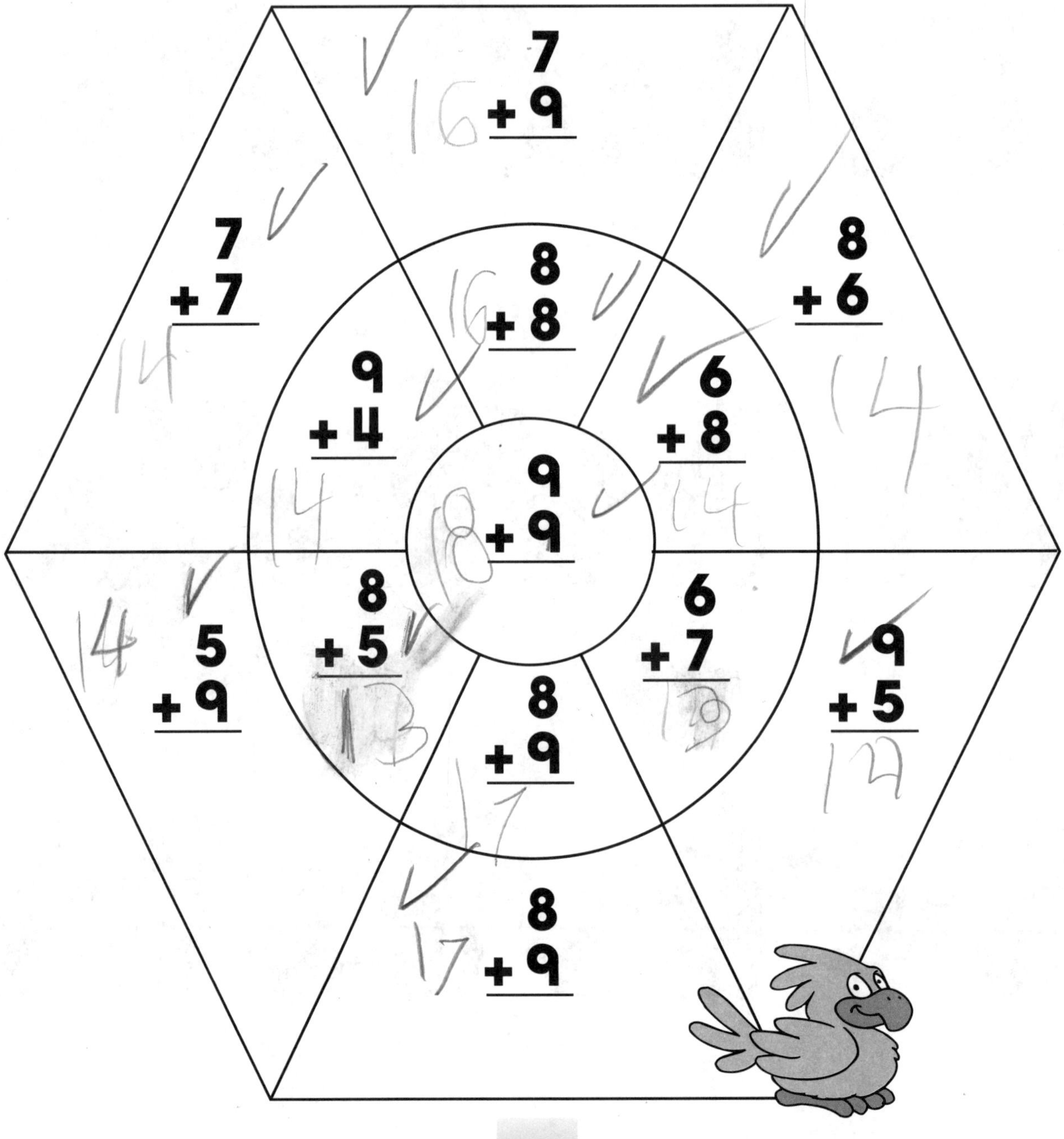

$7 + 9$

$7 + 7$

$8 + 8$

$8 + 6$

$9 + 4$

$6 + 8$

$9 + 9$

$8 + 5$

$6 + 7$

$5 + 9$

$9 + 5$

$8 + 9$

$8 + 9$

Name ______________________________

Counting Up the Coins

Directions: Solve the problem on each bag. Write the answer on the coin below it. Colour the odd sums yellow.

9 + 2	6 + 7	4 + 7	8 + 8	6 + 9
7 + 5	5 + 8	9 + 9	7 + 4	8 + 3
8 + 9	6 + 5	8 + 7	7 + 9	6 + 6

Name ____________________

Mys-sss-terious Music

Directions: Solve the problems. Colour the spaces using the answers.

ANSWER COLOUR KEY:

= 0 - 2

= 3 - 6

= 7 - 9

= 10 - 12

= 13 - 16

= 17 - 20

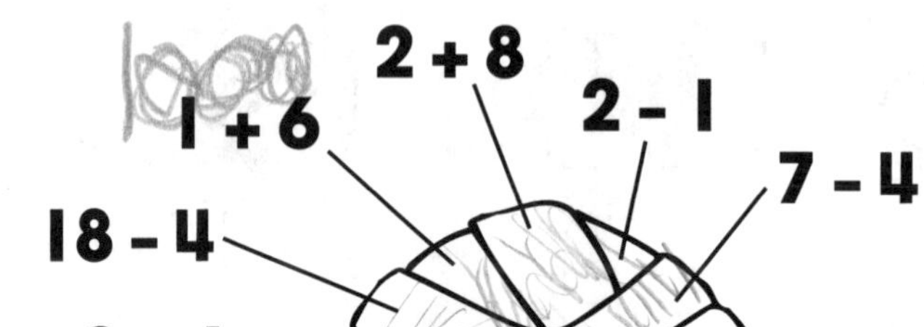

Name ____________________

Food Facts

Directions: Draw pictures to show what happens in each story. Solve the problem.

The squirrel holds 2 s.

He has 8 s in the tree.

How many 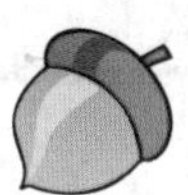s in all?  10 ________

There are 4 s on the tree.

There are 3 s on the ground.

How many s in all? 7 ________

The monkey picked 2 s.

There are 6 more s left on the vine.

How many s in all?  8 ________

There are 5 s in the bag.

There are 4 s in your hand.

How many s in all? 9 ________

Name ____________________

Problem Solving

Directions: Solve each problem.

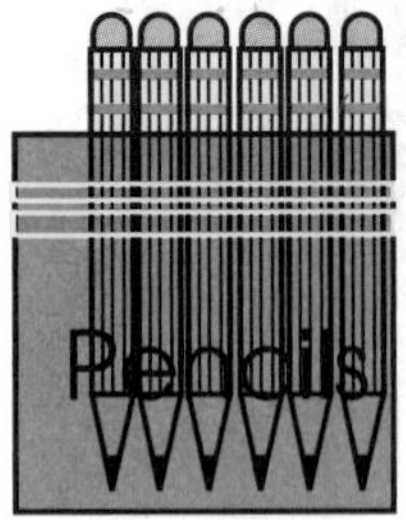
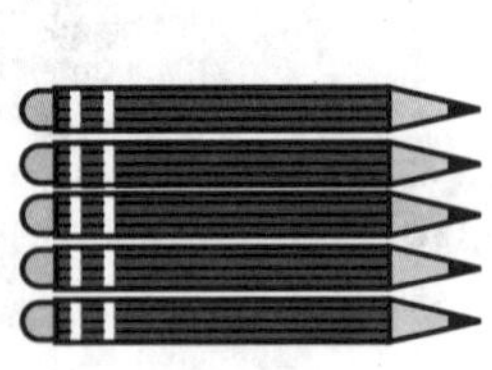

6 pencils in a box
+ 5 more pencils
____ pencils in all

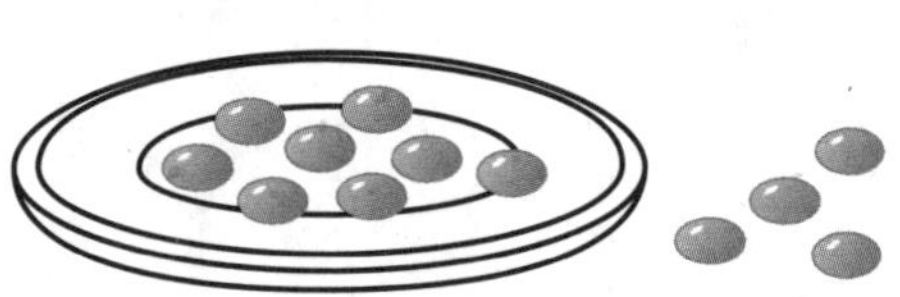

grapes on a plate
more grapes
grapes in all

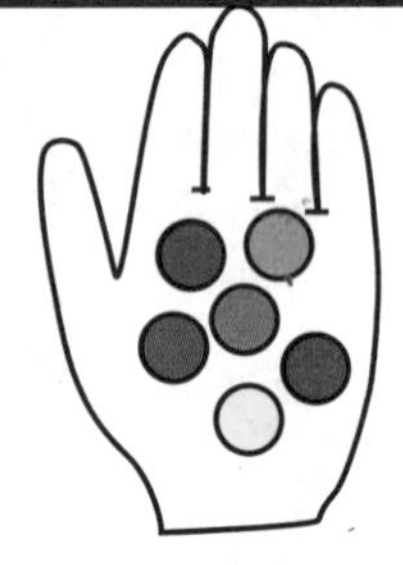
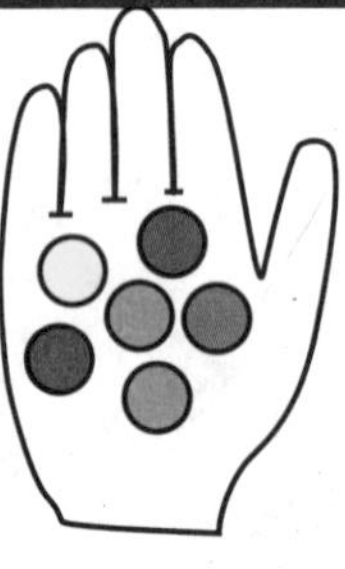

marbles in one hand
marbles in the other hand
marbles in all

people at the table
more people coming in
people in all

black buttons
white buttons
buttons in all

Name ____________________

Problem Solving

Directions: Solve each problem.

Example:

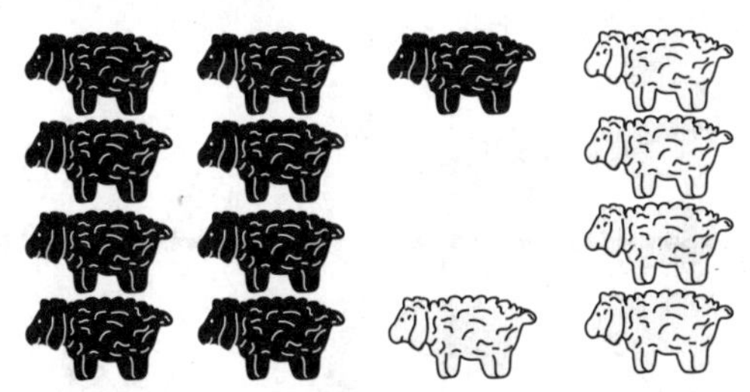

9 black sheep
+ 9 white sheep
sheep in all

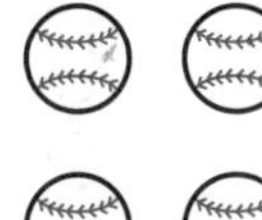
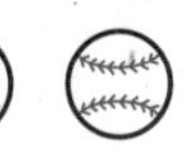

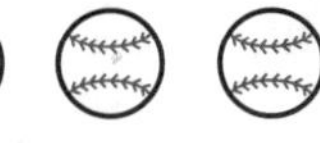

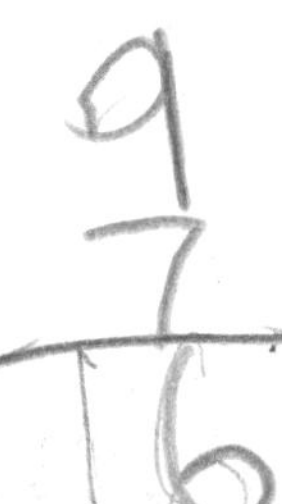

softballs
baseballs
balls in all

glasses of milkshake
empty glasses
glasses in all

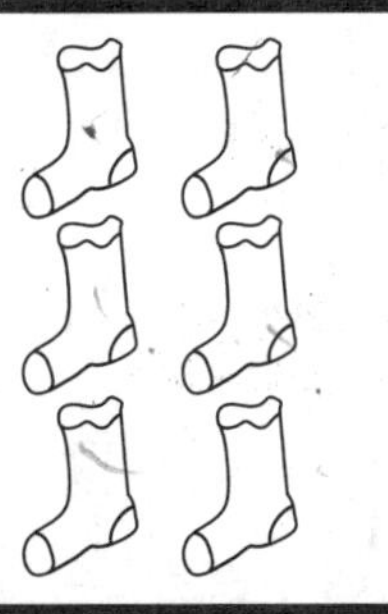
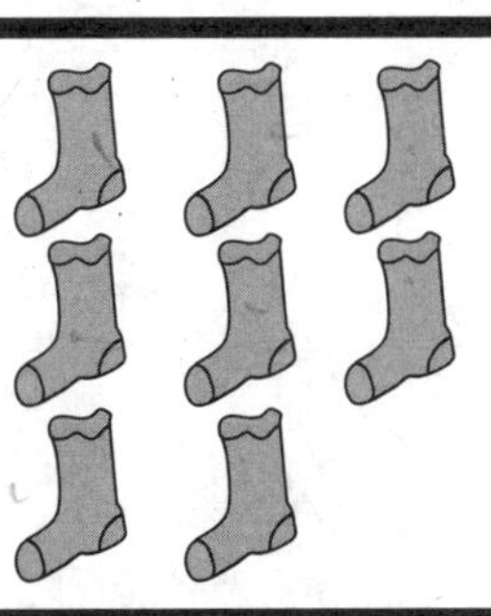

white socks
grey socks
socks in all

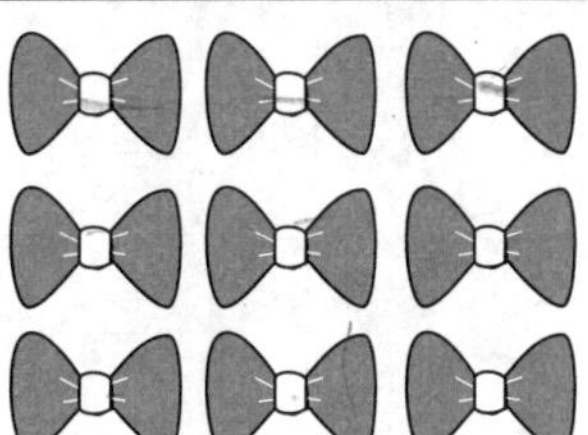
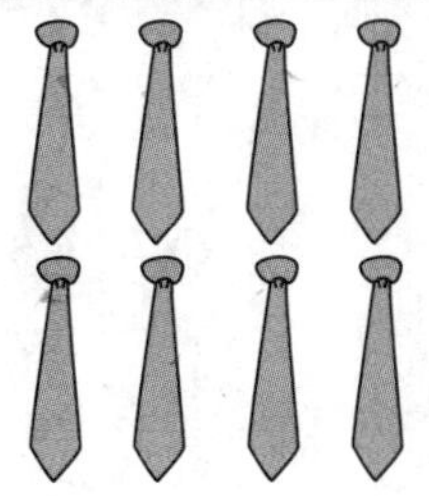

bow ties
regular ties
ties in all

Name ______________________

Fast Tracking Numbers

Directions: Use the number line to count back.

Example: 8, ___7___, ___6___

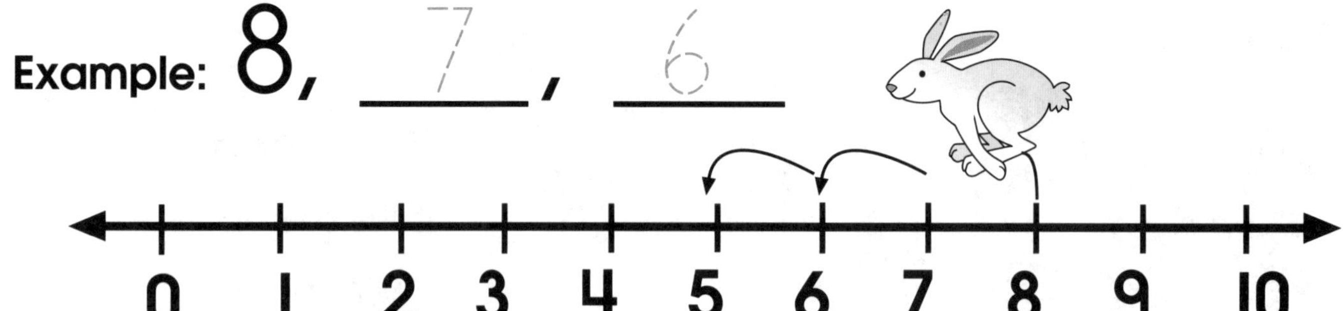

Name ______________________________

Bubbly Baths

Directions: Solve the subtraction sentences below. Write each answer on a rubber duck.

5 - 4

1 - 0

4 - 2

2 - 1

3 - 1

3 - 2

4 - 1

1 - 1

5 - 1

5 - 2

Name ______________________

Leaves Leaving the Limb

Directions: Subtract to find the difference. Use the code to colour the leaves. Code: **0 = green 1 = red 2 = yellow 3 = brown**

$\begin{array}{r} 1 \\ -0 \\ \hline \end{array}$ $\begin{array}{r} 5 \\ -2 \\ \hline \end{array}$ $\begin{array}{r} 3 \\ -3 \\ \hline \end{array}$ $\begin{array}{r} 2 \\ -1 \\ \hline \end{array}$

$\begin{array}{r} 3 \\ -1 \\ \hline \end{array}$ $\begin{array}{r} 2 \\ -2 \\ \hline \end{array}$ $\begin{array}{r} 4 \\ -2 \\ \hline \end{array}$ $\begin{array}{r} 5 \\ -3 \\ \hline \end{array}$

$\begin{array}{r} 3 \\ -0 \\ \hline \end{array}$ $\begin{array}{r} 5 \\ -4 \\ \hline \end{array}$ $\begin{array}{r} 1 \\ -1 \\ \hline \end{array}$ $\begin{array}{r} 2 \\ -1 \\ \hline \end{array}$

How many of each colour?

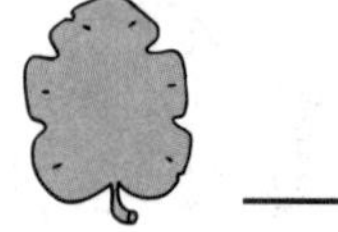 ________ 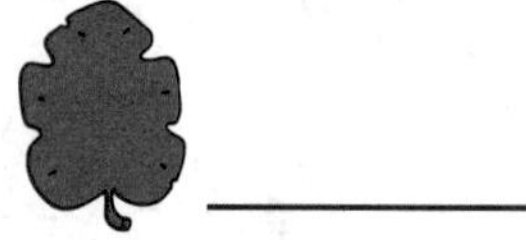 ________ 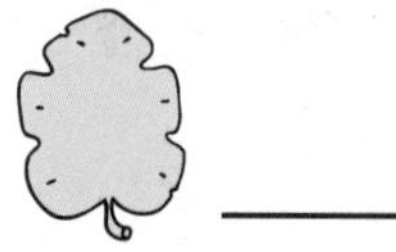 ________  ________

Name ______________________________

Secrets of Subtraction

Directions: Solve the subtraction problems. Use the code to find the secret message.

Code:

7	5	2	6	4	3
K	T	Y	E	W	A

PLEASE, DON'T EVER

8 − 3	10 − 7	9 − 2	10 − 4
___	___	___	___

9 − 6	6 − 2	7 − 4	8 − 6
___	___	___	___

MY MATH!

Name ____________________

Subtraction Makes Al Hungry

Directions: Write a different problem for each answer.

Example:

5 − 4 = 1	8 − ☐ = 1	☐ − ☐ = 2	☐ − ☐ = 2
☐ − ☐ = 3	☐ − ☐ = 3	☐ − ☐ = 4	☐ − ☐ = 4
☐ − ☐ = 5	☐ − ☐ = 6	☐ − ☐ = 7	☐ − ☐ = 8

Name ____________________

Differences in Boxes

Directions: Colour the two numbers in each box that show the given difference.

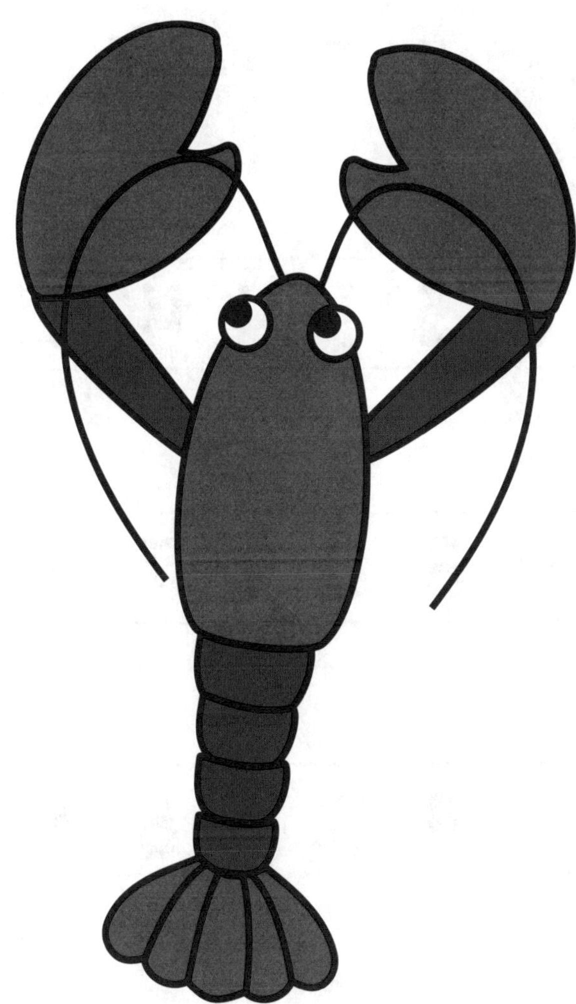

Difference of 1

6	4
3	8

3	1
5	6

4	0
1	7

Difference of 1

3	7
1	8

2	3
5	7

6	3
9	7

Difference of 2

3	0
7	1

3	8
6	9

7	1
4	6

Difference of 2

3	4
8	2

7	4
10	5

10	8
5	4

Difference of 0

2	1
4	2

7	3
8	3

5	6
5	4

Name 

Looping Differences

Directions: Circle the two numbers next to each other that make the given difference. Find as many as you can in each row.

Difference of 1

2	3	0	8	7	2	9	10	6	5	1	4	4	3

Difference of 1

8	4	5	3	7	1	2	4	9	8	0	1	7	6

Difference of 2

5	4	2	3	1	0	3	5	8	9	3	6	8	5

Difference of 2

7	5	10	8	1	4	6	3	2	6	7	9	2	0

Difference of 3

1	6	3	2	8	4	7	6	10	0	3	9	5	2

Name ______________________________

Hidden Differences of 2

Directions: Circle the pairs that have a difference of **2**.

3 1 10 9 7 3 5

4 6 8 5 1 2 6

8 0 2 3 4 0 4

2 4 10 1 10 6 9

6 2 8 10 8 6 7

1 9 3 5 4 4 3

5 7 1 0 2 7 9

Name ________________________________

Hidden Differences of 3

Directions: Circle the pairs that have a difference of **3**.

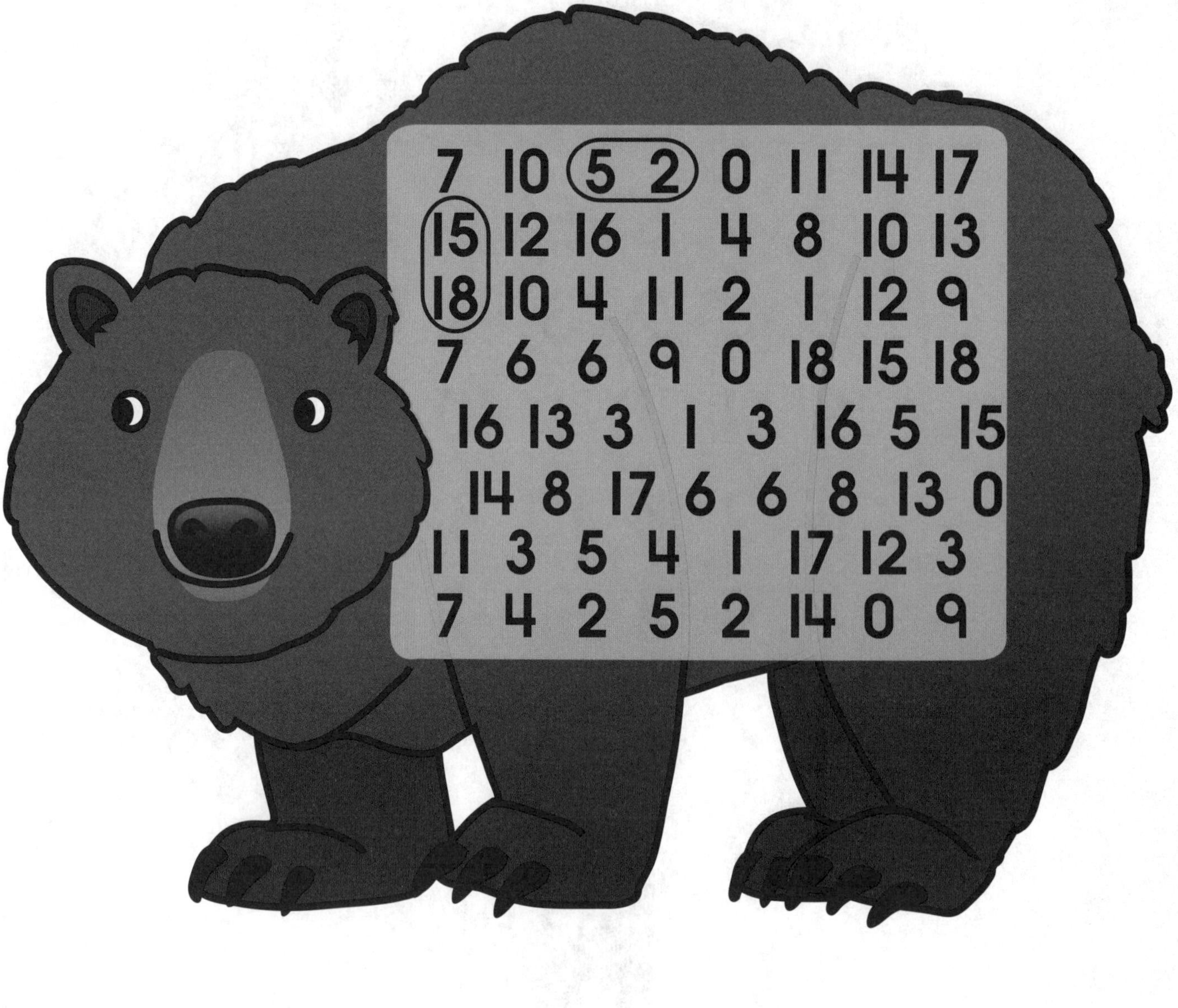

7 10 5 2 0 11 14 17
15 12 16 1 4 8 10 13
18 10 4 11 2 1 12 9
7 6 6 9 0 18 15 18
16 13 3 1 3 16 5 15
14 8 17 6 6 8 13 0
11 3 5 4 1 17 12 3
7 4 2 5 2 14 0 9

Name ____________________

Hidden Differences

Directions: Find the shape with the correct difference. Copy the numbers that make that difference.

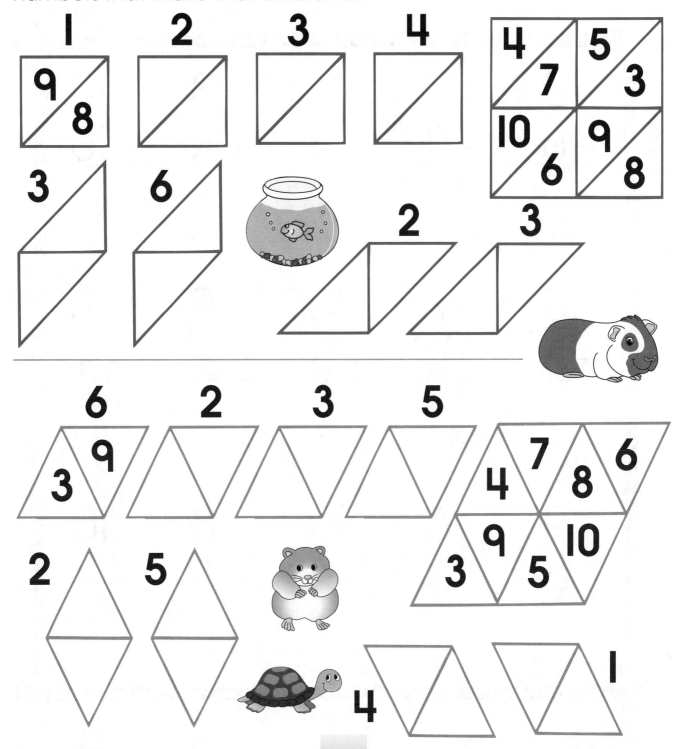

1, 2, 3, 4

9 / 8

4 / 7, 5 / 3, 10 / 6, 9 / 8

3, 6, 2, 3

6, 2, 3, 5

3, 9

4, 7, 8, 6, 3, 9, 5, 10

2, 5, 4, 1

Name ____________________

Subtraction Fun

Directions: Subtract to find each difference.

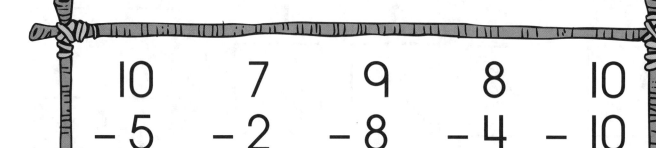

10	7	9	8	10
− 5	− 2	− 8	− 4	− 10

8	7	10	9	9
− 3	− 6	− 3	− 7	− 1

9	6	10	8	10
− 6	− 3	− 9	− 5	− 4

Name ____________________

A Nose for Subtraction

Directions: Cut out the elephant heads at the bottom of the page. Glue each head on the body with the correct answer.

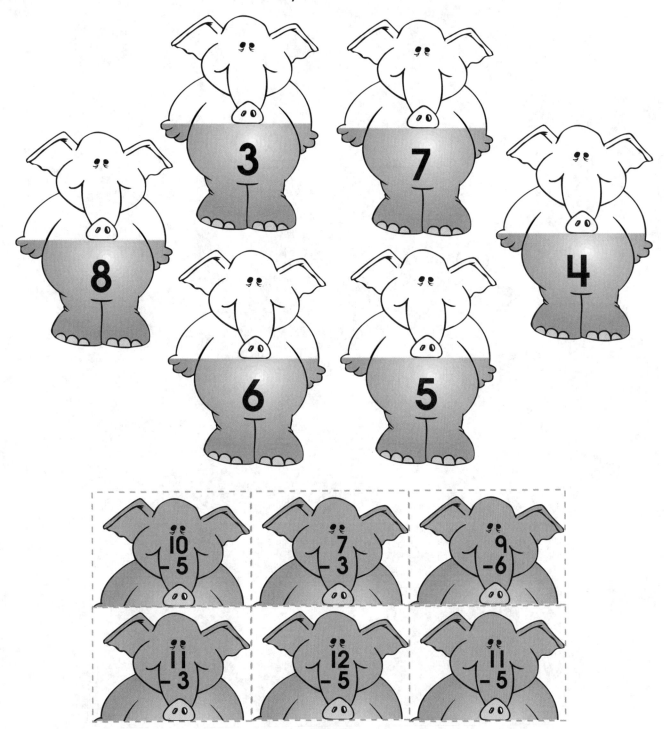

3

7

8

4

6

5

$\begin{array}{r} 10 \\ -5 \end{array}$	$\begin{array}{r} 7 \\ -3 \end{array}$	$\begin{array}{r} 9 \\ -6 \end{array}$
$\begin{array}{r} 11 \\ -3 \end{array}$	$\begin{array}{r} 12 \\ -5 \end{array}$	$\begin{array}{r} 11 \\ -5 \end{array}$

This page was left intentionally blank for cutting activity on previous page.

Name ____________________

Gone Fishing

Directions: Complete the subtraction sentences to make each problem correct.

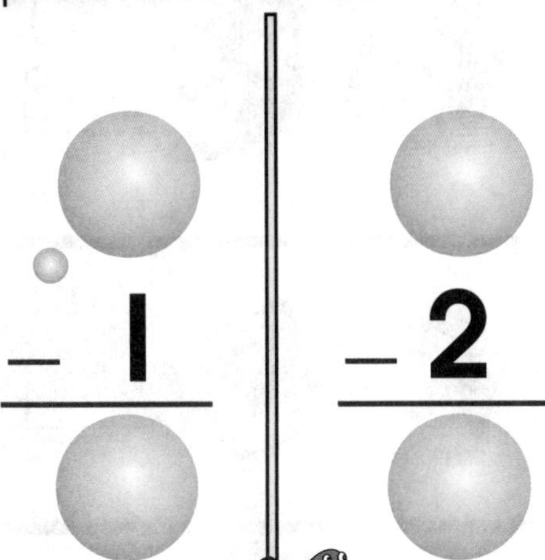

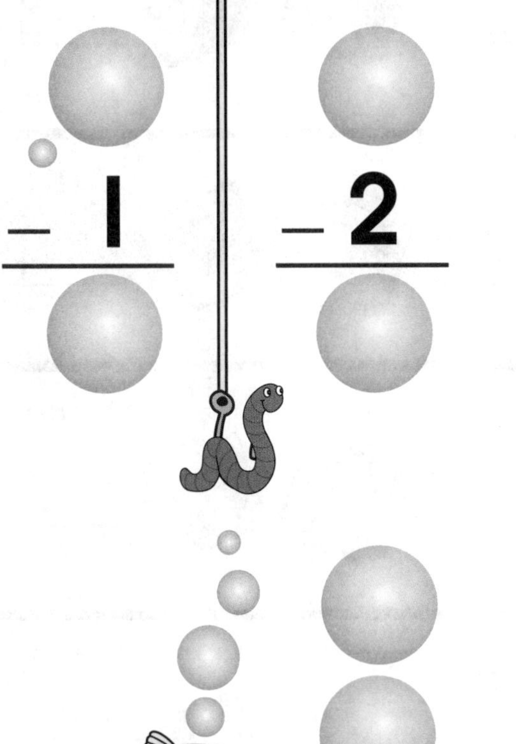

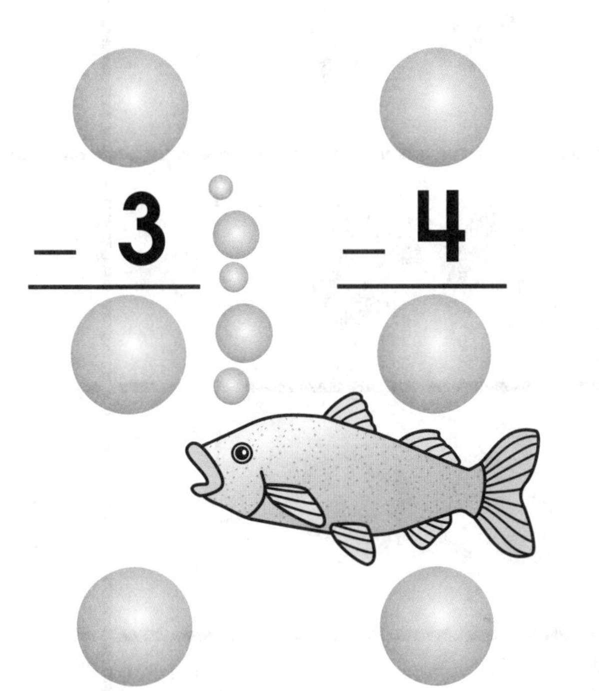

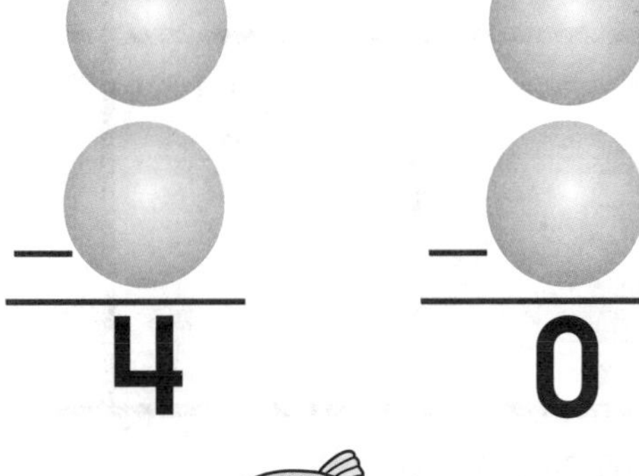

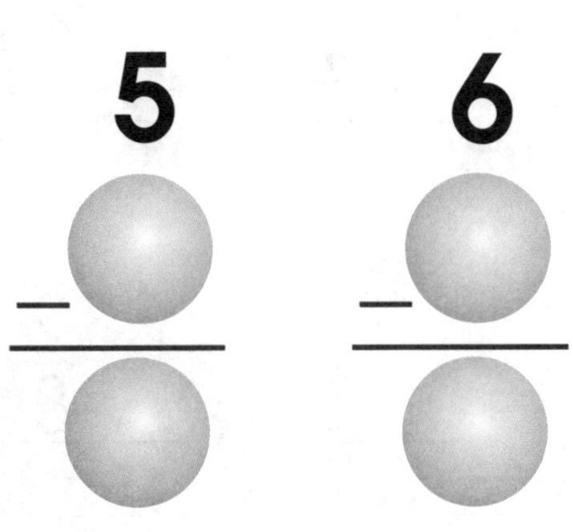

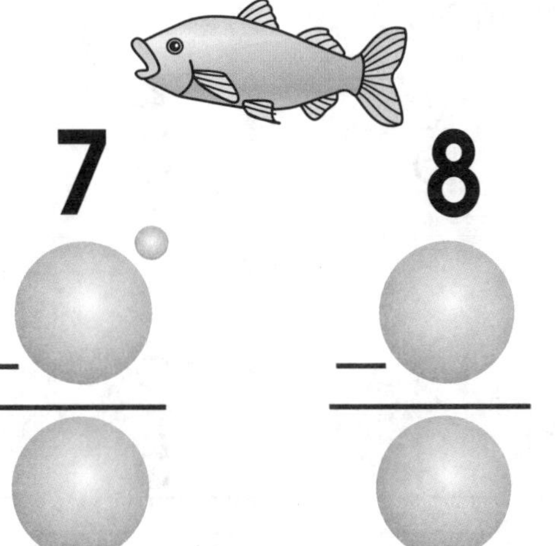

◯	◯	◯	◯	◯
– 1	– 2	– 3	– 4	– 5
◯	◯	◯	◯	◯

◯	◯	◯	◯
– ◯	– ◯	– ◯	– ◯
2	4	0	3

5	6	7	8	9
– ◯	– ◯	– ◯	– ◯	– ◯
◯	◯	◯	◯	◯

Name ____________________

Subtraction Facts Through 12

Directions: Subtract.

11 − 9 = ___
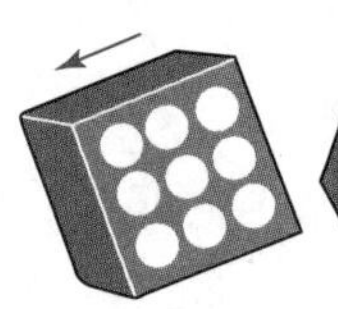
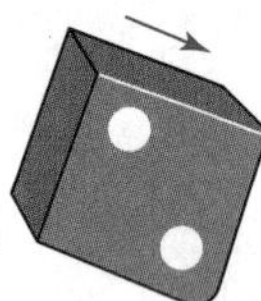
11 − 2 = ___

11 − 8 = ___

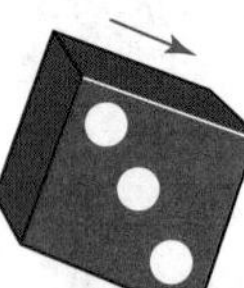
11 − 3 = ___

11 − 6 = ___

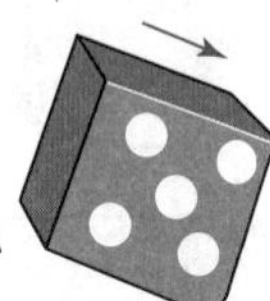
11 − 5 = ___

11 − 7 = ___

11 − 4 = ___

12 − 8 = ___
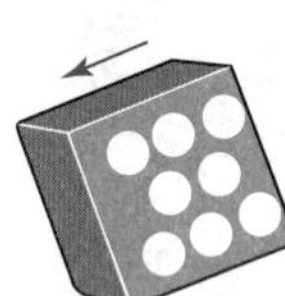
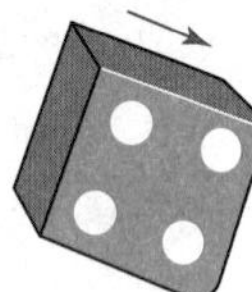
12 − 4 = ___

12 − 7 = ___
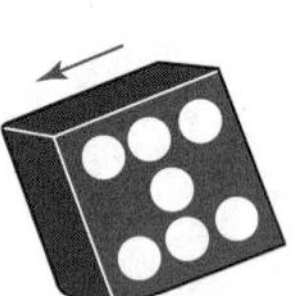
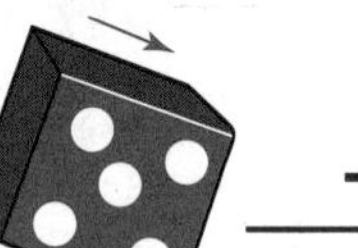
12 − 5 = ___

12 − 9 = ___
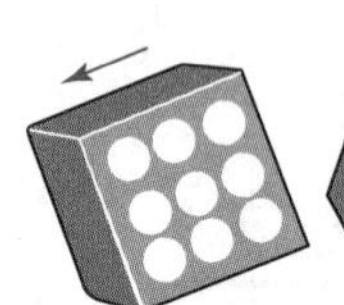
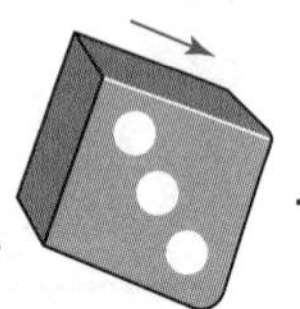
12 − 3 = ___

12 − 6 = ___
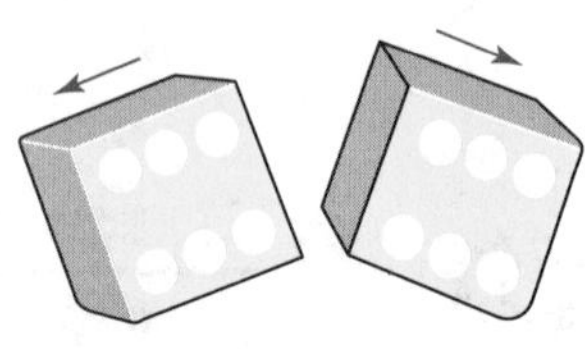

Directions: Subtract.

11 − 3 = ___	11 − 6 = ___	12 − 3 = ___	11 − 8 = ___	12 − 7 = ___	12 − 9 = ___
11 − 7 = ___	12 − 4 = ___	12 − 5 = ___	12 − 6 = ___	11 − 2 = ___	12 − 8 = ___

Name ____________________

Subtraction Facts Through 14

Directions: Subtract.

Examples:

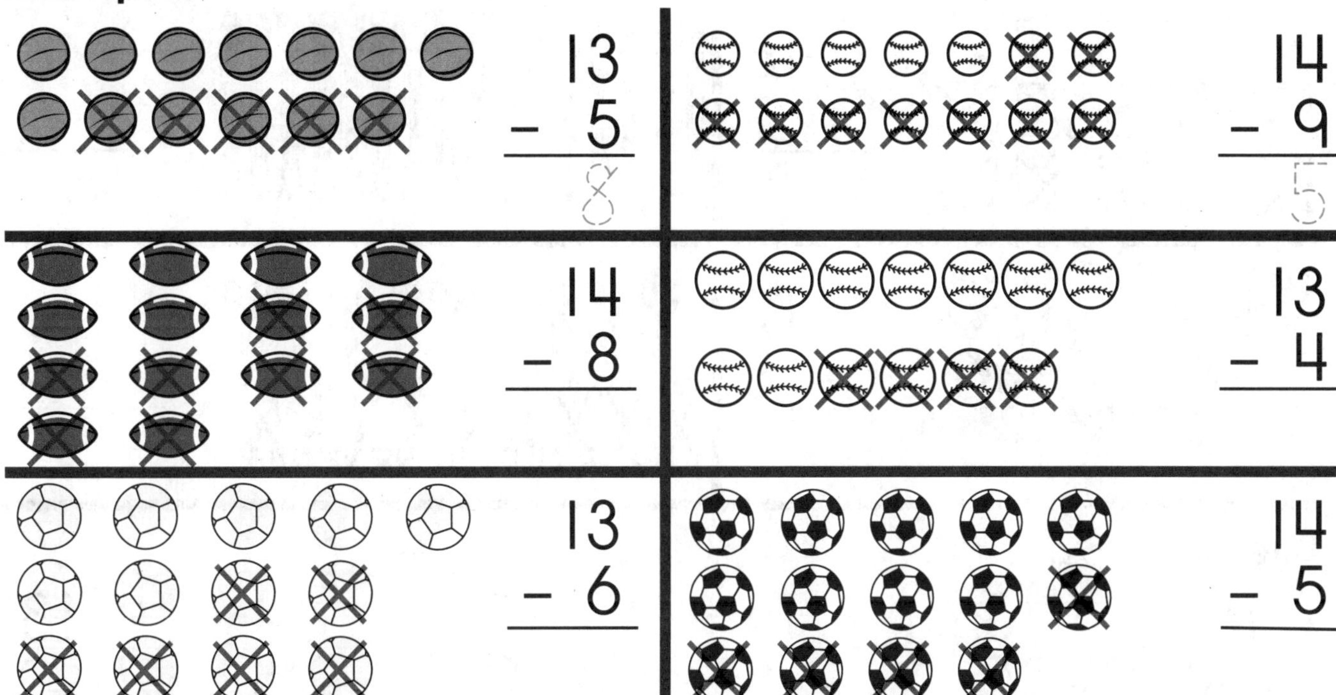

Directions: Subtract.

12 − 7	10 − 2	13 − 4	14 − 9	11 − 8	14 − 5
14 − 6	12 − 8	13 − 5	10 − 6	13 − 6	13 − 7
11 − 6	13 − 9	14 − 8	12 − 3	14 − 7	13 − 8

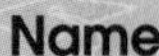

Name ______________________

Subtraction Facts Through 18

Directions: Subtract.

Example:

$$\begin{array}{r} 15 \\ -\ 7 \\ \hline 8 \end{array}$$

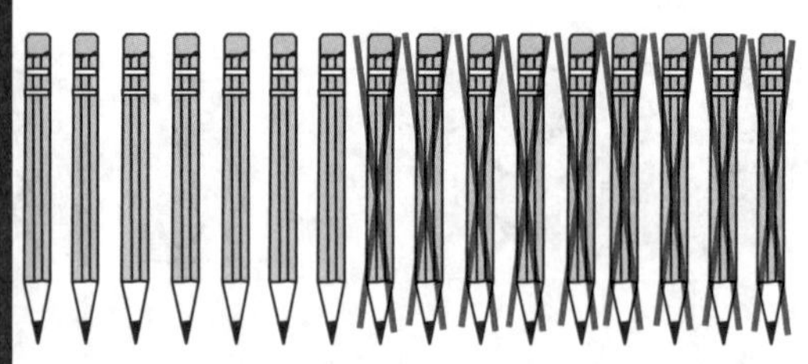

$$\begin{array}{r} 16 \\ -\ 9 \\ \hline \end{array}$$

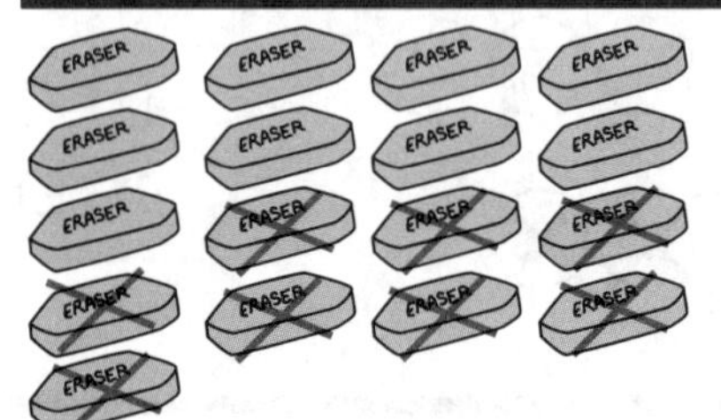

$$\begin{array}{r} 17 \\ -\ 8 \\ \hline \end{array}$$

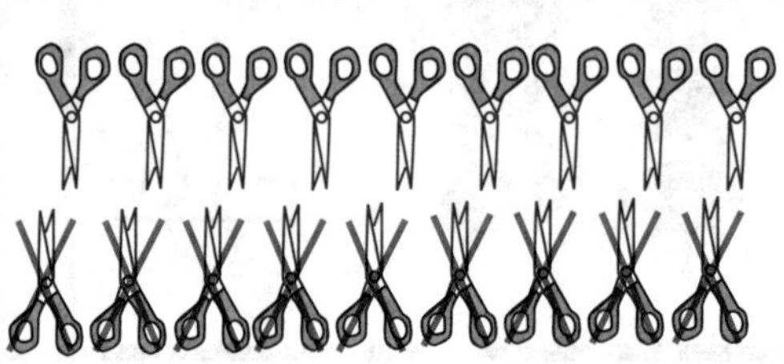

$$\begin{array}{r} 18 \\ -\ 9 \\ \hline \end{array}$$

Directions: Subtract.

$$\begin{array}{r} 18 \\ -\ 9 \\ \hline \end{array} \quad \begin{array}{r} 13 \\ -\ 5 \\ \hline \end{array} \quad \begin{array}{r} 16 \\ -\ 8 \\ \hline \end{array} \quad \begin{array}{r} 17 \\ -\ 9 \\ \hline \end{array} \quad \begin{array}{r} 14 \\ -\ 6 \\ \hline \end{array} \quad \begin{array}{r} 13 \\ -\ 9 \\ \hline \end{array}$$

$$\begin{array}{r} 17 \\ -\ 8 \\ \hline \end{array} \quad \begin{array}{r} 15 \\ -\ 9 \\ \hline \end{array} \quad \begin{array}{r} 14 \\ -\ 5 \\ \hline \end{array} \quad \begin{array}{r} 13 \\ -\ 6 \\ \hline \end{array} \quad \begin{array}{r} 16 \\ -\ 7 \\ \hline \end{array} \quad \begin{array}{r} 12 \\ -\ 4 \\ \hline \end{array}$$

$$\begin{array}{r} 14 \\ -\ 7 \\ \hline \end{array} \quad \begin{array}{r} 15 \\ -\ 8 \\ \hline \end{array} \quad \begin{array}{r} 16 \\ -\ 9 \\ \hline \end{array} \quad \begin{array}{r} 12 \\ -\ 7 \\ \hline \end{array} \quad \begin{array}{r} 15 \\ -\ 7 \\ \hline \end{array} \quad \begin{array}{r} 13 \\ -\ 4 \\ \hline \end{array}$$

$$\begin{array}{r} 15 \\ -\ 6 \\ \hline \end{array} \quad \begin{array}{r} 14 \\ -\ 8 \\ \hline \end{array} \quad \begin{array}{r} 12 \\ -\ 3 \\ \hline \end{array} \quad \begin{array}{r} 13 \\ -\ 9 \\ \hline \end{array} \quad \begin{array}{r} 14 \\ -\ 9 \\ \hline \end{array} \quad \begin{array}{r} 11 \\ -\ 3 \\ \hline \end{array}$$

Name ______________________________

"Grrreat" Picture

Directions: Subtract. Write the answer in the space. Then, colour the spaces according to the answers.

1 = white **2 = purple** **3 = black** **4 = green** **5 = yellow**
6 = blue **7 = pink** **8 = grey** **9 = orange** **10 = red**

8 – 4 7 – 5
5 – 1 4 – 0 6 – 1 6 – 2
7 – 3 10 – 1
1 – 0 15 – 8 11 – 8 4 – 0
10 – 1 3 – 2 10 – 9 9 – 0
9 – 0
8 – 7 14 – 5 4 – 1 2 – 1
8 – 5 12 – 9 10 – 7
11 – 2 13 – 7
13 – 4
12 – 3 3 – 0
9 – 3 12 – 3 11 – 2
12 – 6
8 – 4
6 – 2 15 – 9
7 – 2 10 – 5
11 – 9 13 – 8
8 – 6 10 – 5
14 – 7 10 – 0 6 – 2 5 – 1
7 – 3

Name ______________________

Crayon Count

Directions: Count the crayons. Write the number on the blank. Circle the problems that equal the answer.

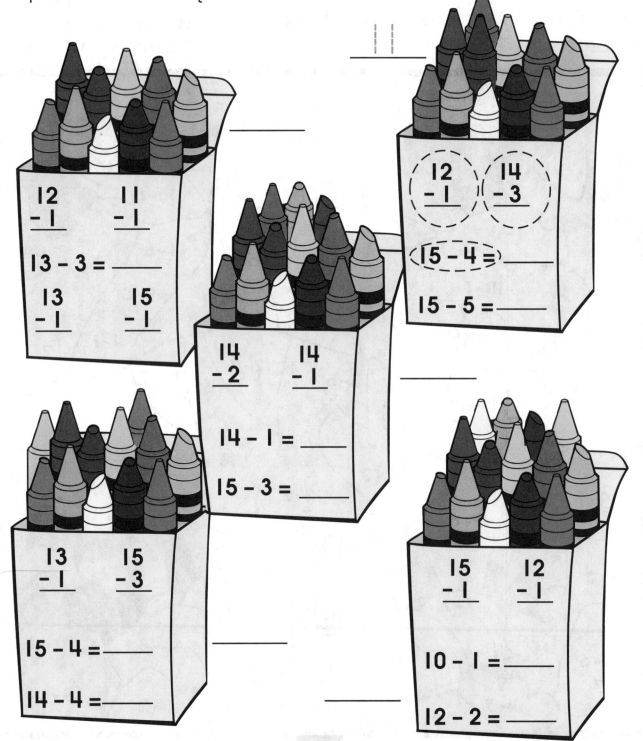

11

$\begin{array}{r}12\\-1\\\hline\end{array}$ $\begin{array}{r}14\\-3\\\hline\end{array}$

15 – 4 = ____

15 – 5 = ____

____

$\begin{array}{r}12\\-1\\\hline\end{array}$ $\begin{array}{r}11\\-1\\\hline\end{array}$

13 – 3 = ____

$\begin{array}{r}13\\-1\\\hline\end{array}$ $\begin{array}{r}15\\-1\\\hline\end{array}$

____

$\begin{array}{r}14\\-2\\\hline\end{array}$ $\begin{array}{r}14\\-1\\\hline\end{array}$

14 – 1 = ____

15 – 3 = ____

____

$\begin{array}{r}13\\-1\\\hline\end{array}$ $\begin{array}{r}15\\-3\\\hline\end{array}$

15 – 4 = ____

14 – 4 = ____

____

$\begin{array}{r}15\\-1\\\hline\end{array}$ $\begin{array}{r}12\\-1\\\hline\end{array}$

10 – 1 = ____

12 – 2 = ____

Name ______________________________

Connect the Facts

Directions: Solve the subtraction problems below.

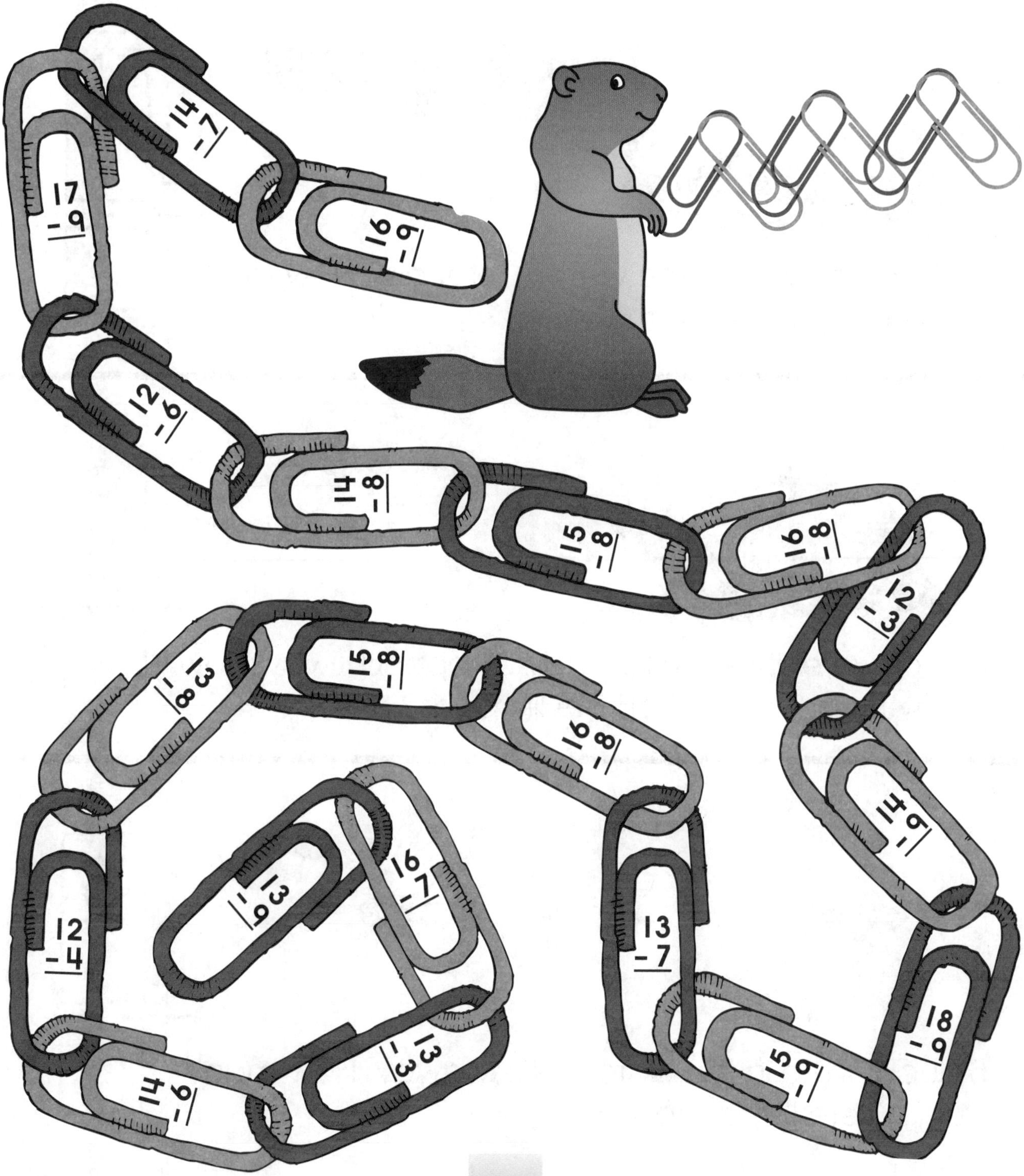

$$\begin{array}{r} 16 \\ -\ 9 \\ \hline \end{array} \quad \begin{array}{r} 14 \\ -\ 7 \\ \hline \end{array} \quad \begin{array}{r} 17 \\ -\ 9 \\ \hline \end{array} \quad \begin{array}{r} 12 \\ -\ 6 \\ \hline \end{array} \quad \begin{array}{r} 14 \\ -\ 8 \\ \hline \end{array}$$

$$\begin{array}{r} 15 \\ -\ 8 \\ \hline \end{array} \quad \begin{array}{r} 16 \\ -\ 8 \\ \hline \end{array} \quad \begin{array}{r} 12 \\ -\ 3 \\ \hline \end{array} \quad \begin{array}{r} 14 \\ -\ 9 \\ \hline \end{array} \quad \begin{array}{r} 18 \\ -\ 9 \\ \hline \end{array}$$

$$\begin{array}{r} 15 \\ -\ 9 \\ \hline \end{array} \quad \begin{array}{r} 13 \\ -\ 7 \\ \hline \end{array} \quad \begin{array}{r} 16 \\ -\ 8 \\ \hline \end{array} \quad \begin{array}{r} 15 \\ -\ 8 \\ \hline \end{array} \quad \begin{array}{r} 13 \\ -\ 8 \\ \hline \end{array}$$

$$\begin{array}{r} 12 \\ -\ 4 \\ \hline \end{array} \quad \begin{array}{r} 14 \\ -\ 9 \\ \hline \end{array} \quad \begin{array}{r} 13 \\ -\ 3 \\ \hline \end{array} \quad \begin{array}{r} 16 \\ -\ 7 \\ \hline \end{array} \quad \begin{array}{r} 13 \\ -\ 9 \\ \hline \end{array}$$

Name ____________________

Swamp Stories

Directions: Read the story. Subtract to find the difference. Write the number in the box.

$$\begin{array}{r} 4 \\ -\ 1 \\ \hline \square \end{array}$$

4 alligators were in the water. 1 got out. How many alligators were left in the water?

$$\begin{array}{r} 6 \\ -\ 2 \\ \hline \square \end{array}$$

6 frogs were sitting on lily pads. 2 hopped away. How many frogs were left on the lily pads?

$$\begin{array}{r} 5 \\ -\ 3 \\ \hline \square \end{array}$$

5 ducks were in the water. 3 flew away. How many ducks were left in the water?

Name ____________________

More Animal Stories

Directions: Subtract to find the difference. Cut out the subtraction sentences and glue them in the correct boxes. Write the difference in each small box.

How many toucans were left?

How many lion cubs were left?

How many monkeys were left?

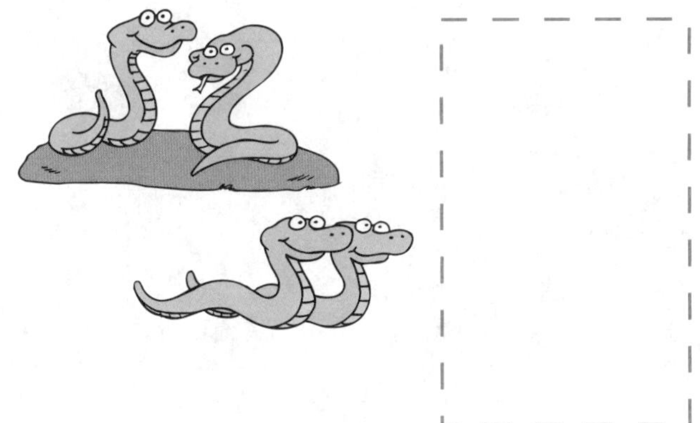

How many snakes were left?

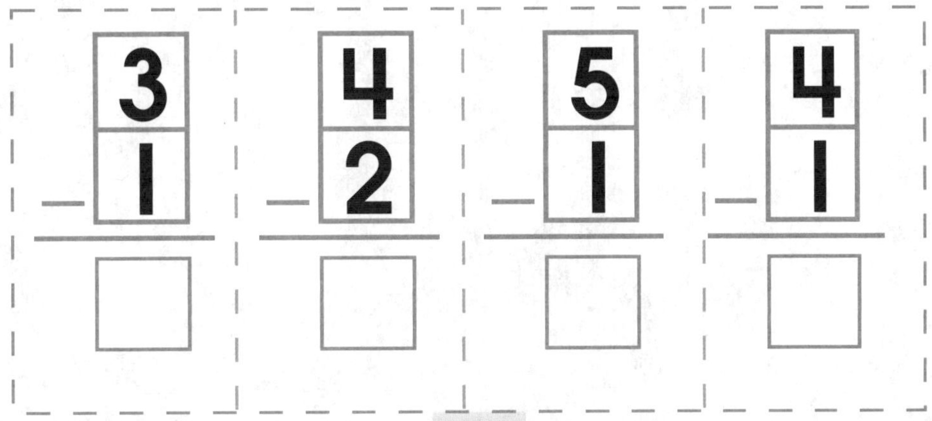

This page was left intentionally blank for cutting activity on previous page.

Name ____________________

Facts Through 5

Directions: Add or subtract.

Examples:

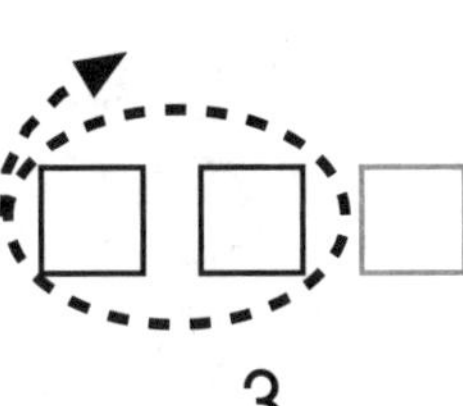

$$\begin{array}{r} 1 \\ +\ 1 \\ \hline 2 \end{array} \quad \begin{array}{r} 2 \\ -\ 1 \\ \hline 1 \end{array} \quad \begin{array}{r} 2 \\ +\ 1 \\ \hline \end{array} \quad \begin{array}{r} 1 \\ +\ 2 \\ \hline \end{array} \quad \begin{array}{r} 3 \\ -\ 1 \\ \hline \end{array} \quad \begin{array}{r} 3 \\ -\ 2 \\ \hline \end{array}$$

$$\begin{array}{r} 3 \\ +\ 1 \\ \hline \end{array} \quad \begin{array}{r} 1 \\ +\ 3 \\ \hline \end{array} \quad \begin{array}{r} 2 \\ +\ 2 \\ \hline \end{array} \quad \begin{array}{r} 4 \\ +\ 0 \\ \hline \end{array} \quad \begin{array}{r} 0 \\ +\ 4 \\ \hline \end{array}$$

$$\begin{array}{r} 4 \\ -\ 1 \\ \hline \end{array} \quad \begin{array}{r} 4 \\ -\ 3 \\ \hline \end{array} \quad \begin{array}{r} 4 \\ -\ 2 \\ \hline \end{array} \quad \begin{array}{r} 4 \\ -\ 0 \\ \hline \end{array} \quad \begin{array}{r} 4 \\ -\ 4 \\ \hline \end{array}$$

$$\begin{array}{r} 3 \\ +\ 2 \\ \hline \end{array} \quad \begin{array}{r} 2 \\ +\ 3 \\ \hline \end{array} \quad \begin{array}{r} 4 \\ +\ 1 \\ \hline \end{array} \quad \begin{array}{r} 1 \\ +\ 4 \\ \hline \end{array} \quad \begin{array}{r} 5 \\ +\ 0 \\ \hline \end{array} \quad \begin{array}{r} 0 \\ +\ 5 \\ \hline \end{array}$$

$$\begin{array}{r} 5 \\ -\ 2 \\ \hline \end{array} \quad \begin{array}{r} 5 \\ -\ 3 \\ \hline \end{array} \quad \begin{array}{r} 5 \\ -\ 1 \\ \hline \end{array} \quad \begin{array}{r} 5 \\ -\ 4 \\ \hline \end{array} \quad \begin{array}{r} 5 \\ -\ 0 \\ \hline \end{array} \quad \begin{array}{r} 5 \\ -\ 5 \\ \hline \end{array}$$

Name ____________________

Facts for 6 and 7

Directions: Add or subtract.

Examples:

$\begin{array}{r} 5 \\ +1 \\ \hline 6 \end{array}$ $\begin{array}{r} 1 \\ +5 \\ \hline \end{array}$ $\begin{array}{r} 6 \\ -1 \\ \hline 5 \end{array}$ $\begin{array}{r} 6 \\ -5 \\ \hline \end{array}$

$\begin{array}{r} 3 \\ +3 \\ \hline \end{array}$ $\begin{array}{r} 6 \\ -3 \\ \hline \end{array}$

$\begin{array}{r} 4 \\ +2 \\ \hline \end{array}$ $\begin{array}{r} 2 \\ +4 \\ \hline \end{array}$ $\begin{array}{r} 6 \\ -2 \\ \hline \end{array}$ $\begin{array}{r} 6 \\ -4 \\ \hline \end{array}$

$\begin{array}{r} 4 \\ +3 \\ \hline \end{array}$ $\begin{array}{r} 3 \\ +4 \\ \hline \end{array}$ $\begin{array}{r} 7 \\ -3 \\ \hline \end{array}$ $\begin{array}{r} 7 \\ -4 \\ \hline \end{array}$

$\begin{array}{r} 5 \\ +2 \\ \hline \end{array}$ $\begin{array}{r} 2 \\ +5 \\ \hline \end{array}$ $\begin{array}{r} 7 \\ -2 \\ \hline \end{array}$ $\begin{array}{r} 7 \\ -5 \\ \hline \end{array}$

$\begin{array}{r} 6 \\ +1 \\ \hline \end{array}$ $\begin{array}{r} 1 \\ +6 \\ \hline \end{array}$ $\begin{array}{r} 7 \\ -1 \\ \hline \end{array}$ $\begin{array}{r} 7 \\ -6 \\ \hline \end{array}$

$\begin{array}{r} 3 \\ +3 \\ \hline \end{array}$ $\begin{array}{r} 5 \\ +2 \\ \hline \end{array}$ $\begin{array}{r} 6 \\ +0 \\ \hline \end{array}$ $\begin{array}{r} 7 \\ -7 \\ \hline \end{array}$ $\begin{array}{r} 7 \\ -4 \\ \hline \end{array}$ $\begin{array}{r} 6 \\ -2 \\ \hline \end{array}$

Name ____________________

Facts for 8

Directions: Add or subtract.

Examples:

$$\begin{array}{r}5\\+3\\\hline\end{array}\qquad\begin{array}{r}3\\+5\\\hline\end{array}\qquad\begin{array}{r}8\\-3\\\hline\end{array}\qquad\begin{array}{r}8\\-5\\\hline\end{array}$$

$$\begin{array}{r}4\\+4\\\hline\end{array}$$

$$\begin{array}{r}8\\-4\\\hline\end{array}$$

$$\begin{array}{r}6\\+2\\\hline\end{array}\qquad\begin{array}{r}2\\+6\\\hline\end{array}$$

$$\begin{array}{r}8\\-2\\\hline\end{array}\qquad\begin{array}{r}8\\-6\\\hline\end{array}$$

$$\begin{array}{r}7\\+1\\\hline\end{array}\qquad\begin{array}{r}1\\+7\\\hline\end{array}$$

$$\begin{array}{r}8\\-1\\\hline\end{array}\qquad\begin{array}{r}8\\-7\\\hline\end{array}$$

$$\begin{array}{r}2\\+6\\\hline\end{array}\qquad\begin{array}{r}4\\+3\\\hline\end{array}\qquad\begin{array}{r}5\\+1\\\hline\end{array}\qquad\begin{array}{r}3\\+5\\\hline\end{array}\qquad\begin{array}{r}7\\+1\\\hline\end{array}\qquad\begin{array}{r}0\\+8\\\hline\end{array}$$

$$\begin{array}{r}8\\-1\\\hline\end{array}\qquad\begin{array}{r}7\\-6\\\hline\end{array}\qquad\begin{array}{r}8\\-5\\\hline\end{array}\qquad\begin{array}{r}6\\-3\\\hline\end{array}\qquad\begin{array}{r}8\\-0\\\hline\end{array}\qquad\begin{array}{r}8\\-2\\\hline\end{array}$$

Name ____________________

Facts for 9

Directions: Add or subtract.

Examples:

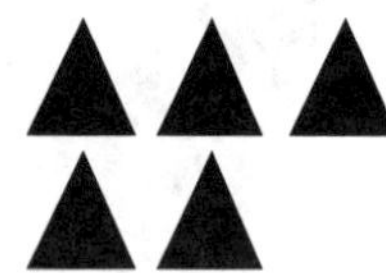    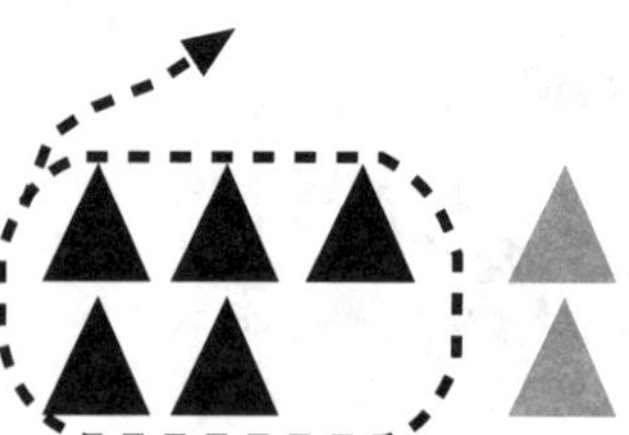

$\begin{array}{r} 5 \\ +4 \\ \hline 9 \end{array}$ $\begin{array}{r} 4 \\ +5 \\ \hline \end{array}$ $\begin{array}{r} 9 \\ -4 \\ \hline 5 \end{array}$ $\begin{array}{r} 9 \\ -5 \\ \hline \end{array}$

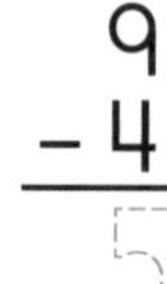

$\begin{array}{r} 6 \\ +3 \\ \hline \end{array}$ $\begin{array}{r} 3 \\ +6 \\ \hline \end{array}$

$\begin{array}{r} 9 \\ -3 \\ \hline \end{array}$ $\begin{array}{r} 9 \\ -6 \\ \hline \end{array}$

 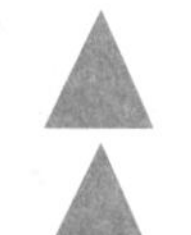

$\begin{array}{r} 7 \\ +2 \\ \hline \end{array}$ $\begin{array}{r} 2 \\ +7 \\ \hline \end{array}$

$\begin{array}{r} 9 \\ -2 \\ \hline \end{array}$ $\begin{array}{r} 9 \\ -7 \\ \hline \end{array}$

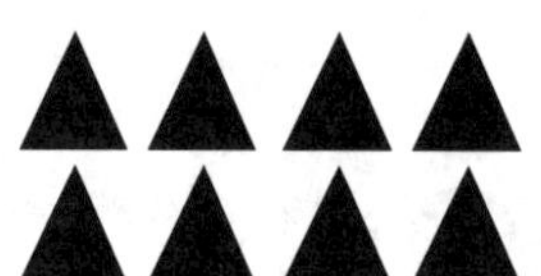

$\begin{array}{r} 8 \\ +1 \\ \hline \end{array}$ $\begin{array}{r} 1 \\ +8 \\ \hline \end{array}$

$\begin{array}{r} 9 \\ -1 \\ \hline \end{array}$ $\begin{array}{r} 9 \\ -8 \\ \hline \end{array}$

$\begin{array}{r} 5 \\ +4 \\ \hline \end{array}$ $\begin{array}{r} 2 \\ +7 \\ \hline \end{array}$ $\begin{array}{r} 6 \\ +1 \\ \hline \end{array}$ $\begin{array}{r} 9 \\ +0 \\ \hline \end{array}$ $\begin{array}{r} 1 \\ +8 \\ \hline \end{array}$ $\begin{array}{r} 4 \\ +4 \\ \hline \end{array}$

$\begin{array}{r} 9 \\ -5 \\ \hline \end{array}$ $\begin{array}{r} 7 \\ -3 \\ \hline \end{array}$ $\begin{array}{r} 9 \\ -8 \\ \hline \end{array}$ $\begin{array}{r} 9 \\ -3 \\ \hline \end{array}$ $\begin{array}{r} 9 \\ -9 \\ \hline \end{array}$ $\begin{array}{r} 9 \\ -0 \\ \hline \end{array}$

Name ______________________________

Facts for 10

Directions: Add or subtract.

Examples:

$$\begin{array}{r} 5 \\ +5 \\ \hline 10 \end{array} \qquad \begin{array}{r} 10 \\ -5 \\ \hline 5 \end{array}$$

$$\begin{array}{r} 6 \\ +4 \\ \hline \end{array} \qquad \begin{array}{r} 4 \\ +6 \\ \hline \end{array} \qquad \begin{array}{r} 10 \\ -4 \\ \hline \end{array} \qquad \begin{array}{r} 10 \\ -6 \\ \hline \end{array}$$

$$\begin{array}{r} 7 \\ +3 \\ \hline \end{array} \qquad \begin{array}{r} 3 \\ +7 \\ \hline \end{array} \qquad \begin{array}{r} 10 \\ -3 \\ \hline \end{array} \qquad \begin{array}{r} 10 \\ -7 \\ \hline \end{array}$$

$$\begin{array}{r} 8 \\ +2 \\ \hline \end{array} \qquad \begin{array}{r} 2 \\ +8 \\ \hline \end{array} \qquad \begin{array}{r} 10 \\ -2 \\ \hline \end{array} \qquad \begin{array}{r} 10 \\ -8 \\ \hline \end{array}$$

$$\begin{array}{r} 9 \\ +1 \\ \hline \end{array} \qquad \begin{array}{r} 1 \\ +9 \\ \hline \end{array} \qquad \begin{array}{r} 10 \\ -1 \\ \hline \end{array} \qquad \begin{array}{r} 10 \\ -9 \\ \hline \end{array}$$

$$\begin{array}{r} 4 \\ +6 \\ \hline \end{array} \qquad \begin{array}{r} 5 \\ +5 \\ \hline \end{array} \qquad \begin{array}{r} 9 \\ +1 \\ \hline \end{array} \qquad \begin{array}{r} 10 \\ -8 \\ \hline \end{array} \qquad \begin{array}{r} 10 \\ -3 \\ \hline \end{array} \qquad \begin{array}{r} 10 \\ -0 \\ \hline \end{array}$$

Name 

Facts Through 10

Directions: Add.

Example:

5	4	1	5	4	4
+ 4	+ 3	+ 2	+ 3	+ 6	+ 4
9					

0	4	8	9	8	2
+ 6	+ 1	+ 1	+ 1	+ 2	+ 2

2	5	1	5	4	6
+ 7	+ 2	+ 6	+ 5	+ 5	+ 2

Directions: Subtract.

Example:

10	8	5	7	4	10
− 6	− 2	− 3	− 6	− 3	− 5
4					

9	10	7	8	10	8
− 3	− 2	− 2	− 6	− 9	− 8

10	9	9	8	10	7
− 4	− 6	− 8	− 1	− 7	− 4

Name ____________________

Problem Solving

Directions: Solve each problem.

Example:

4	leaves on the ground
+ 3	leaves falling
7	leaves in all

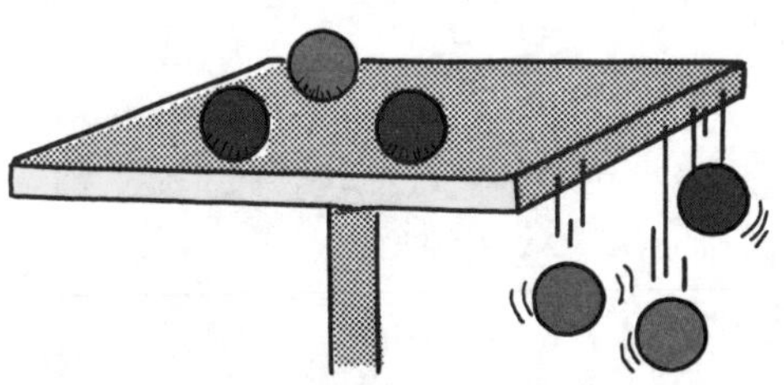

___	balls in all
− ___	balls falling
___	balls not falling

___	fish by a rock
+ ___	more fish coming
___	fish in all

___	pencils in all
− ___	pencils taken
___	pencils not taken

___	puppies on a rug
+ ___	more puppies coming
___	puppies in all

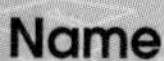

Name ____________________

Checkup

Directions: Add.

$2 + 4$	$7 + 3$	$4 + 5$	$6 + 2$	$2 + 3$	$0 + 4$
$4 + 3$	$1 + 5$	$2 + 8$	$3 + 3$	$6 + 4$	$2 + 1$
$3 + 1$	$7 + 0$	$8 + 1$	$5 + 2$	$3 + 6$	$5 + 5$

Directions: Subtract.

$3 - 3$	$5 - 2$	$10 - 6$	$9 - 2$	$7 - 3$	$10 - 5$
$9 - 1$	$8 - 7$	$1 - 0$	$6 - 4$	$8 - 5$	$10 - 8$
$9 - 6$	$4 - 3$	$6 - 3$	$7 - 5$	$10 - 9$	$8 - 4$

Name ____________________

Addition and Subtraction Fun

Directions: Solve the number problem under each picture. Write **+** or **–** to show if you should add or subtract.

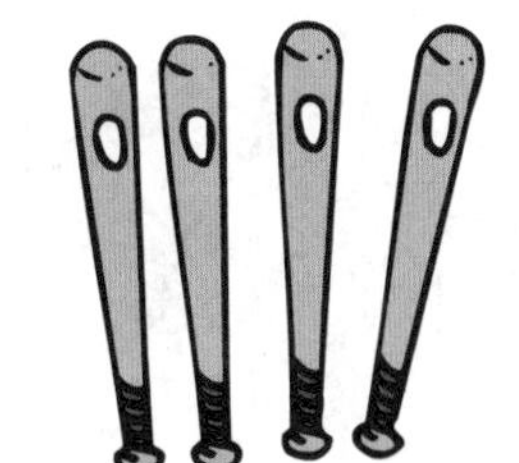

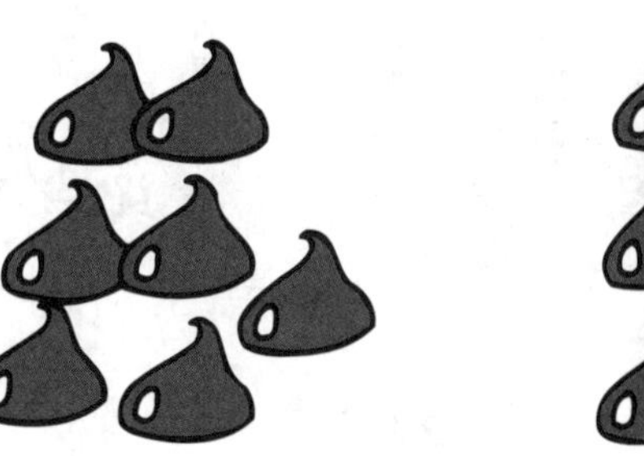

Example:

How many  s in all?

4 + 5 = 9

How many s in all?

7   5 = ________

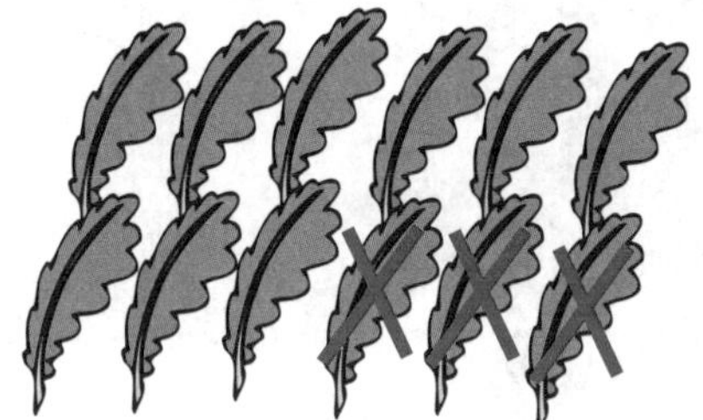

Example:

How many s are left?

12 – 3 = 9

How many s are left?

15   8 = ________

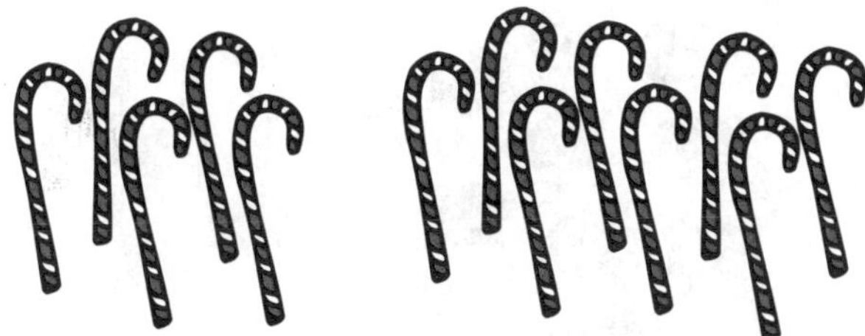

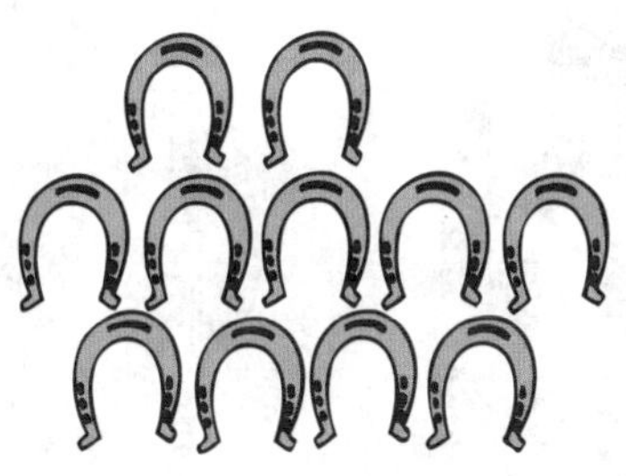

How many s in all?

5   8 = ________

How many s are left?

11   4 = ________

Name ______________________

Addition and Subtraction

Directions: Solve the number problem under each picture. Write **+** or **–** to show if you should add or subtract.

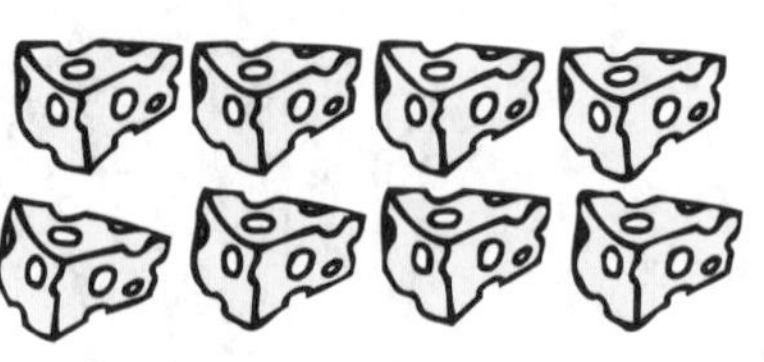 

Example:

How many s in all?

7 + **5 =** 12

How many s in all?

8 3 = ______

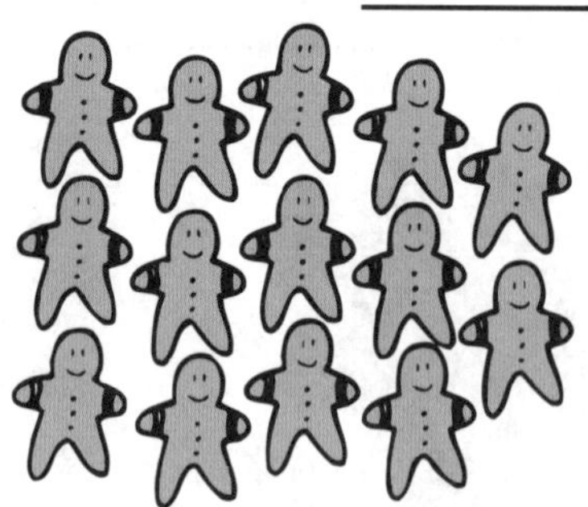

Example:

How many  s are left?

9 – **4 =** 5

How many  s are left?

14 1 = ______

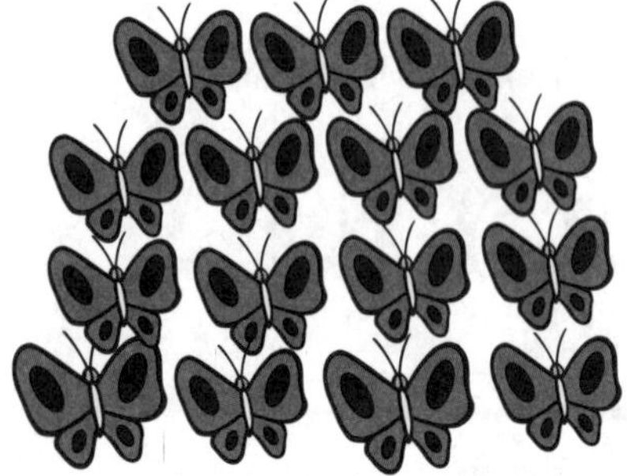 

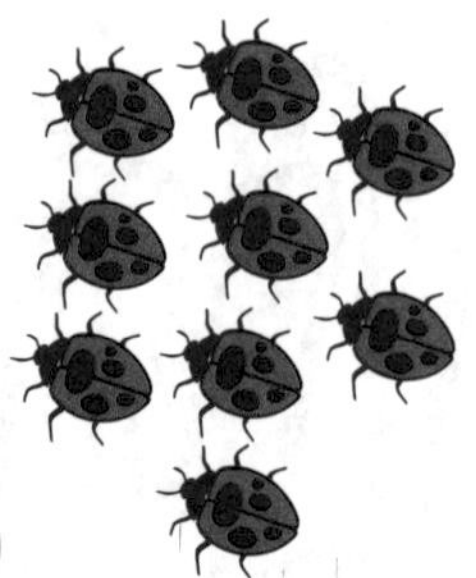

How many s in all?

15 6 = ______

How many s are left?

9 5 =

Name ____________________

Hopping Around

Directions: Write the number sentence on the line below each number line.

Example:

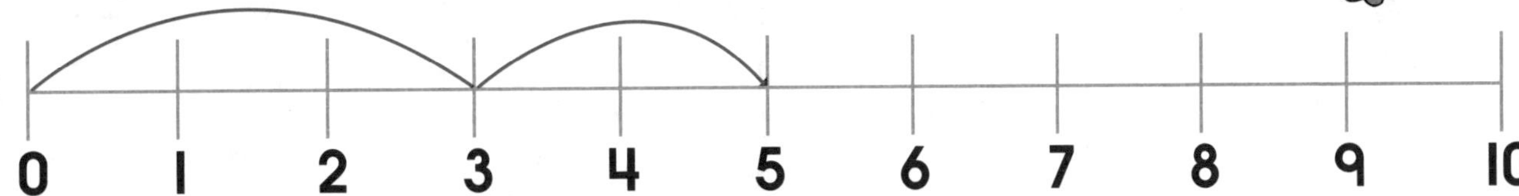

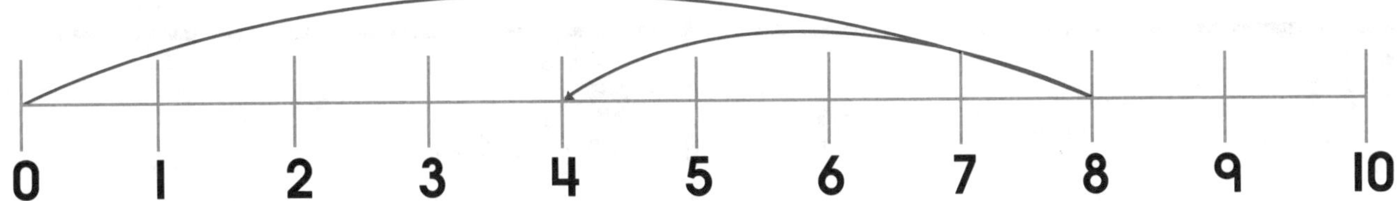

____

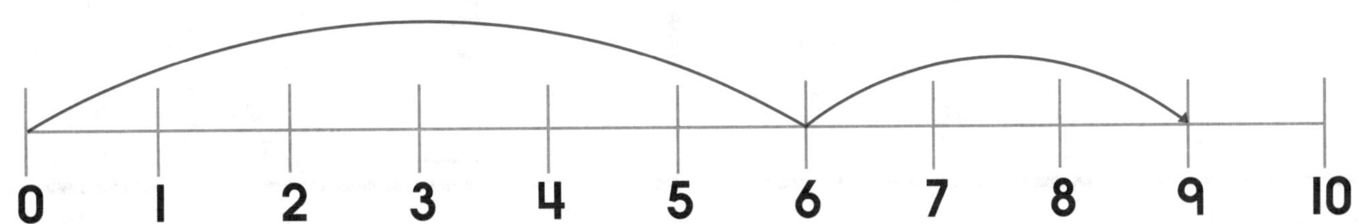

____

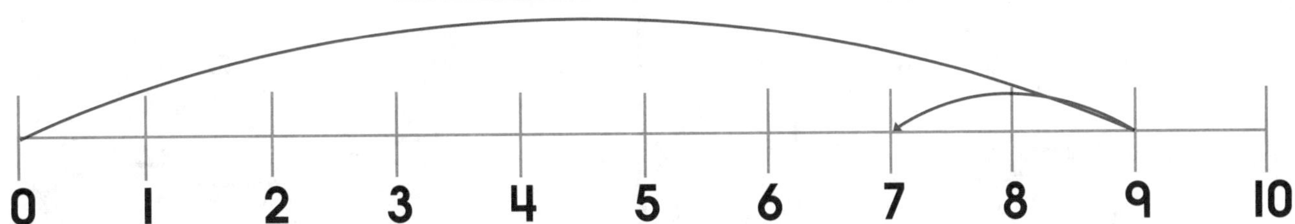

____

Name ______________________

Big Families

Directions: Complete each number sentence in each number family.

2

0 + __2__ = 2
2 + 0 = __2__
__2__ − 0 = 2
2 − 2 = __0__

3

1 + 2 = ___
___ + 1 = 3
3 − ___ = 2
3 − 2 = ___

4

___ + 3 = 4
3 + 1 = ___
4 − ___ = 3
___ − 3 = 1

5

2 + 3 = ___
___ + 2 = 5
5 − ___ = 3
___ − 3 = 2

6

2 + ___ = 6
4 + 2 = ___
6 − ___ = 4
6 − 4 = ___

6

5 + ___ = 6
___ + ___ = ___
6 − ___ = 5
___ − 5 = ___

Name ____________________

Sums and Differences

Directions: Colour two numbers in each box to show the given sum or difference.

Sum of 8

3	7	3	6	6	5	3	8
1	4	7	2	4	4	1	5

Difference of 1

6	3	5	9	8	5	5	2
1	5	10	7	3	2	4	0

Sum of 9

0	5	4	3	8	3	5	5
6	4	6	2	1	2	7	2

Difference of 2

6	9	4	10	5	8	0	2
1	4	7	5	1	10	7	3

Name ______________________________

Help the Hippo

Directions: Use the numbers in each thought bubble to write the number family.

Example:

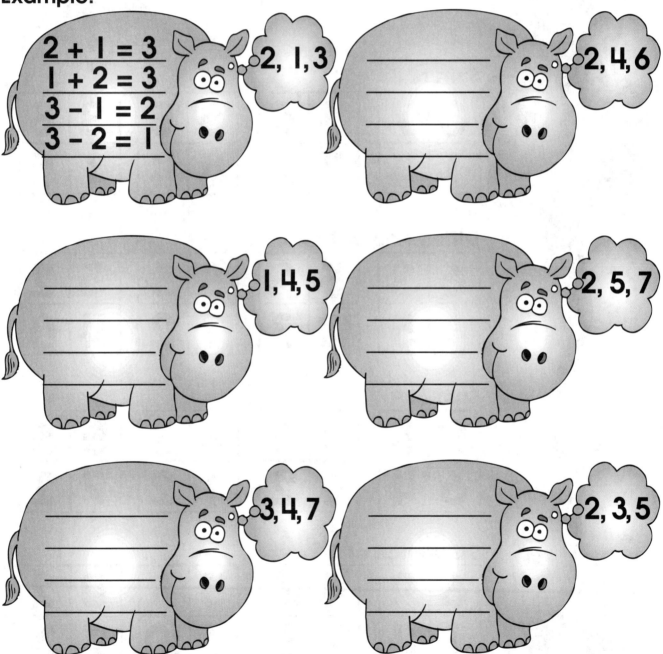

2 + 1 = 3
1 + 2 = 3
3 - 1 = 2
3 - 2 = 1

2, 1, 3

2, 4, 6

1, 4, 5

2, 5, 7

3, 4, 7

2, 3, 5

Name ______________________

Bigger Families

Directions: Complete each number sentence in the families.

7 ___ + 4 = 7 4 + 3 = ___ ___ − 3 = 4 7 − ___ = 3	**8** 3 + ___ = 8 5 + 3 = ___ 8 − ___ = 5 ___ − 5 = 3
9 4 + 5 = ___ ___ + 4 = 9 9 − ___ = 5 ___ − 5 = 4	**10** ___ + 6 = 10 6 + 4 = ___ 10 − 4 = ___ ___ − ___ = ___
11 3 + ___ = ___ ___ + ___ = ___ 11 − ___ = 8 ___ − ___ = ___	**12** 5 + ___ = 12 ___ + ___ = ___ 12 − ___ = ___ ___ + ___ = ___

Name ______________________________

Place Value: Ones, Tens

The **place value** of a digit or numeral is shown by where it is in the number. For example, in the number **23, 2** has the place value of **tens**, and **3** is **ones**.

Directions: Add the tens and ones and write your answers in the blanks.

Example:

+ = 33

3 tens + 3 ones = 33

	tens ones		tens ones
7 tens + 5 ones =	________	4 tens + 0 ones =	________
2 tens + 3 ones =	________	8 tens + 1 one =	________
5 tens + 2 ones =	________	1 ten + 1 one =	________
5 tens + 4 ones =	________	6 tens + 3 ones =	________
9 tens + 5 ones =	________		

Directions: Draw a line to the correct number.

6 tens + 7 ones	73
4 tens + 2 ones	67
8 tens + 0 ones	51
7 tens + 3 ones	80
5 tens + 1 one	42

Name ____________________

Finding Place Value: Ones and Tens

Directions: Write the numbers for the tens and ones. Then add.

Example:

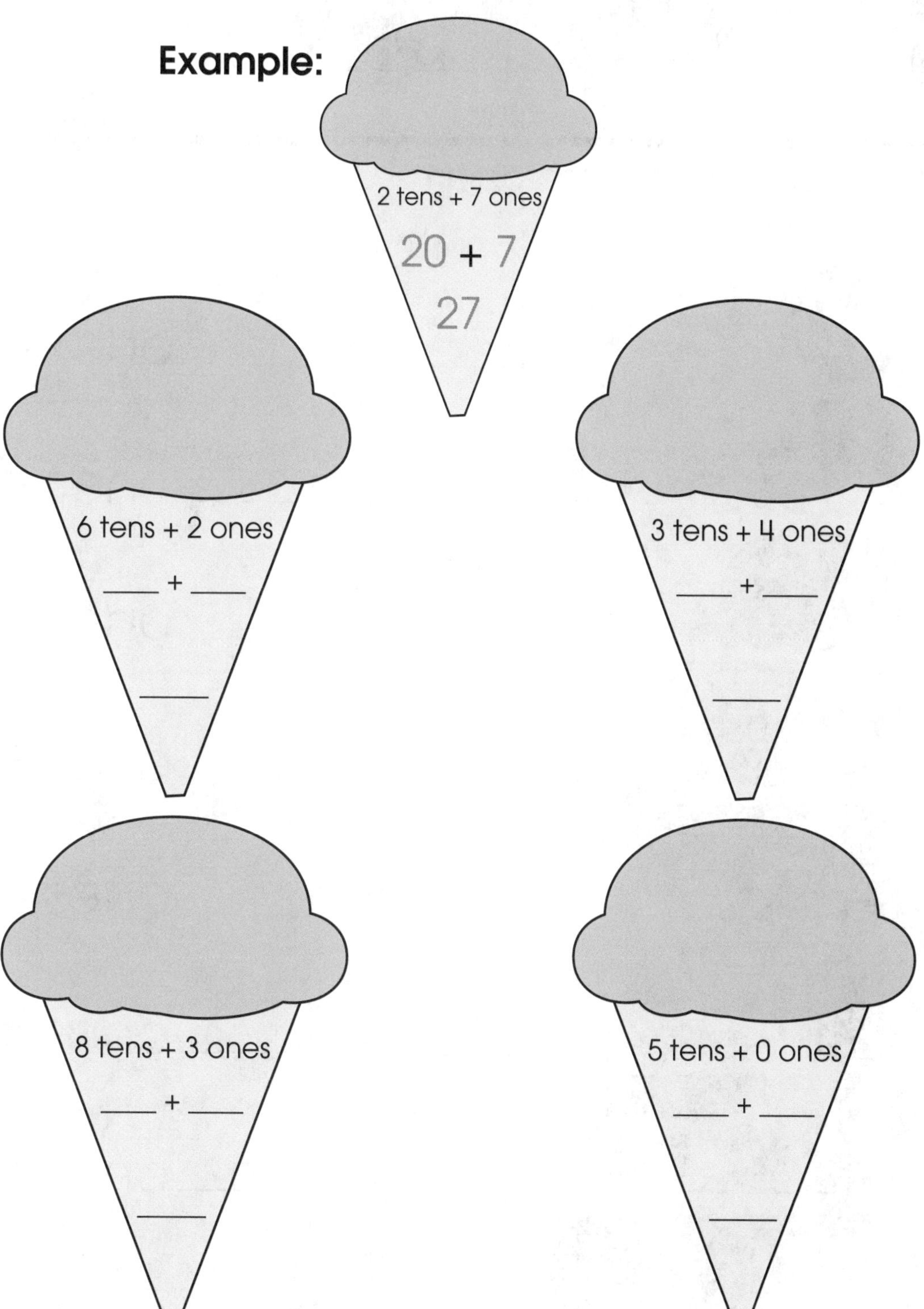

2 tens + 7 ones
20 + 7
27
6 tens + 2 ones
____ + ____
3 tens + 4 ones
____ + ____
8 tens + 3 ones
____ + ____
5 tens + 0 ones
____ + ____

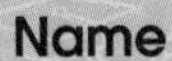

Name ______________________

Numbers 11 Through 18

Note: Although pennies are no longer in circulation, they are useful as counters.

1¢

10¢

10¢

Directions: Complete the problems.

Example:

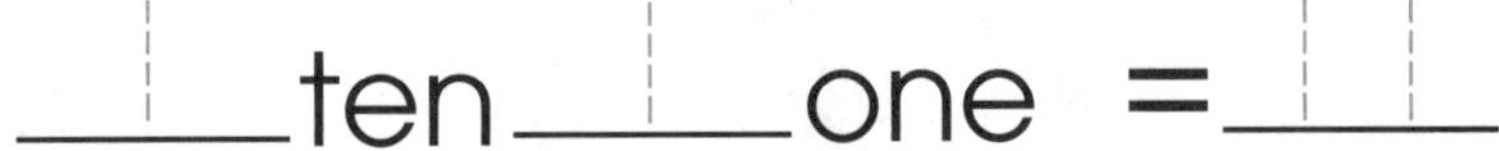

____ten ____ones =____

____ten ____ones =____

____ten ____ones =____

____ten ____ones =____

____ten ____ones =____

____ten ____ones =____

____ten ____ones =____

Name ________________________

Numbers 19 Through 39

Note: Although pennies are no longer in circulation, they are useful as counters.

Directions: Complete the problems.

Example:

__2__ tens = __20__

_____ tens _____ ones = _____

_____ten _____ones = _____

_____tens _____ones = _____

_____ tens = _____

_____tens _____ones = _____

_____tens _____ones = _____

_____tens _____ones = _____

Name ______________________________

Numbers 40 Through 99

Note: Although pennies are no longer in circulation, they are useful as counters.

Directions: Complete the problems.

Example:

__4__ tens ______ ones = __40__

______ tens ______ ones = ______

______ tens ______ ones = ______

______ tens ______ ones = ______

______ tens ______ ones = ______

______ tens ______ ones = ______

______ tens ______ ones = ______

______ tens ______ ones = ______

Name ______________________

Numbers 40 Through 99

Directions: Complete the problems.

Example:

_____ tens _____ ones = _____

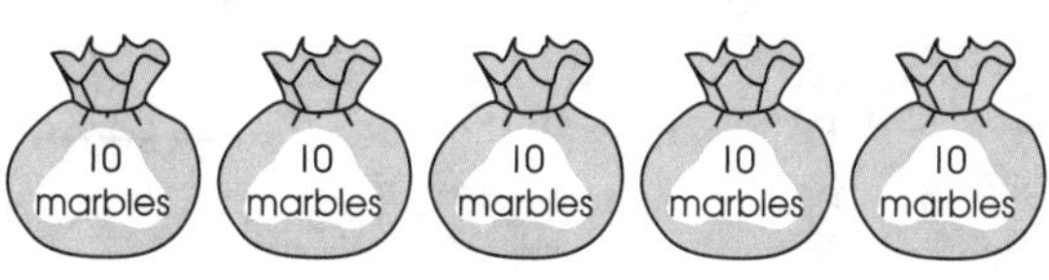

_____ tens = _____

_____ tens _____ ones = _____

_____ tens _____ ones = _____

_____ tens _____ ones = _____

_____ tens = _____

_____ tens _____ ones = _____

Name ____________________

Numbers Through 99

Directions: Complete the problems.

Example:

4 tens 6 ones = 46		2 tens 1 one = _____	
1 ten 2 ones = _____		5 tens 7 ones = _____	
3 tens 7 ones = _____		1 ten 9 ones = _____	
2 tens 4 ones = _____		8 tens 8 ones = _____	
9 tens = _____		6 tens 7 ones = _____	
6 tens = _____		7 tens 2 ones = _____	
5 tens 3 ones = _____		9 tens 5 ones = _____	
7 tens 8 ones = _____		4 tens 1 one = _____	
1 ten 1 one = _____		3 tens 4 ones = _____	
8 tens 4 ones = _____		6 tens 6 ones = _____	
3 tens 5 ones = _____		8 tens 9 ones = _____	
4 tens 9 ones = _____		2 tens = _____	
9 tens 6 ones = _____		5 tens = _____	

Name ____________________

Hundreds, Tens, and Ones

Directions: Count the groups of crayons. Write the number of hundreds, tens, and ones.

Example:

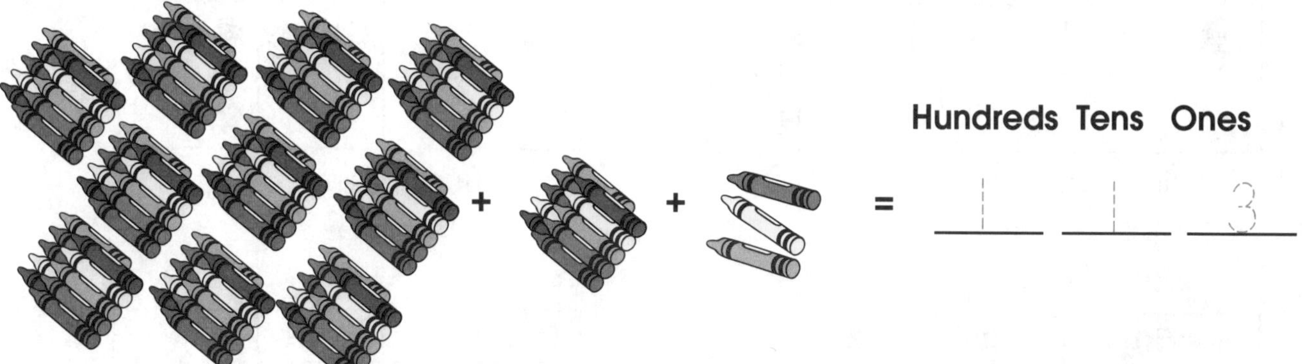

Hundreds Tens Ones

+ + = 1 1 3

1 Hundred + 1 Ten + 3 Ones

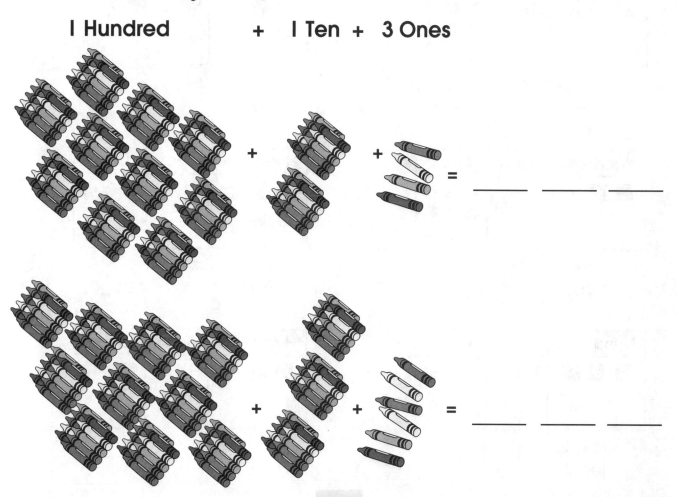

+ + = ______ ______ ______

+ + = ______ ______ ______

Name ______________________________

What Big Numbers!

Directions: Write each number.

Example:

Hundreds	Tens	Ones

1 hundreds
3 tens
2 ones = 132

Hundreds	Tens	Ones

___ hundreds
___ tens
___ ones = _______

Hundreds	Tens	Ones

___ hundreds
___ tens
___ ones = _______

Hundreds	Tens	Ones

___ hundreds
___ tens
___ ones = _______

Hundreds	Tens	Ones

___ hundreds
___ tens
___ ones = _______

Hundreds	Tens	Ones

___ hundreds
___ tens
___ ones = _______

Hundreds	Tens	Ones

___ hundreds
___ tens
___ ones = _______

Hundreds	Tens	Ones

___ hundreds
___ tens
___ ones = _______

Name ______________________________

Count 'Em Up!

Directions: Look at the example. Then, write the missing numbers in the blanks.

Example:

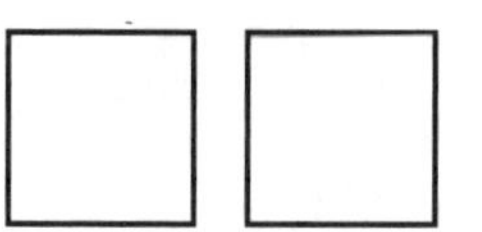
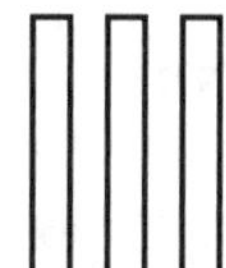

2 hundreds + 3 tens + 6 ones =

hundreds	tens	ones	
2	3	6	= 236

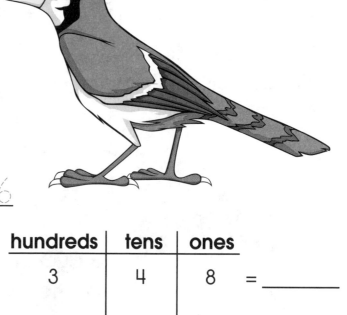

	hundreds	tens	ones	
3 hundreds + 4 tens + 8 ones =	3	4	8	= ______
___ hundreds + ___ ten + ___ ones =	2	1	7	= ______
___ hundreds + ___ tens + ___ ones =	6	3	5	= ______
___ hundreds + ___ tens + ___ ones =	4	7	9	= ______
___ hundreds + ___ tens + ___ ones =	2	9	4	= ______
___ hundreds + ___ tens + ___ ones =	4	2	0	= ______
3 hundreds + 1 ten + 3 ones =	____	____	____	= ______
3 hundreds + ___ tens + 7 ones =	____	5	____	= ______
6 hundreds + 2 tens + ___ ones =	____	____	8	= ______

Name ______________________

Up, Up, and Away

Directions: Use the code to colour the balloons. If the answer has:

7 hundreds, colour it **red.**

6 hundreds, colour it **green.**
5 hundreds, colour it **orange.**

8 tens, colour it **yellow.**
3 ones, colour it **brown.**

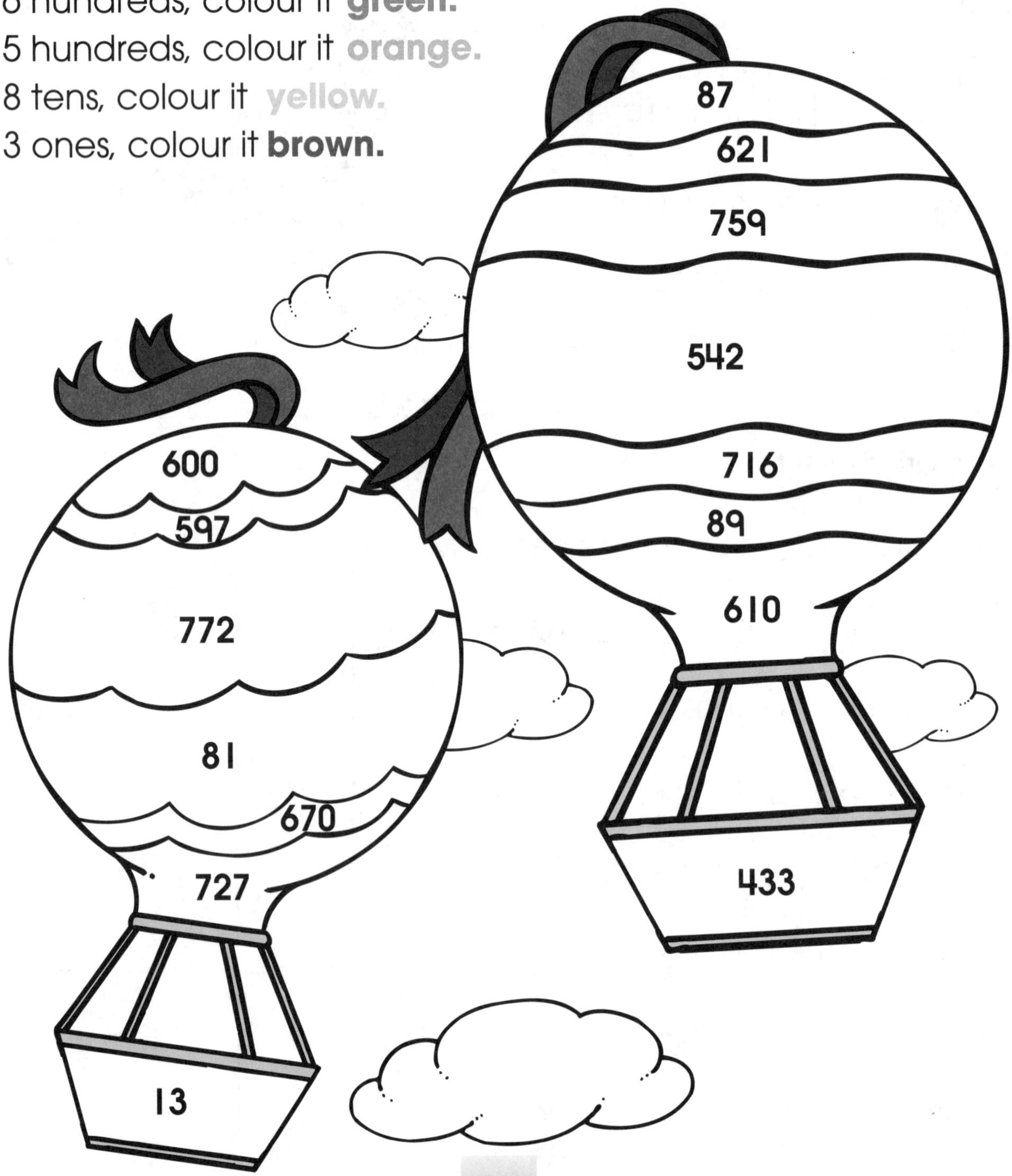

87
621
759
542
716
89
610
433

600
597
772
81
670
727
13

Name ____________________

Place Value: Hundreds

Directions: Study the example. Write the missing numbers.

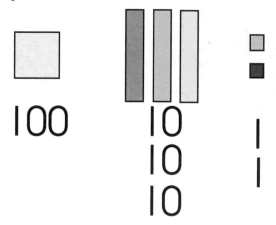

Example:

100 | 10 10 10 | 1 1

1 hundred + __3__ tens + 2 ones = __132__

286 = ____ hundreds + ____ tens + ____ ones

831 = ____ hundreds + ____ tens + ____ one

972 = ____ hundreds + ____ tens + ____ ones

528 = ____ hundreds + ____ tens + ____ ones

177 = ____ hundred + ____ tens + ____ ones

Directions: Draw a line to the number that has:

8 hundreds	862
5 ones	996
9 tens	485

Name ______________________________

Place Value: Hundreds

4	3	1
hundreds	tens	ones

Directions: Tell which number is in each place.

 Tens place:

4 286 ______

1 234 ______

5 678 ______

 Hundreds place:

6 321 ______

3 210 ______

7 871 ______

☆ Ones place:

5 432 ______

6 531 ______

9 980 ______

Name ______________________________

Place Value: Hundreds

Directions: Use the code to colour the fan.

If the answer has:

9 tens, colour it **pink.**

8 tens, colour it **red.**

6 hundreds, colour it **green.**

3 ones, colour it **blue.**

5 hundreds, colour it **orange.**

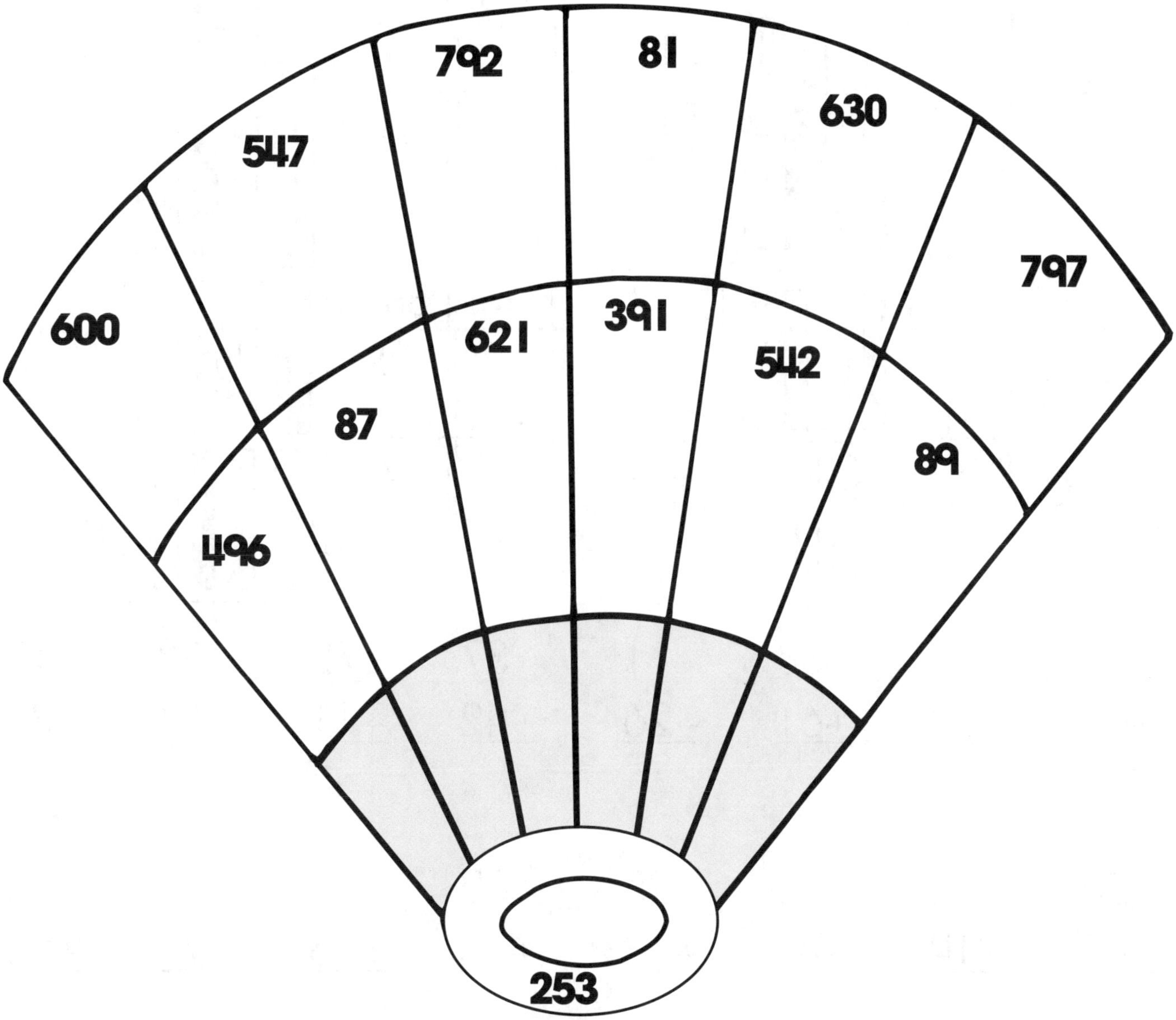

792 81 547 630 600 797 621 391 542 87 89 496 253

Name ________________________

2-Digit Addition

Directions: Study the example. Follow the steps to add.

Example:

```
 33
+41
```

Step 1: Add the ones.

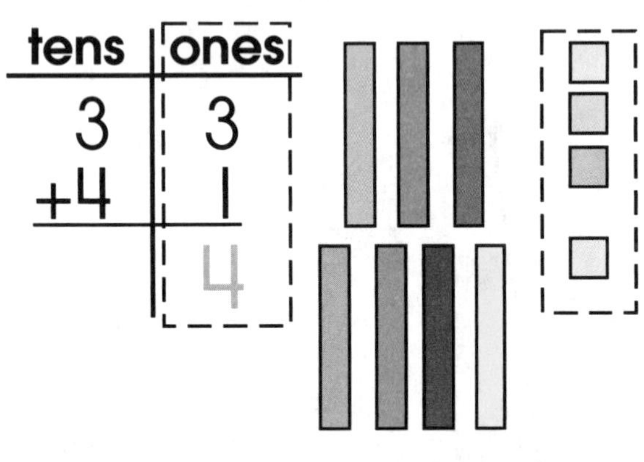

tens	ones
4	2
+2	4
6	6

Step 2: Add the tens.

tens	ones
3	3
+4	1
7	4

tens	ones
5	0
+4	7
9	7

24	15	38	11	37	72	33	10
+62	+23	+61	+26	+42	+11	+51	+30

25	62	32	25	82	91	16	55
+42	+14	+44	+13	+ 6	+ 5	+71	+ 3

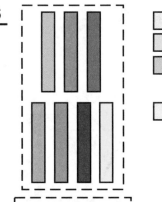

Name ____________________

2-Digit Addition

Directions: Add the total points scored in each game. Remember to add **ones** first and **tens** second.

Example:

Total 39

Total ________

Total ________

Total ________

Total ________

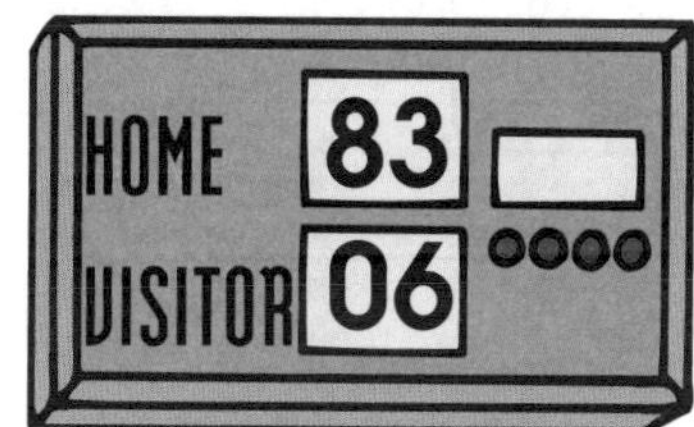

Total ________

Total ________

Total ________

Total ________

Total ________

Name ____________________

Adding Tens

3 tens + 4 tens 7 tens	30 + 40 70	6 tens + 2 tens 8 tens	60 + 20 80

Directions: Add.

2 tens + 4 tens ___ tens	20 + 40	6 tens + 2 tens ___ tens	60 + 20

20 + 20	10 + 50	40 + 20	30 + 40	50 + 30
30 + 20	60 + 10	20 + 50	70 + 10	10 + 10
10 + 20	40 + 40	80 + 10	60 + 30	20 + 60
70 + 20	40 + 10	30 + 10	50 + 40	30 + 30

Name ____________________

Problem Solving

Directions: Solve each problem.

Example:

There are 20 men in the plane.

30 women get in the plane.

How many men and women are in the plane?

Jill buys 10 apples.

Carol buys 20 apples.

How many apples in all?

There are 30 ears of corn in one pile.

There are 50 ears of corn in another pile.

How many ears of corn in all?

Henry cut 40 pieces of wood.

Art cut 20 pieces of wood.

How many pieces of wood were cut?

Adolpho had 60 baseball cards.

Maria had 30 baseball cards.

How many baseball cards in all?

Name ______________________

Picture This

Directions: Add the ones, then the tens in each problem. Then, write the sum in the blank.

Example:

2 tens and 6 ones	1 ten and 4 ones
+ 1 ten and 3 ones	+ 3 tens and 3 ones
3 tens and 9 ones = 39	___ tens and ___ ones = ____

2 tens and 5 ones	1 ten and 6 ones
+ 2 tens and 3 ones	+ 5 tens and 1 one
___ tens and ___ ones = ____	___ tens and ___ ones = ____

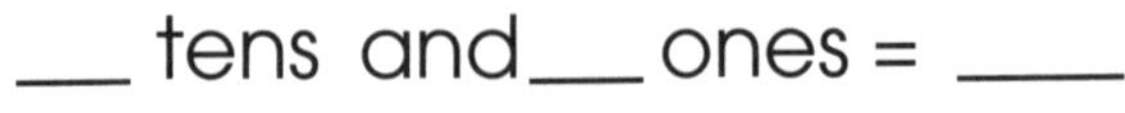

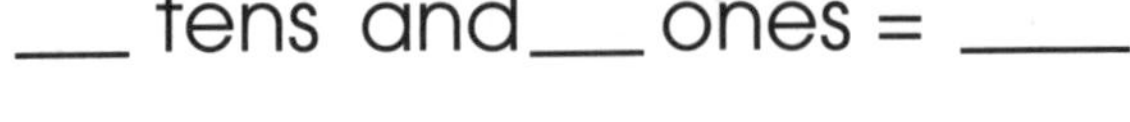

1 ten and 3 ones	2 tens and 5 ones
+ 1 ten and 1 one	+ 2 tens and 0 ones
___ tens and ___ ones = ____	___ tens and ___ ones = ____

1 ten and 5 ones	7 tens and 6 ones
+ 2 tens and 4 ones	+ 2 tens and 2 ones
___ tens and ___ ones = ____	___ tens and ___ ones = ____

Name ____________________

Digital Addition

Add the ones.

tens	ones
2	4
+3	2
	6

Then, add the tens.

tens	ones
2	4
+3	2
5	6

Directions: Solve the addition problems below.

tens	ones
1	7
+2	1

tens	ones
3	4
+5	2

tens	ones
	5
+6	2

tens	ones
	6
+5	2

tens	ones
2	0
+4	0

tens	ones
5	1
+	8

tens	ones
7	2
+1	7

tens	ones
4	7
+2	1

tens	ones
2	5
+6	2

tens	ones
4	2
+2	4

tens	ones
8	3
+1	4

tens	ones
3	2
+2	5

Name ____________________

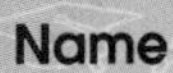

Circus Fun

Directions: Add to solve the problems. Add the ones first. Then, add the tens.

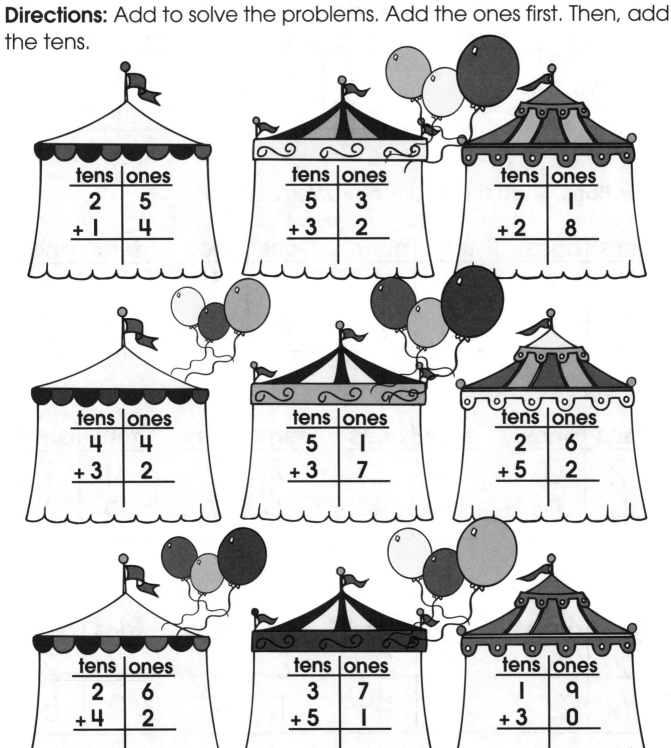

tens	ones
2	5
+ 1	4

tens	ones
5	3
+ 3	2

tens	ones
7	1
+ 2	8

tens	ones
4	4
+ 3	2

tens	ones
5	1
+ 3	7

tens	ones
2	6
+ 5	2

tens	ones
2	6
+ 4	2

tens	ones
3	7
+ 5	1

tens	ones
1	9
+ 3	0

Name ____________________

Scoreboard Sums

Directions: Add the total points scored in each game.
add the ones first, then the tens.

Example:

HOME 22
VISITOR 17

Total 39

HOME 28
VISITOR 30

Total ________

HOME 55
VISITOR 21

Total ________

HOME 14
VISITOR 33

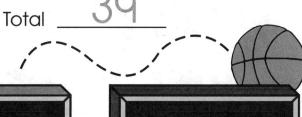

Total ________

HOME 24
VISITOR 13

Total ________

HOME 46
VISITOR 32

Total ________

HOME 83
VISITOR 06

Total ________

HOME 30
VISITOR 20

Total ________

HOME 17
VISITOR 41

Total ________

HOME 24
VISITOR 45

Total ________

Name ______________________________

Raccoon Roundup

Directions: Solve the addition problems. Write your answers inside the ropes.

$$\begin{array}{r} 26 \\ +\ 43 \\ \hline \end{array}$$

$$\begin{array}{r} 43 \\ +\ 31 \\ \hline \end{array}$$

$$\begin{array}{r} 34 \\ +\ 10 \\ \hline \end{array}$$

$$\begin{array}{r} 48 \\ +\ 20 \\ \hline \end{array}$$

$$\begin{array}{r} 57 \\ +\ 20 \\ \hline \end{array}$$

$$\begin{array}{r} 52 \\ +\ 34 \\ \hline \end{array}$$

$$\begin{array}{r} 43 \\ +\ 55 \\ \hline \end{array}$$

$$\begin{array}{r} 67 \\ +\ 22 \\ \hline \end{array}$$

Name ____________________

Anchors Away

Directions: Solve the addition problems. Use the code to find the answer to this riddle:

What did the pirate have to do before every trip out to sea?

48	36	58	96	69	75	89	29
O	H	G	B	T	E	N	A

Example:

42 + 16	34 + 41	60 + 9
58		
G		

17 + 31	55 + 34

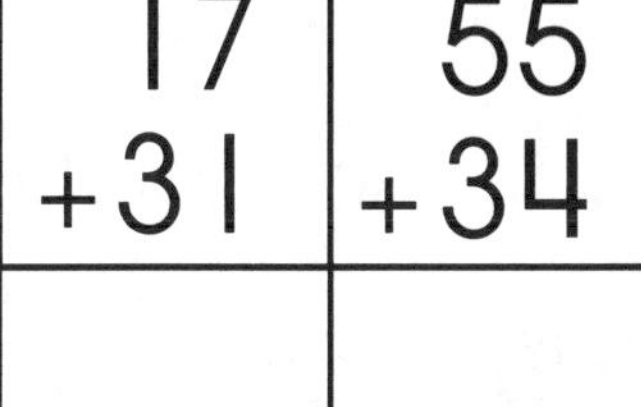

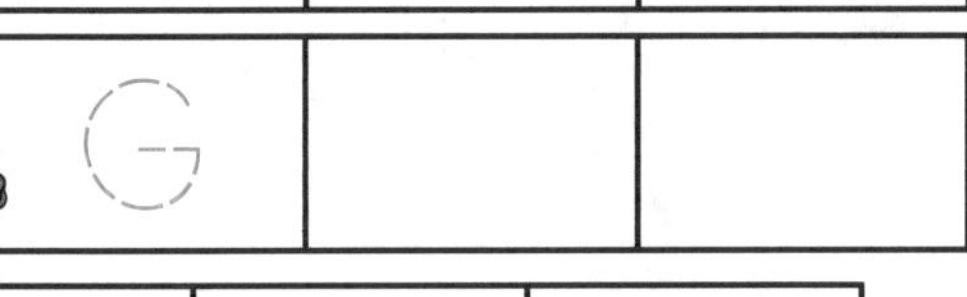

26 + 43	14 + 22	52 + 23

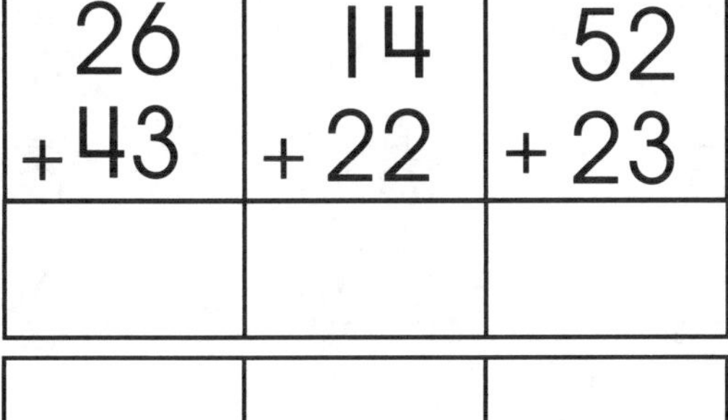

83 + 13	24 + 24	5 + 24	52 + 17
			!

Name ________________________

Two-Digit Subtraction

Directions: Look at the example.
Follow the steps to subtract.

Examples:

28	24
-14	-12

Step 1: Subtract the ones.

tens	ones
2	8
-1	4
	4

Step 2: Subtract the tens.

tens	ones
2	8
-1	4
1	4

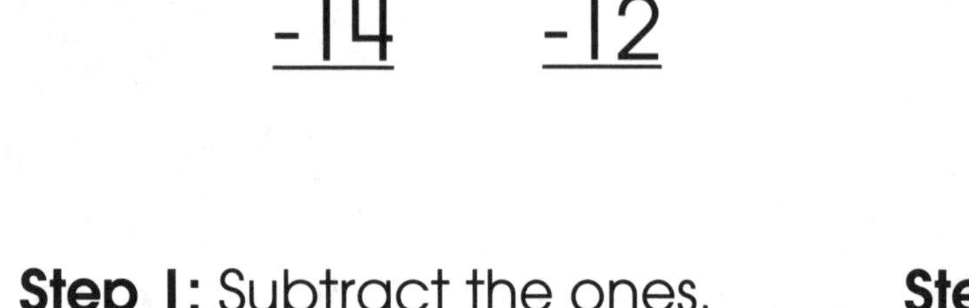

Step 1: Subtract the ones.

tens	ones
2	4
-1	2
	2

Step 2: Subtract the tens.

tens	ones
2	4
-1	2
1	2

24	61	77	85	57	87
– 12	– 30	– 44	– 24	– 23	– 33

Name ______________________

Subtracting Tens

Examples:

6 tens − 3 tens 3 tens	60 −30 30	8 tens − 2 tens 6 tens	80 −20 60

Directions: Subtract.

7 tens − 5 tens tens	70 −50	4 tens − 2 tens tens	40 −20

50 −30	60 −20	20 −10	80 −40	40 −40
90 −50	80 −20	70 −30	30 −20	50 −40
60 −30	40 −10	80 −30	90 −20	70 −50
80 −70	90 −80	70 −40	60 −40	50 −20

Name ____________________

Problem Solving

Directions: Solve each problem.

Example:

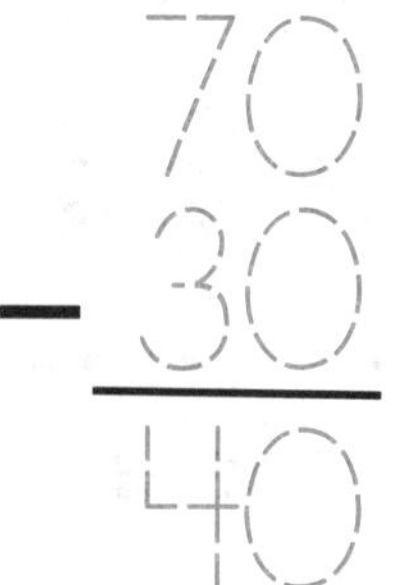

Mr. Cobb counts 70 s.

He sells 30 s.

How many s are left?

Keith has 20 s.

Leon has 10 s.

How many more s does Keith have than Leon?

Tina plants 60 s.

Melody plants 30 s.

How many more s did Tina plant than Melody?

Link has 80 s.

Jessica has 50 s .

How many more s does Link have than Jessica?

Maranda hits 40 s.

Harold hits 30 s.

How many more s does Maranda hit than Harold?

Name ____________________

All Aboard

Directions: Count the tens and ones and write the numbers. Then, subtract to solve the problems.

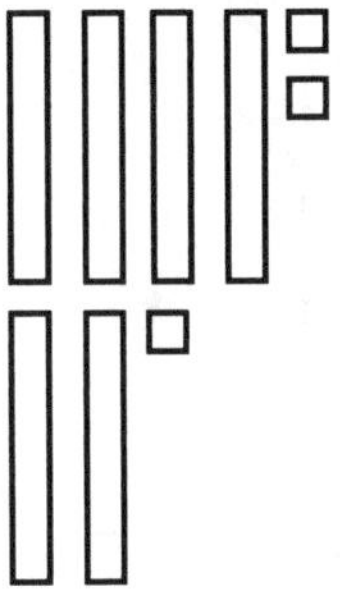

	tens	ones
	4	2
−	2	1

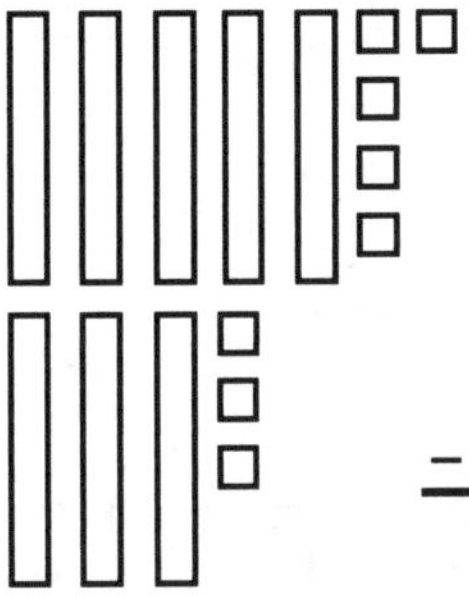

	tens	ones
−		

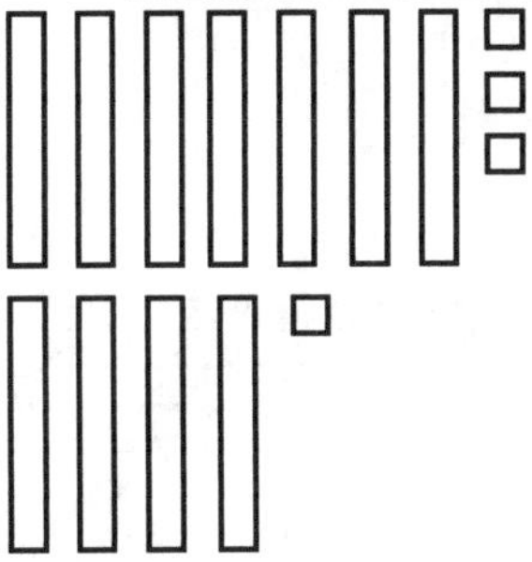

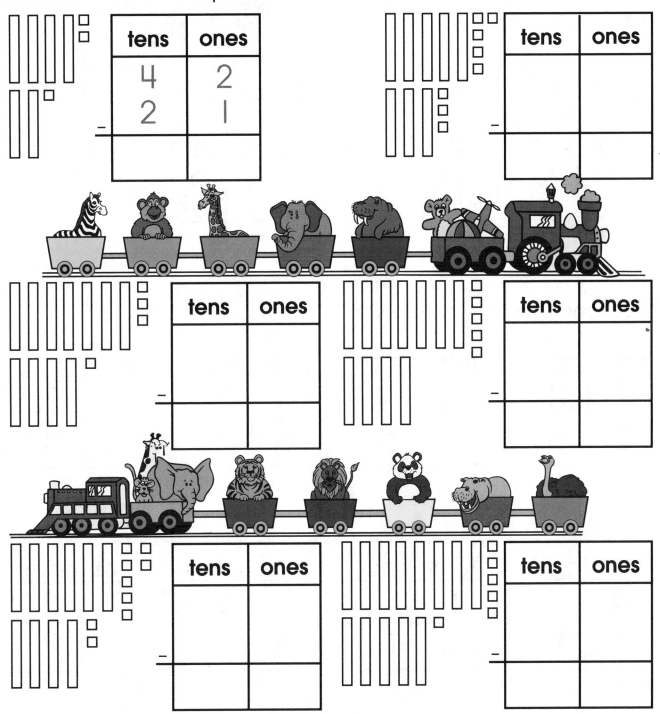

	tens	ones
−		

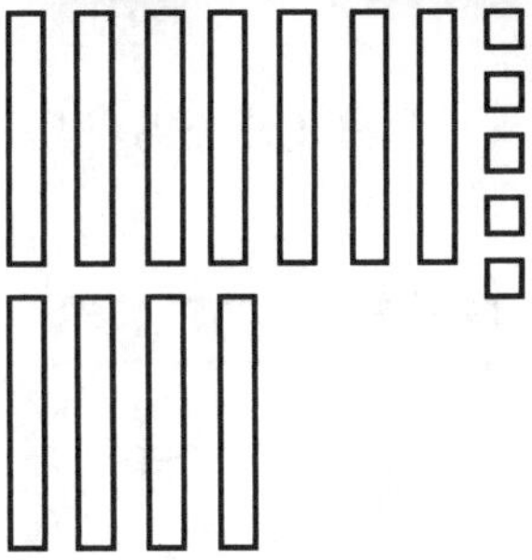

	tens	ones
−		

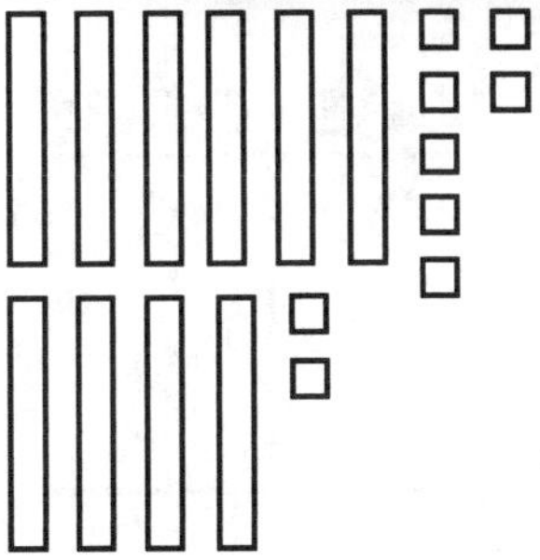

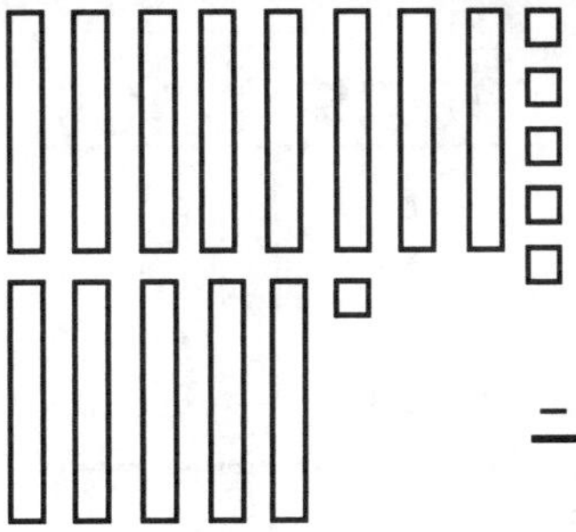

	tens	ones
−		

	tens	ones
−		

Name ____________________

Cookie Mania

There are 46 cookies.
Bill eats 22 cookies.
How many are left?

$$\begin{array}{r} 46 \\ -\ 22 \\ \hline \end{array}$$

1. Subtract the ones.

tens	ones
4	6
- 2	2
	4

2. Subtract the tens.

tens	ones
4	6
- 2	2
2	4

Directions: Subtract the ones first. Then, subtract the tens.

tens	ones
7	8
- 2	5

tens	ones
5	9
- 3	6

tens	ones
8	3
- 6	1

tens	ones
6	7
- 4	3

tens	ones
9	7
- 1	4

tens	ones
5	4
- 3	0

tens	ones
4	2
- 3	1

tens	ones
2	8
- 1	8

Name ____________________

Cookie Craze!

Directions: Subtract to solve the problems. Circle the answers. Colour the cookies with answers greater than 30.

49 − 23	67 − 41	58 − 37
16 (26) 25	26 15 62	81 11 21
 75 − 50	86 − 21	64 − 52
20 25 35	67 86 65	12 26 16
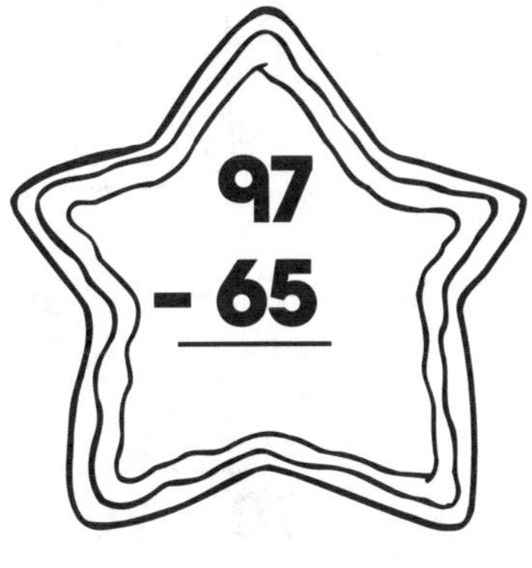 97 − 65	77 − 43	49 − 13
31 33 32	34 43 39	56 36 37

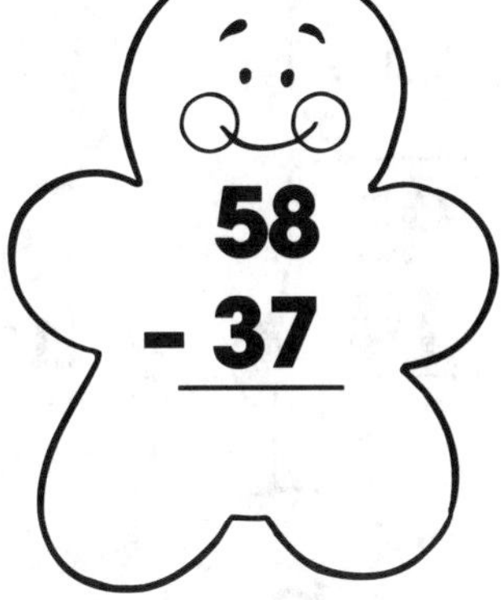

Name ______________________

How's Your Pitch?

Directions: Solve the subtraction problems. Write each answer.

u	n	t	r	a
95 - 14	68 - 47	80 - 20	79 - 38	83 - 52

h	y	i	c
84 - 23	75 - 31	99 - 29	98 - 36

o	e	g	s	p
84 - 30	98 - 16	74 - 42	58 - 38	82 - 40

Use the answers and the letters on the baseballs to solve the code.

__ __ __ __   __ __ __ __ __   __ __

44 54 81 41   42 70 60 62 61   70 20

__ __ __ __ __   __ __   __ __ __ __ __ __ !

41 70 32 61 60   54 21   60 31 41 32 82 60

Name ____________________

Prehistoric Problems

Directions: Solve the subtraction problems. Use the code to colour picture.

Code:

25 = blue	57 = green
31 = yellow	14 = orange
21 = brown	11 = red

$$\begin{array}{r} 52 \\ -\ 21 \\ \hline \end{array}$$

$$\begin{array}{r} 47 \\ -\ 22 \\ \hline \end{array}$$

$$\begin{array}{r} 25 \\ -\ 11 \\ \hline \end{array}$$

$$\begin{array}{r} 62 \\ -\ 31 \\ \hline \end{array}$$

$$\begin{array}{r} 77 \\ -\ 20 \\ \hline \end{array}$$

$$\begin{array}{r} 51 \\ -\ 40 \\ \hline \end{array}$$

$$\begin{array}{r} 69 \\ -\ 12 \\ \hline \end{array}$$

$$\begin{array}{r} 98 \\ -\ 41 \\ \hline \end{array}$$

$$\begin{array}{r} 55 \\ -\ 34 \\ \hline \end{array}$$

Name ____________________

2-Digit Addition: Regrouping

Addition is "putting together" or adding two or more numbers to find the sum. Regrouping is using **ten ones** to form **one ten, ten tens** to form **one 100, fifteen ones** to form **one ten** and **five ones,** and so on.

Directions: Study the examples. Follow the steps to add.

Example:

```
 14
+ 8
```

Step 1:
Add the ones.

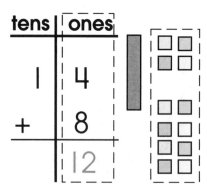

tens	ones
1	4
+	8
	12

Step 2:
Regroup the tens.

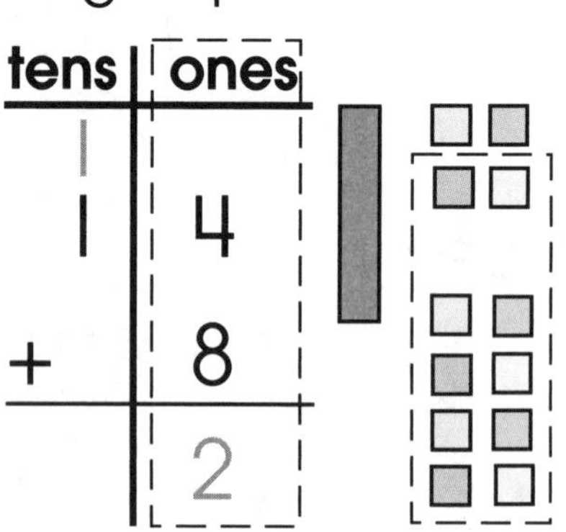

tens	ones
1	
1	4
+	8
	2

Step 3:
Add the tens.

tens	ones
1	
1	4
+	8
2	2

tens	ones
1	
1	6
+3	7
5	3

tens	ones
1	
3	8
+5	3
9	1

tens	ones
1	
2	4
+4	7
7	1

```
 28    32    54    19    44    25    29    79
+17   +38   +25   +55   +48   +64   +33   +15
```

Name ____________________

2-Digit Addition: Regrouping

Directions: Add the total points scored in the game. Remember to add the ones, regroup, and then add the tens.

Example:

Total 85

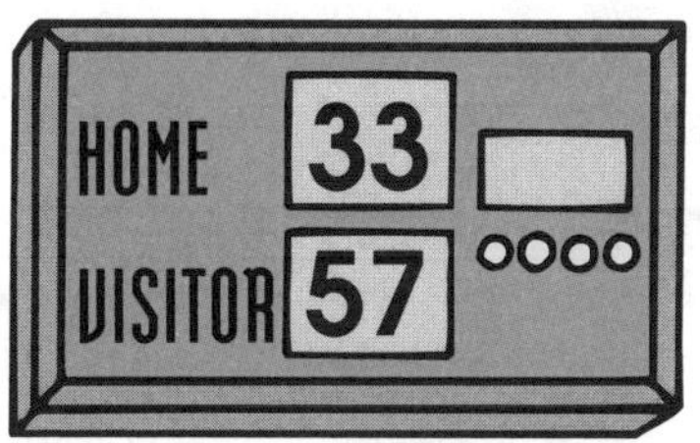

Total ________

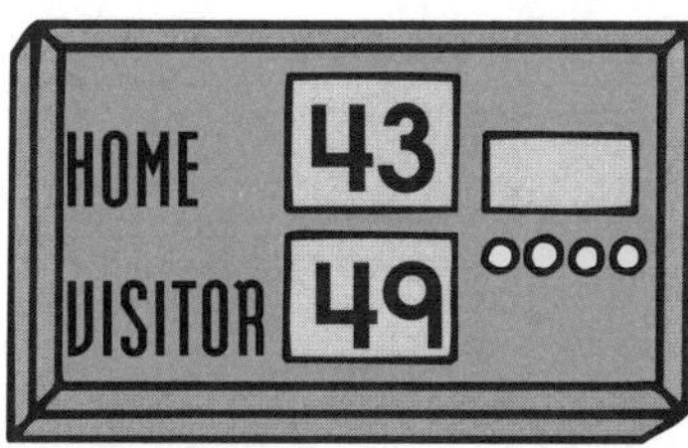

Total ________

Total ________

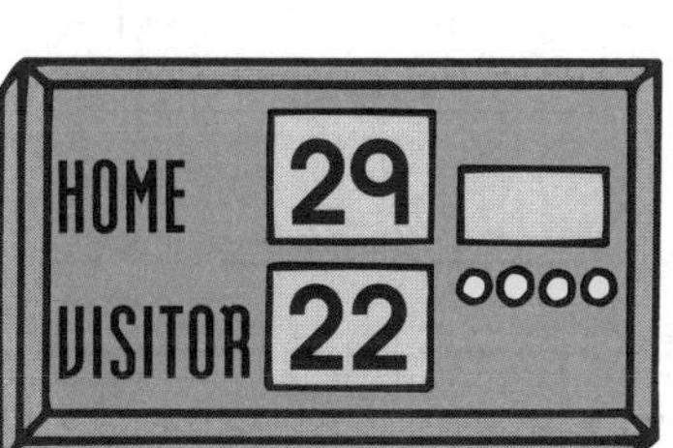

Total ________

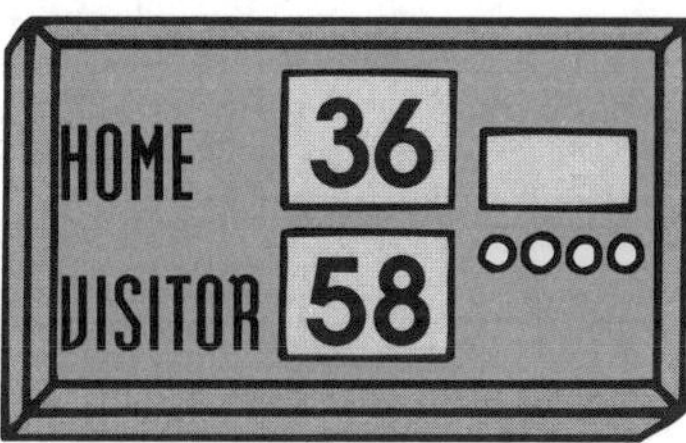

Total ________

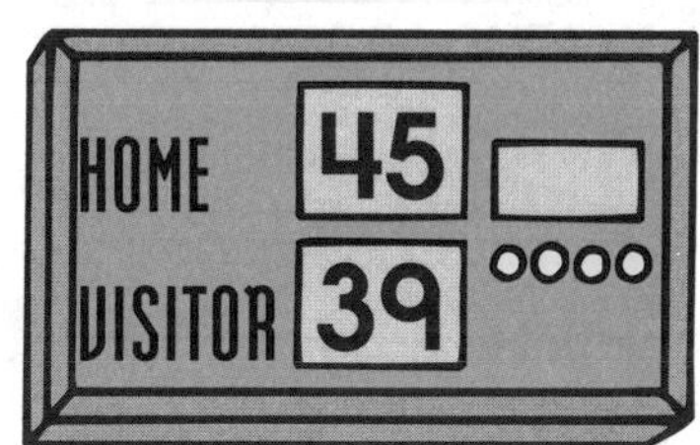

Total ________

Total ________

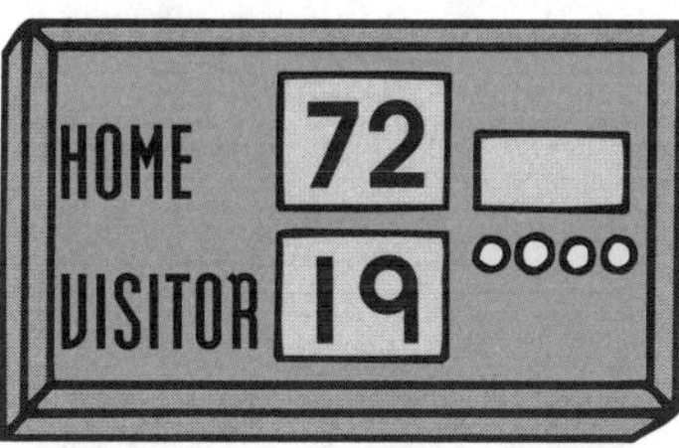

Total ________

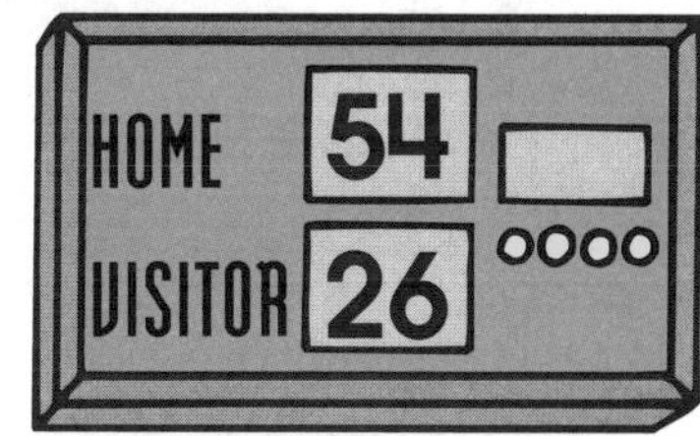

Total ________

Name ______________________

2-Digit Addition

Directions: Add the ones. Rename 15 as 10 + 5. Add the tens.

$$\begin{array}{r} 56 \\ +29 \\ \hline \end{array} \qquad \begin{array}{r} 6 \\ +\ 9 \\ \hline 15 \text{ or } 10 + 5 \end{array} \quad \Rightarrow \quad \begin{array}{r} 1\ \ \\ 56 \\ +29 \\ \hline 5 \end{array}$$

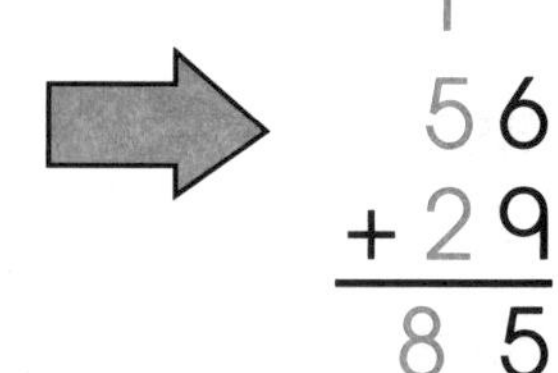

$$\begin{array}{r} 1\ \ \\ 56 \\ +29 \\ \hline 85 \end{array}$$

Directions: Add the ones. Rename 12 as 10 + 2. Add the tens.

$$\begin{array}{r} 47 \\ +35 \\ \hline \end{array} \qquad \begin{array}{r} 7 \\ +\ 5 \\ \hline 12 \text{ or } 10 + 2 \end{array} \quad \Rightarrow \quad \begin{array}{r} 1\ \ \\ 47 \\ +35 \\ \hline 2 \end{array} \quad \Rightarrow \quad \begin{array}{r} 1\ \ \\ 47 \\ +35 \\ \hline 82 \end{array}$$

Directions: Add.

Examples:

$$\begin{array}{r} 45 \\ +28 \\ \hline 73 \end{array} \quad \begin{array}{r} 13 \\ +19 \\ \hline 32 \end{array} \quad \begin{array}{r} 48 \\ +35 \\ \hline \end{array} \quad \begin{array}{r} 69 \\ +18 \\ \hline \end{array} \quad \begin{array}{r} 54 \\ +39 \\ \hline \end{array}$$

$$\begin{array}{r} 44 \\ +17 \\ \hline \end{array} \quad \begin{array}{r} 37 \\ +18 \\ \hline \end{array} \quad \begin{array}{r} 28 \\ +36 \\ \hline \end{array} \quad \begin{array}{r} 73 \\ +18 \\ \hline \end{array} \quad \begin{array}{r} 66 \\ +29 \\ \hline \end{array}$$

$$\begin{array}{r} 52 \\ +39 \\ \hline \end{array} \quad \begin{array}{r} 38 \\ +47 \\ \hline \end{array} \quad \begin{array}{r} 64 \\ +18 \\ \hline \end{array} \quad \begin{array}{r} 29 \\ +45 \\ \hline \end{array} \quad \begin{array}{r} 75 \\ +17 \\ \hline \end{array}$$

Name ____________________

2-Digit Addition

Directions: Add the ones. Rename 11 as 10 + 1. Add the tens.

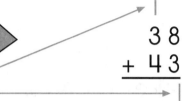

38 + 43	8 + 3 = 11 or 10 + 1	38 + 43 (carry 1) = 1	38 + 43 = 81

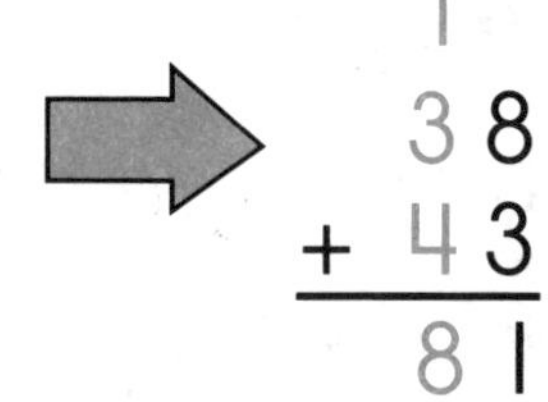

Directions: Add.

Example:

17 + 34 = 51	26 + 47	47 + 35	68 + 24	37 + 28
29 + 48	58 + 27	69 + 17	78 + 13	19 + 44
55 + 28	27 + 35	39 + 52	57 + 27	38 + 36
49 + 43	65 + 18	23 + 18	64 + 18	46 + 39
54 + 27	38 + 44	66 + 26	28 + 34	19 + 56

Name ____________________

Problem Solving

Directions: Solve each problem.

Example:

16 boys ride their bikes to school.

18 girls ride their bikes to school.

How many bikes are ridden to school?

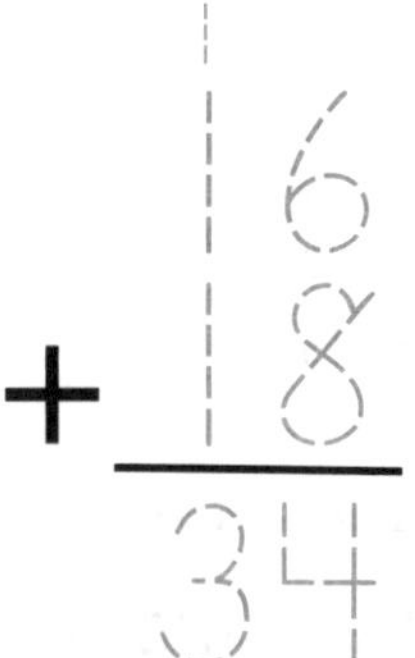

Dad reads 26 pages.

Mike reads 37 pages.

How many pages did Dad and Mike read?

Tiffany counts 46 stars.

Mike counts 39 stars.

How many stars did they count?

Mom has 29 golf balls.

Dad has 43 golf balls.

How many golf balls do they have?

Vicki ran in 26 races.

Kay ran in 14 races.

How many races did they run?

Name ____________________

2-Digit Subtraction: Regrouping

Subtraction is "taking away" or subtracting one number from another to find the difference. Regrouping is using **one ten** to form **ten ones, one 100** to form **ten tens,** and so on.

Directions: Study the examples. Follow the steps to subtract.

Example: 37 − 19

Step 1: Regroup.

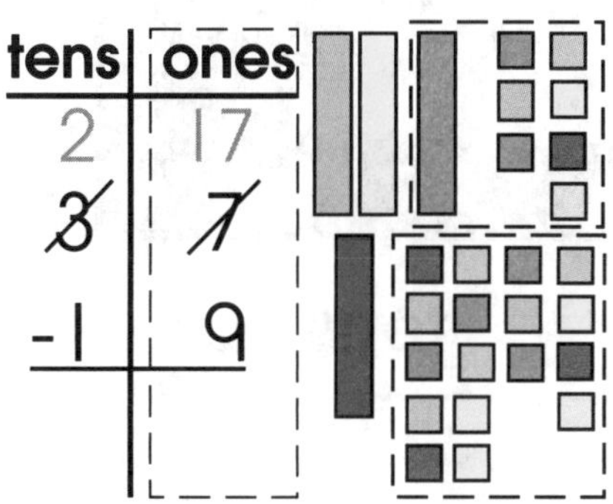

tens	ones
2	17
~~3~~	~~7~~
-1	9

Step 2: Subtract the ones.

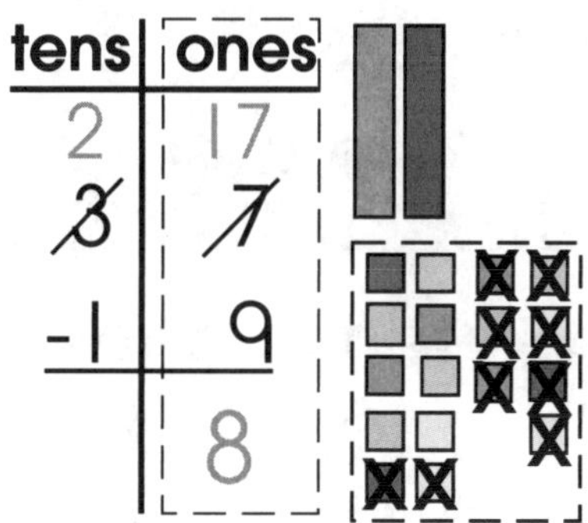

tens	ones
2	17
~~3~~	~~7~~
-1	9
	8

Step 3: Subtract the tens.

tens	ones
2	17
~~3~~	~~7~~
-1	9
1	8

tens	ones
0	12
~~1~~	~~2~~
-	9
	3

tens	ones
2	14
~~3~~	~~4~~
-1	6
1	8

tens	ones
3	15
~~4~~	~~5~~
-2	9
1	6

28 − 19 =

46 − 18 =

12 − 8 =

30 − 12 =

52 − 25 =

47 − 35 =

21 − 13 =

45 − 25 =

Name ______________________________

2-Digit Subtraction: Regrouping

Directions: Study the steps for subtracting. Solve the problems using the steps.

STEPS FOR SUBTRACTING

1. DO YOU REGROUP?
   YES, WHEN BOTTOM NUMBER IS BIGGER THAN THE TOP.
2. SUBTRACT THE ONES.
3. SUBTRACT THE TENS.

TENS	ONES	
3 ~~4~~	12	REGROUP? YES
−2	4	
1	8	

TENS	ONES	
3	7	REGROUP? NO
−1	4	
2	3	

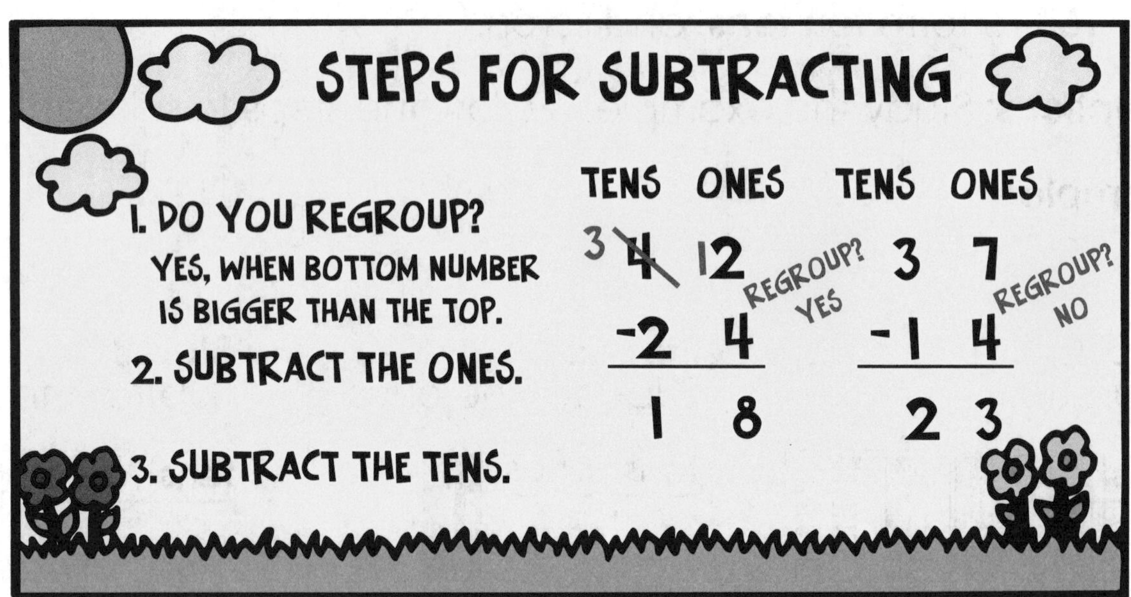

tens	ones
4	7
− 2	8

tens	ones
6	4
− 3	4

tens	ones
5	3
− 3	9

$$\begin{array}{r} 56 \\ -\ 27 \\ \hline \end{array} \quad \begin{array}{r} 83 \\ -\ 47 \\ \hline \end{array} \quad \begin{array}{r} 43 \\ -\ 39 \\ \hline \end{array} \quad \begin{array}{r} 75 \\ -\ 53 \\ \hline \end{array} \quad \begin{array}{r} 91 \\ -\ 18 \\ \hline \end{array}$$

$$\begin{array}{r} 73 \\ -\ 66 \\ \hline \end{array} \quad \begin{array}{r} 35 \\ -\ 14 \\ \hline \end{array} \quad \begin{array}{r} 67 \\ -\ 58 \\ \hline \end{array} \quad \begin{array}{r} 26 \\ -\ 7 \\ \hline \end{array} \quad \begin{array}{r} 68 \\ -\ 45 \\ \hline \end{array}$$

Name ____________________

Sea Shell Subtraction

Ellen found 32 shells on the beach. She gave 15 shells to Cindy. How many shells does Ellen have now?

Directions: Look at the problem below. Follow the steps to subtract.

Put the numbers on the tens and ones table.

tens	ones
3	2
–1	5

Subtract the ones. Ask: Do I need to regroup?

tens	ones
2	12
~~3~~	~~2~~
–1	5
	7

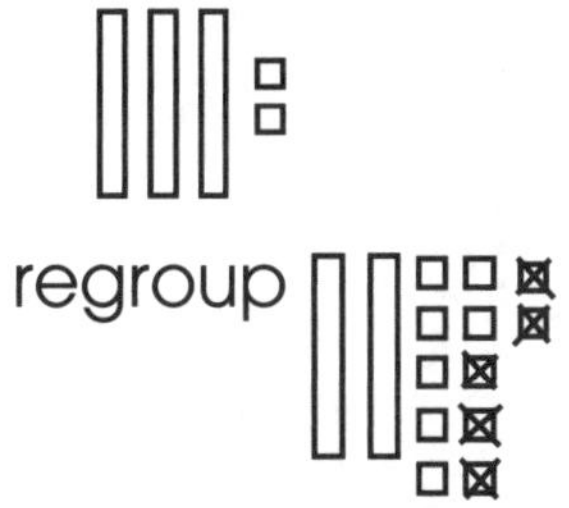

regroup

32 = 2 tens and 12 ones.

Subtract the tens.

tens	ones
2	12
~~3~~	~~2~~
–1	5
1	7

Ellen has 17 shells now.

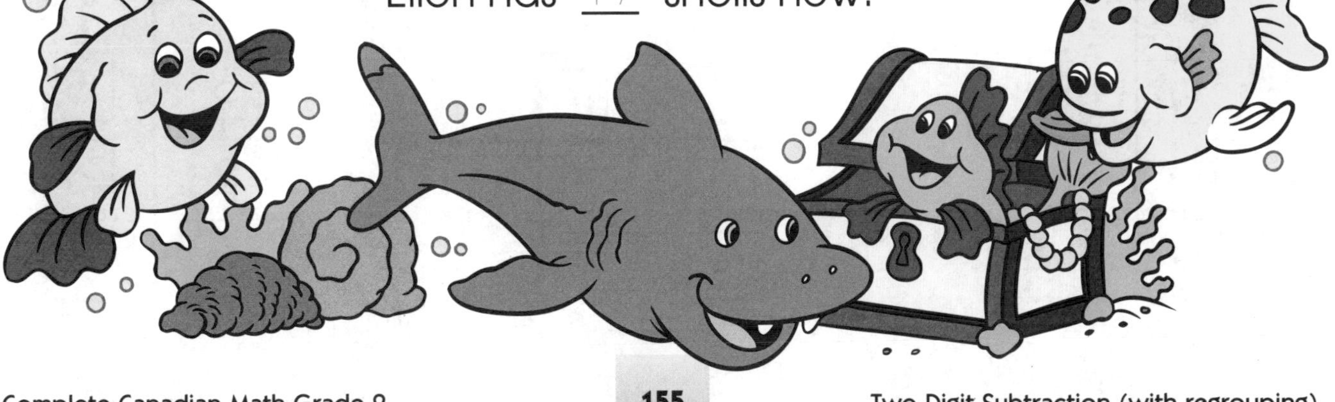

Name ____________________

Subtraction With Regrouping

Directions: Use manipulatives to find the difference.

Example:

1.

tens	ones
4	14
~~5~~	~~4~~
– 1	7
3	7

2.

tens	ones
3	3
– 1	5

3.

tens	ones
6	1
– 3	3

4.

tens	ones
2	7
– 1	6

5.

tens	ones
4	2
– 2	4

6.

tens	ones
5	2
– 2	6

7.

tens	ones
9	4
– 4	8

8.

tens	ones
7	7
– 3	4

9.

tens	ones
6	5
– 2	6

Name ____________________

Subtraction With Regrouping

Directions: Subtract to find the difference. Regroup as needed. Colour the spaces with differences of:

10–19 = red **50–59 = brown** **30–39 = green**
40–49 = yellow **20–29 = blue** **60–69 = orange**

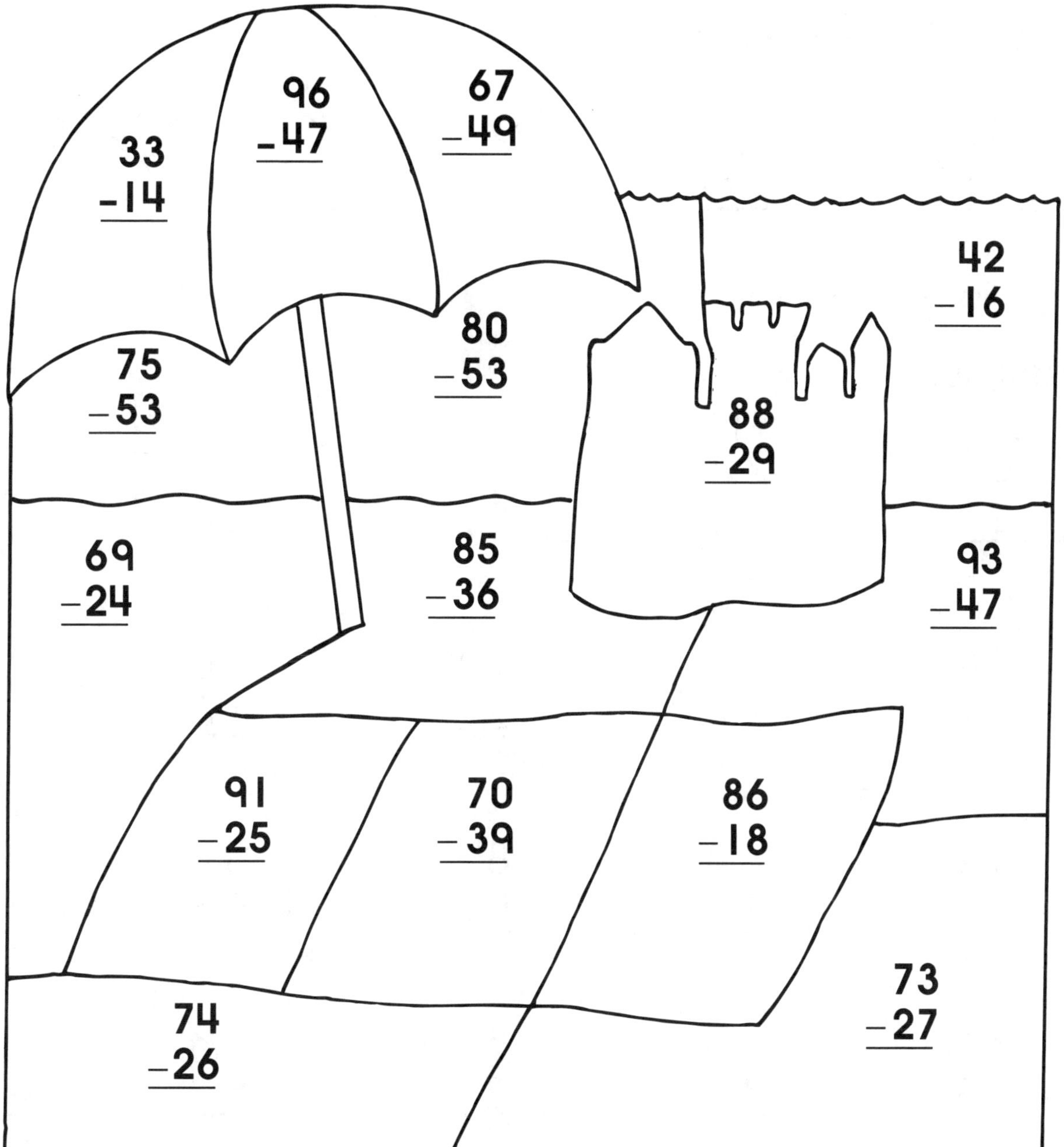

Name ________________________________

2-Digit Subtraction

Directions: Rename 53 as 4 tens and 13 ones.

			Subtract the ones.		Subtract the tens.
	4 13		4 13		
53	~~5~~ ~~3~~	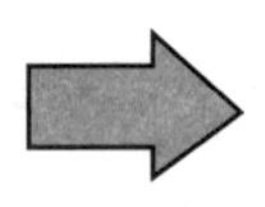	~~5~~ ~~3~~	→	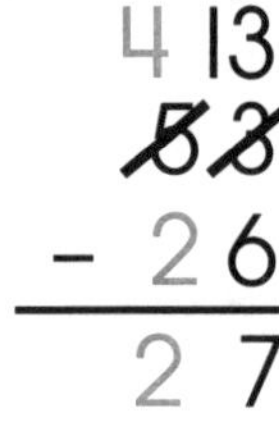
− 26	− 26		− 26		
			7		

4 13
~~5~~ ~~3~~
− 26
2 7

Rename 45 as 3 tens and 15 ones.

	3 15		3 15		3 15
45	~~4~~ ~~5~~	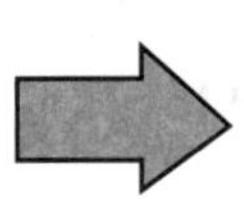	~~4~~ ~~5~~		~~4~~ ~~5~~
− 18	− 18		− 18		− 18
			7		2 7

Directions: Subtract.

Examples:

5 13 ~~6~~ ~~3~~ − 28 35	6 14 ~~7~~ ~~4~~ − 39 35	47 − 28	52 − 26	64 − 36
84 − 47	93 − 56	71 − 23	26 − 18	67 − 48
44 − 28	53 − 37	82 − 46	94 − 66	55 − 39
86 − 58	34 − 18	54 − 29	73 − 59	86 − 69

Name ____________________

2-Digit Subtraction

Directions: Rename 73 as 6 tens and 13 ones.

73 − 48

6 13
73 − 48

Subtract the ones.

6 13
73 − 48 = 5

Subtract the tens.

6 13
73 − 48 = 25

Directions: Subtract.

Example:

5 13
63 − 48 = 15

63 − 48	83 − 45	74 − 29	94 − 48	62 − 25
45 − 27	33 − 24	24 − 8	86 − 37	72 − 48
36 − 17	26 − 18	43 − 19	63 − 48	93 − 18
82 − 26	73 − 28	95 − 69	57 − 38	41 − 25
54 − 18	61 − 34	91 − 37	81 − 44	32 − 15

Name ____________________

Problem Solving

Directions: Solve each problem.

Example:

Dad cooks 23 potatoes.

He uses 19 potatoes in the potato salad.

How many potatoes are left?

Susan draws 32 butterflies.

She coloured 15 of them brown.

How many butterflies does she have left to colour?

A book has 66 pages.

Pedro reads 39 pages.

How many pages are left to read?

Jerry picks up 34 sea shells.

He puts 15 of them in a box.

How many does he have left?

Beth buys 72 sheets of paper.

She uses 44 sheets for her school work.

How many sheets of paper are left?

Name ____________

Addition and Subtraction Review

Directions: Add.

4 + 9	8 + 6	9 + 8	7 + 6	5 + 7	6 + 5
9 + 6	5 + 8	7 + 4	9 + 9	8 + 7	7 + 9
30 + 40	20 + 30	45 + 23	52 + 23	60 + 25	83 + 15

Directions: Subtract.

16 − 7	15 − 9	13 − 4	12 − 7	11 − 9	17 − 8
18 − 9	17 − 9	16 − 8	15 − 8	14 − 7	16 − 9
40 − 30	60 − 10	85 − 23	73 − 41	96 − 43	54 − 44

Name ______________________

Addition and Subtraction Review

Directions: Add.

4 + 8	9 + 2	5 + 9	6 + 6	7 + 5	9 + 4
8 + 8	7 + 6	3 + 9	7 + 7	6 + 9	6 + 5
40 + 20	50 + 30	75 + 20	66 + 31	47 + 51	34 + 23

Directions: Subtract.

17 − 9	15 − 6	12 − 3	13 − 7	14 − 6	16 − 8
15 − 7	14 − 9	13 − 6	15 − 7	12 − 9	11 − 8
30 − 10	50 − 30	65 − 30	87 − 34	75 − 23	66 − 43

Name ____________________

Review: 2-Digit Addition

Directions: Add the ones. Rename 12 as 10 + 2. Add the tens.

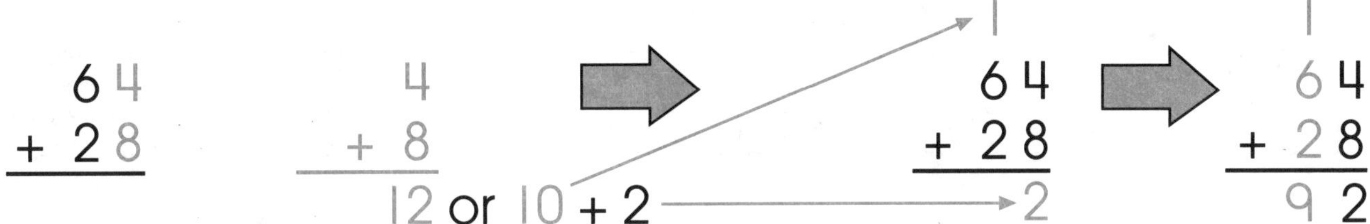

Directions: Add.

Example:

28 + 19 = 47	34 + 49	25 + 16	46 + 29	54 + 39
16 + 39	64 + 28	58 + 24	39 + 17	34 + 19
57 + 39	14 + 48	37 + 39	61 + 19	29 + 44
17 + 35	39 + 14	44 + 37	25 + 49	18 + 18
26 + 48	39 + 27	14 + 27	65 + 25	59 + 18

Name ______________________________

Review: 2-Digit Addition

Directions: Add.

36 + 55	14 + 28	57 + 38	44 + 48	33 + 29
23 + 18	27 + 27	68 + 25	23 + 19	42 + 19
56 + 28	49 + 27	38 + 49	36 + 18	49 + 24
18 + 54	51 + 39	74 + 17	35 + 28	52 + 19
48 + 26	25 + 28	39 + 33	29 + 44	54 + 27

Name ______________________________

Problem Solving

Directions: Solve each problem.

Example:

Simon sees 36 birds flying.

Julie sees 28 birds flying.

How many birds do they see flying?

$$\begin{array}{r} 36 \\ + \underline{28} \\ 64 \end{array}$$

Brandon ran the race in 35 seconds.

Ryan ran the race in 28 seconds.

How many seconds did they run?

Tom has 63 nickels.

Connie has 29 nickels.

How many nickels do they have?

Pam sees 48 monkeys at the zoo.

Brenda sees 35 different monkeys.

How many monkeys did they see?

There are 29 cows in one pen.

There are 47 cows in the other pen.

How many cows in all?

Name ______________________

Keep on Truckin'

Directions: Write each sum. Connect the sums of 83 to make a road for the truck.

$$\begin{array}{r} 17 \\ +66 \\ \hline \end{array} \quad \begin{array}{r} 48 \\ +26 \\ \hline \end{array} \quad \begin{array}{r} 42 \\ +19 \\ \hline \end{array}$$

$$\begin{array}{r} 28 \\ +38 \\ \hline \end{array} \quad \begin{array}{r} 64 \\ +19 \\ \hline \end{array} \quad \begin{array}{r} 26 \\ +57 \\ \hline \end{array} \quad \begin{array}{r} 58 \\ +25 \\ \hline \end{array} \quad \begin{array}{r} 17 \\ +75 \\ \hline \end{array} \quad \begin{array}{r} 65 \\ +29 \\ \hline \end{array}$$

$$\begin{array}{r} 37 \\ +39 \\ \hline \end{array} \quad \begin{array}{r} 48 \\ +35 \\ \hline \end{array} \quad \begin{array}{r} 58 \\ +37 \\ \hline \end{array} \quad \begin{array}{r} 65 \\ +16 \\ \hline \end{array} \quad \begin{array}{r} 38 \\ +25 \\ \hline \end{array} \quad \begin{array}{r} 39 \\ +59 \\ \hline \end{array}$$

$$\begin{array}{r} 59 \\ +27 \\ \hline \end{array} \quad \begin{array}{r} 55 \\ +28 \\ \hline \end{array} \quad \begin{array}{r} 39 \\ +44 \\ \hline \end{array}$$

Name ____________________

Shoot for the Stars

Directions: Add the total points scored in the game. Remember to add the ones first and regroup. Then, add the tens.

Example:

Total 80

HOME 29
VISITOR 45

Total ____________

Total ____________

Total ____________

HOME 66
VISITOR 28

Total ____________

Total ____________

Total ____________

Total ____________

Total ____________

Total ____________

Name ____________________

Review: 2-Digit Subtraction

Directions: Rename 61 as 5 tens and 11 ones.

Subtract the ones.

Subtract the tens.

$$\begin{array}{r} 61 \\ -\ 43 \\ \hline \end{array} \qquad \begin{array}{r} 5\ 11 \\ \not{6}\not{1} \\ -\ 43 \\ \hline \end{array}$$

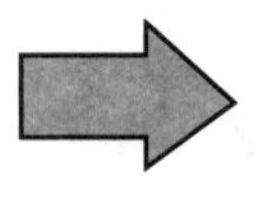

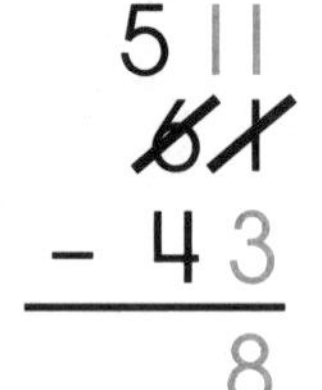

$$\begin{array}{r} 5\ 11 \\ \not{6}\not{1} \\ -\ 43 \\ \hline 8 \end{array}$$

$$\begin{array}{r} 5\ 11 \\ \not{6}\not{1} \\ -\ 43 \\ \hline 18 \end{array}$$

Directions: Subtract.

Example:

$$\begin{array}{r} 3\ 17 \\ \not{4}\not{7} \\ -\ 28 \\ \hline 19 \end{array}$$

73 − 48 = ___	84 − 66 = ___	95 − 18 = ___	64 − 29 = ___

56 − 38 = ___	31 − 15 = ___	25 − 17 = ___	33 − 19 = ___	46 − 29 = ___
93 − 64 = ___	82 − 55 = ___	72 − 14 = ___	45 − 28 = ___	61 − 23 = ___
51 − 44 = ___	62 − 48 = ___	37 − 19 = ___	50 − 32 = ___	83 − 47 = ___
92 − 73 = ___	82 − 75 = ___	76 − 38 = ___	47 − 29 = ___	74 − 39 = ___

Name ____________________

Review: 2-Digit Subtraction

Directions: Subtract.

85 − 16	93 − 48	72 − 35	63 − 27	43 − 38
56 − 29	75 − 49	84 − 38	91 − 65	37 − 18
21 − 14	35 − 18	42 − 29	72 − 47	81 − 54
64 − 38	53 − 28	94 − 57	48 − 39	23 − 18
74 − 58	83 − 36	62 − 26	54 − 28	32 − 17

Name ____________________

Go "Fore" It!

Directions: Add or subtract using regrouping.

tens	ones
2	15
~~3~~	5
-2	7
	8

$$\begin{array}{r} 56 \\ -\ 27 \\ \hline \end{array}$$

$$\begin{array}{r} 40 \\ -\ 16 \\ \hline \end{array}$$

$$\begin{array}{r} 35 \\ +27 \\ \hline \end{array}$$

$$\begin{array}{r} 93 \\ -\ 39 \\ \hline \end{array}$$

$$\begin{array}{r} 44 \\ +28 \\ \hline \end{array}$$

$$\begin{array}{r} 42 \\ -14 \\ \hline \end{array}$$

$$\begin{array}{r} 97 \\ -\ 48 \\ \hline \end{array}$$

$$\begin{array}{r} 33 \\ +18 \\ \hline \end{array}$$

$$\begin{array}{r} 73 \\ -\ 24 \\ \hline \end{array}$$

$$\begin{array}{r} 56 \\ -\ 17 \\ \hline \end{array}$$

$$\begin{array}{r} 68 \\ -\ 49 \\ \hline \end{array}$$

$$\begin{array}{r} 49 \\ +32 \\ \hline \end{array}$$

$$\begin{array}{r} 77 \\ -\ 68 \\ \hline \end{array}$$

$$\begin{array}{r} 27 \\ +19 \\ \hline \end{array}$$

Name ____________________

Monster Math

Directions: Add or subtract using regrouping.

$$\begin{array}{r} 84 \\ -\ 56 \\ \hline \end{array}$$

$$\begin{array}{r} 41 \\ -\ 17 \\ \hline \end{array}$$

$$\begin{array}{r} 52 \\ -\ 28 \\ \hline \end{array}$$

$$\begin{array}{r} 84 \\ -\ 27 \\ \hline \end{array}$$

$$\begin{array}{r} 57 \\ -\ 39 \\ \hline \end{array}$$

$$\begin{array}{r} 72 \\ -\ 19 \\ \hline \end{array}$$

$$\begin{array}{r} 33 \\ -\ 15 \\ \hline \end{array}$$

$$\begin{array}{r} 64 \\ +\ 17 \\ \hline \end{array}$$

$$\begin{array}{r} 36 \\ -\ 19 \\ \hline \end{array}$$

$$\begin{array}{r} 65 \\ -\ 28 \\ \hline \end{array}$$

$$\begin{array}{r} 48 \\ -\ 30 \\ \hline \end{array}$$

$$\begin{array}{r} 33 \\ +\ 18 \\ \hline \end{array}$$

$$\begin{array}{r} 25 \\ +\ 35 \\ \hline \end{array}$$

Name ____________________

Adding Hundreds

Examples:

5 hundreds	500
+ 3 hundreds	+ 300
8 hundreds	800

4 hundreds	400
+ 5 hundreds	+ 500
9 hundreds	900

Directions: Add.

3 hundreds	300
+ 1 hundreds	+ 100
4 hundreds	400

6 hundreds	600
+ 2 hundreds	+ 200
___ hundreds	

$$\begin{array}{r} 200 \\ +\ 200 \\ \hline \end{array} \qquad \begin{array}{r} 100 \\ +\ 700 \\ \hline \end{array} \qquad \begin{array}{r} 600 \\ +\ 300 \\ \hline \end{array} \qquad \begin{array}{r} 400 \\ +\ 500 \\ \hline \end{array}$$

$$\begin{array}{r} 300 \\ +\ 400 \\ \hline \end{array} \qquad \begin{array}{r} 800 \\ +\ 100 \\ \hline \end{array} \qquad \begin{array}{r} 400 \\ +\ 400 \\ \hline \end{array} \qquad \begin{array}{r} 700 \\ +\ 200 \\ \hline \end{array}$$

$$\begin{array}{r} 500 \\ +\ 100 \\ \hline \end{array} \qquad \begin{array}{r} 100 \\ +\ 600 \\ \hline \end{array} \qquad \begin{array}{r} 500 \\ +\ 200 \\ \hline \end{array} \qquad \begin{array}{r} 300 \\ +\ 200 \\ \hline \end{array}$$

$$\begin{array}{r} 300 \\ +\ 300 \\ \hline \end{array} \qquad \begin{array}{r} 400 \\ +\ 200 \\ \hline \end{array} \qquad \begin{array}{r} 300 \\ +\ 500 \\ \hline \end{array} \qquad \begin{array}{r} 200 \\ +\ 100 \\ \hline \end{array}$$

Name ______________________________

Problem Solving

Directions: Solve each problem.

Example:

Ria packed 300 boxes.

Melvin packed 200 boxes.

How many boxes did Ria and Melvin pack?

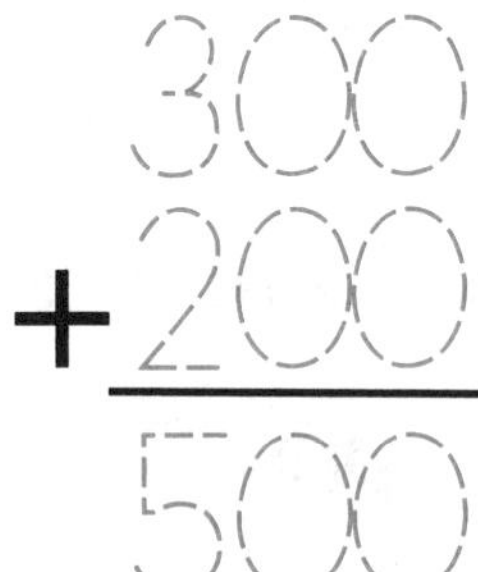

Santo typed 500 letters.

Hale typed 400 letters.

How many letters did they type?

Paula used 100 paper clips.

Milton used 600 paper clips.

How many paper clips did they use?

The grocery store sold 400 red apples.

The grocery store also sold 100 yellow apples.

How many apples did the grocery store sell in all?

Miles worked 200 days.

Julia worked 500 days.

How many days did they work?

Name ____________________

Challenge! 3-Digit Addition

$\begin{array}{r} 245 \\ +\ 253 \\ \hline 8 \end{array}$  $\begin{array}{r} 245 \\ +\ 253 \\ \hline 98 \end{array}$ 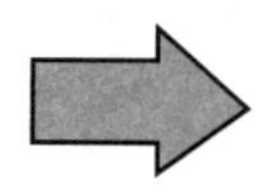 $\begin{array}{r} 245 \\ +\ 253 \\ \hline 498 \end{array}$

Directions: Add.

Example:

$\begin{array}{r} 745 \\ +\ 23 \\ \hline 768 \end{array}$

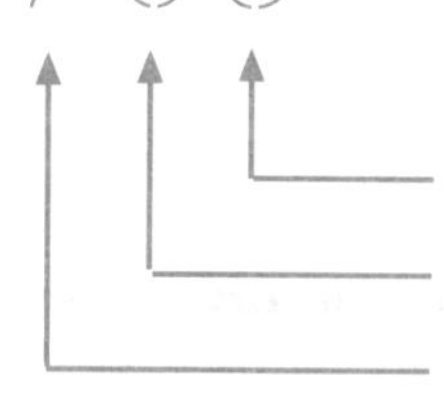

Add the ones.
Add the tens.
Add the hundreds.

$\begin{array}{r} 623 \\ +\ 156 \\ \hline \end{array}$

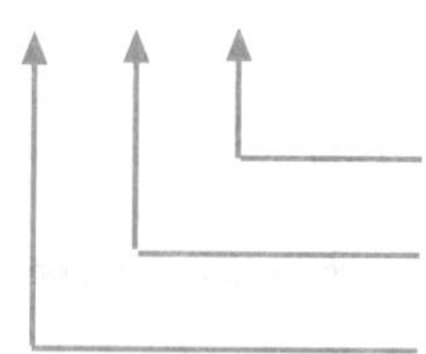

Add the ones.
Add the tens.
Add the hundreds.

$\begin{array}{r} 415 \\ +\ 342 \\ \hline \end{array}$ $\begin{array}{r} 566 \\ +\ 33 \\ \hline \end{array}$ $\begin{array}{r} 373 \\ +\ 221 \\ \hline \end{array}$ $\begin{array}{r} 160 \\ +\ 334 \\ \hline \end{array}$

$\begin{array}{r} 835 \\ +\ 42 \\ \hline \end{array}$ $\begin{array}{r} 642 \\ +\ 251 \\ \hline \end{array}$ $\begin{array}{r} 287 \\ +\ 412 \\ \hline \end{array}$ $\begin{array}{r} 723 \\ +\ 45 \\ \hline \end{array}$

$\begin{array}{r} 133 \\ +\ 522 \\ \hline \end{array}$ $\begin{array}{r} 454 \\ +\ 324 \\ \hline \end{array}$ $\begin{array}{r} 314 \\ +\ 602 \\ \hline \end{array}$ $\begin{array}{r} 654 \\ +\ 235 \\ \hline \end{array}$

Problem Solving

Directions: Solve each problem.

Example:

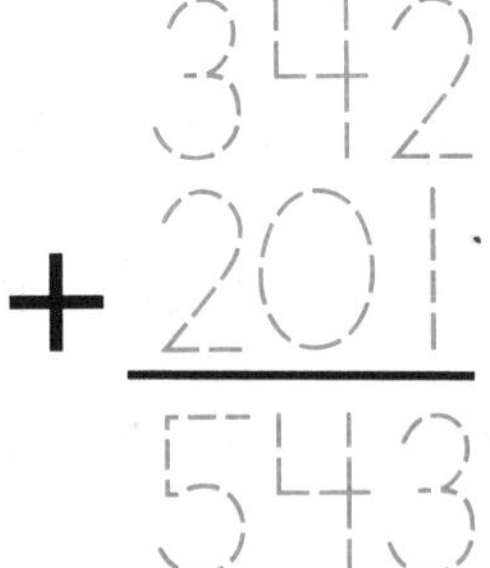

Gene collected 342 rocks.

Lester collected 201 rocks.

How many rocks did they collect?

Tina jumped the rope 403 times.

Henry jumped the rope 426 times.

How many times did they jump?

There are 210 people wearing blue hats.

There are 432 people wearing red hats.

How many hats in all?

Asta used 135 paper plates.

Clyde used 143 paper plates.

How many paper plates did they use in all?

Aunt Mary had 536 dollars.

Uncle Lewis had 423 dollars.

How many dollars did they have in all?

Name ______________________

Challenge!

Problem Solving

Directions: Solve each problem.

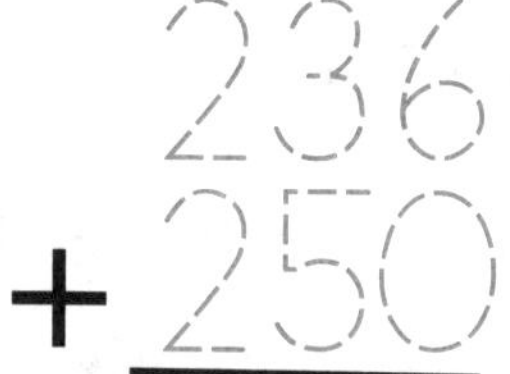

There are 236 boys in school.

There are 250 girls in school.

How many boys and girls are in school?

Mary saw 131 cars.

Marvin saw 268 trucks.

How many cars and trucks did they see in all?

Jack has 427 pennies.

Jill has 370 pennies.

How many pennies do they have in all?

There are 582 red apples.

There are 206 yellow apples.

How many apples are there in all?

Ann found 122 shells.

Pedro found 76 shells.

How many shells did they find?

Name ____________________

Subtracting Hundreds

8 hundreds - 3 hundreds 5 hundreds	800 - 300 500	6 hundreds - 2 hundreds 4 hundreds	600 - 200 400

Directions: Subtract.

Example:

9 hundreds - 7 hundreds 2 hundreds	900 - 700 200	3 hundreds - 1 hundreds ___ hundreds	300 - 100 ___

700 - 300	500 - 400	900 - 400	800 - 500
600 - 500	300 - 200	500 - 100	400 - 200
900 - 100	800 - 400	600 - 200	500 - 300
400 - 100	700 - 600	800 - 200	900 - 600

Name ________________________________

Problem Solving

Directions: Solve each problem.

Example:

There were 400 apples in a box.

Jesse took 100 apples from the box.

How many apples are still in the box?

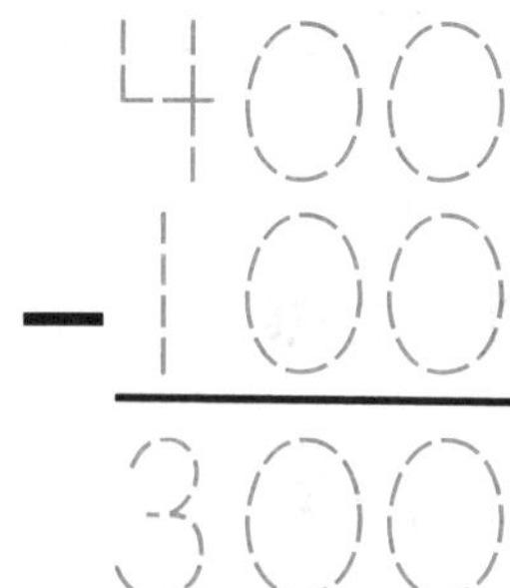

Tommy bought 300 golf balls.

He gave Irene 200 golf balls.

How many golf balls does he have left?

The black horse ran 900 feet.

The brown horse ran 700 feet.

How many more feet did the black horse run?

The paint store has 800 gallons of paint.

It sells 300 gallons of paint.

How many gallons of paint are left?

There are 700 children.

There are 200 boys.

How many girls are there?

Name ____________________

Challenge! 3-Digit Subtraction

Directions: Subtract the ones.

$$\begin{array}{r} 746 \\ -\underline{424} \\ 2 \end{array}$$

Subtract the tens.

$$\begin{array}{r} 746 \\ -\underline{424} \\ 22 \end{array}$$

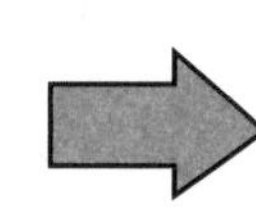

Subtract the hundreds.

$$\begin{array}{r} 746 \\ -\underline{424} \\ 322 \end{array}$$

Directions: Add.

Example:

$$\begin{array}{r} 879 \\ -\underline{46} \end{array}$$

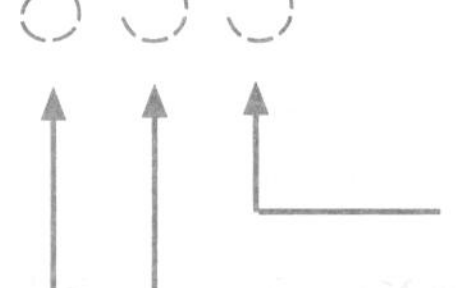

Subtract the ones.
Subtract the tens.
Subtract the hundreds.

$$\begin{array}{r} 586 \\ -\underline{142} \end{array}$$

Subtract the ones.
Subtract the tens.
Subtract the hundreds.

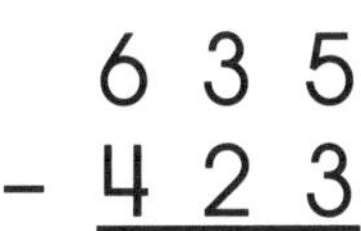

$$\begin{array}{r} 635 \\ -\underline{423} \end{array} \quad \begin{array}{r} 478 \\ -\underline{241} \end{array} \quad \begin{array}{r} 338 \\ -\underline{27} \end{array} \quad \begin{array}{r} 957 \\ -\underline{734} \end{array}$$

$$\begin{array}{r} 297 \\ -\underline{145} \end{array} \quad \begin{array}{r} 846 \\ -\underline{325} \end{array} \quad \begin{array}{r} 769 \\ -\underline{514} \end{array} \quad \begin{array}{r} 653 \\ -\underline{142} \end{array}$$

$$\begin{array}{r} 569 \\ -\underline{333} \end{array} \quad \begin{array}{r} 365 \\ -\underline{213} \end{array} \quad \begin{array}{r} 818 \\ -\underline{618} \end{array} \quad \begin{array}{r} 936 \\ -\underline{424} \end{array}$$

Name ____________________

Challenge!

Problem Solving

Directions: Solve each problem.

Example:

The grocery store buys 568 cans of beans.

It sells 345 cans of beans.

How many cans of beans are left?

$$\begin{array}{r} 568 \\ -\ 345 \\ \hline 223 \end{array}$$

The cooler holds 732 gallons of milk.

It has 412 gallons of milk in it.

How many more gallons of milk
will it take to fill the cooler?

Ann does 635 push-ups.

Carl does 421 push-ups.

How many more push-ups does Ann do?

Kurt has 386 pennies.

Neal has 32 pennies.

How many more pennies does Kurt have?

It takes 874 nails to build a tree house.

Jillian has 532 nails.

How many more nails does she need?

Name ____________________

Challenge! Problem Solving

Directions: Solve each problem.

Example:

There were 787 bales of hay.

Glenda fed the cows 535 bales.

How many bales of hay are left?

$$\begin{array}{r} 787 \\ -\ 535 \\ \hline 252 \end{array}$$

There are 673 bolts in a box.

Maria took 341 bolts out of the box.

How many bolts are left in the box?

The secretary types 459 letters.

138 of the letters were mailed.

How many letters are left?

Mr. Jones had 569 dollars.

He spent 203 dollars.

How many dollars does he have left?

There are 342 riding horses in the rodeo.

There are 132 bucking horses in the rodeo.

How many more riding horses are there?

Name ____________________

Review: Addition and Subtraction

Directions: Add.

$$\begin{array}{r} 124 \\ +\ 323 \\ \hline \end{array} \qquad \begin{array}{r} 520 \\ +\ 407 \\ \hline \end{array} \qquad \begin{array}{r} 739 \\ +\ 150 \\ \hline \end{array} \qquad \begin{array}{r} 861 \\ +\ \ \ \ 6 \\ \hline \end{array}$$

Directions: Subtract.

$$\begin{array}{r} 900 \\ -\ 600 \\ \hline \end{array} \qquad \begin{array}{r} 800 \\ -\ 200 \\ \hline \end{array} \qquad \begin{array}{r} 974 \\ -\ 564 \\ \hline \end{array} \qquad \begin{array}{r} 508 \\ -\ \ \ \ 7 \\ \hline \end{array}$$

$$\begin{array}{r} 728 \\ -\ 326 \\ \hline \end{array} \qquad \begin{array}{r} 657 \\ -\ \ 45 \\ \hline \end{array} \qquad \begin{array}{r} 894 \\ -\ 464 \\ \hline \end{array} \qquad \begin{array}{r} 596 \\ -\ 352 \\ \hline \end{array}$$

Directions: Solve each problem.

There are 275 nails in a box.

123 nails are taken out of the box.

How many nails are still in the box?

Gerald peeled 212 apples.

Anna peeled 84 apples.

How many apples did they peel in all?

Name ______________________________

Challenge! Review: 3-Digit Addition

Directions: Add.

Examples:

$340 + 225 = 565$	$754 + 32 = 786$	$826 + 3$	$632 + 322$
$198 + 200$	$456 + 31$	$541 + 333$	$273 + 415$
$900 + 34$	$847 + 131$	$721 + 176$	$402 + 383$
$156 + 423$	$644 + 251$	$215 + 542$	$372 + 417$
$518 + 351$	$783 + 5$	$684 + 14$	$710 + 260$

Name ____________________

Review: 3-Digit Subtraction

Directions: Subtract.

Examples:

$$\begin{array}{r} 856 \\ -\underline{352} \\ 504 \end{array} \qquad \begin{array}{r} 432 \\ -\underline{21} \\ 411 \end{array} \qquad \begin{array}{r} 598 \\ -\underline{416} \end{array} \qquad \begin{array}{r} 769 \\ -\underline{345} \end{array}$$

$$\begin{array}{r} 319 \\ -\underline{6} \end{array} \qquad \begin{array}{r} 954 \\ -\underline{731} \end{array} \qquad \begin{array}{r} 275 \\ -\underline{3} \end{array} \qquad \begin{array}{r} 643 \\ -\underline{313} \end{array}$$

$$\begin{array}{r} 775 \\ -\underline{261} \end{array} \qquad \begin{array}{r} 834 \\ -\underline{12} \end{array} \qquad \begin{array}{r} 942 \\ -\underline{111} \end{array} \qquad \begin{array}{r} 478 \\ -\underline{324} \end{array}$$

$$\begin{array}{r} 562 \\ -\underline{431} \end{array} \qquad \begin{array}{r} 444 \\ -\underline{212} \end{array} \qquad \begin{array}{r} 385 \\ -\underline{152} \end{array} \qquad \begin{array}{r} 754 \\ -\underline{3} \end{array}$$

$$\begin{array}{r} 868 \\ -\underline{234} \end{array} \qquad \begin{array}{r} 943 \\ -\underline{843} \end{array} \qquad \begin{array}{r} 689 \\ -\underline{417} \end{array} \qquad \begin{array}{r} 577 \\ -\underline{37} \end{array}$$

Name ____________________

Multiplication

Multiplication is a short way to find the sum of adding the same number a certain amount of times. For example, 7 x 4 = 28 instead of 7 + 7 + 7 + 7 = 28.

Directions: Study the example. Solve the problems.

Example:

3 + 3 + 3 = 9
3 threes = 9
3 x 3 = 9

7 + 7 = ____
2 sevens = ____
2 x 7 = ____

4 + 4 + 4 + 4 = ____
4 fours = ____
4 x ____ = ____

5 + 5 = ____
2 fives = ____
2 x ____ = ____

2 + 2 + 2 + 2 = ____
4 twos = ____
4 x ____ = ____

6 + 6 = ____
2 sixes = ____
2 x ____ = ____

Name ______________________

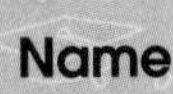

Multiplication

Multiplication is repeated addition.

Directions: Draw a picture for each problem.
Then, write the missing numbers.

Example:
Draw 2 groups of three apples.

$3 + 3 = 6$

or $2 \times 3 = 6$

Draw 3 groups of four hearts.

4 + 4 + 4 = ____

or 3 x ____ = ____

Draw 2 groups of five boxes.

5 + ____ = ____

or 2 x ____ = ____

Draw 6 groups of two circles.

2 + ____ + ____ + ____ + ____ + ____ = ____

or 6 x ____ = ____

Draw 7 groups of three triangles.

3 + ____ + ____ + ____ + ____ + ____ + ____ = ____

or ____ x ____ = ____

Name ______________________

Multiplication

Directions: Study the example. Draw the groups and write the total.

Example: 3x2
2+2+2 = 6
●● ●● ●●

3x4

___ + ___ + ___ = _________

2x5

____ + ____ = _________

5x3

___ + ___ + ___ + ___ + ___ = _________

Name ____________________

Multiplication

Directions: Solve the problems.

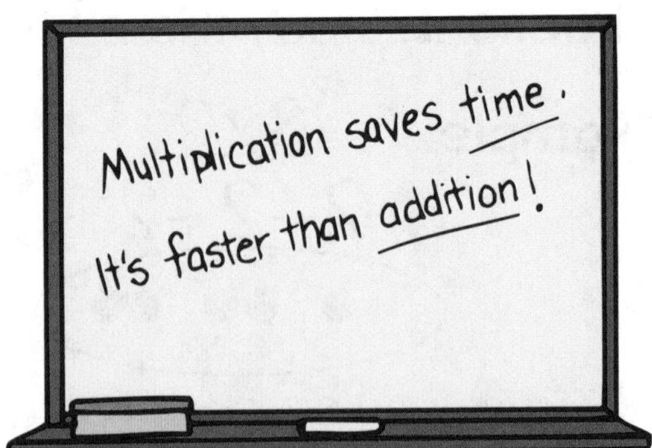
Multiplication saves time.
It's faster than addition!

9 + 9 = ____ 7 + 7 = ____

2 nines = ____ 2 sevens = ____

2 x 9 = ____ 2 x ____ = ____

4 + 4 + 4 + 4 = ____ 8 + 8 + 8 + 8 + 8 = ____

____ fours = ____ ____ eights = ____

____ x 4 = ____ ____ x 8 = ____

5 + 5 + 5 = ____ 9 + 9 = ____ 6 + 6 + 6 = ____

____ fives = ____ ____ nines = ____ ____ sixes = ____

____ x 5 = ____ ____ x 9 = ____ ____ x 6 = ____

3 + 3 = ____ 7 + 7 + 7 + 7 = ____ 2 + 2 = ____

____ threes = ____ ____ sevens = ____ ____ twos = ____

____ x 3 = ____ ____ x 7 = ____ ____ x 2 = ____

Name ______________________________

Multiplication

Directions: Use the code to colour the fish.

If the answer is:

 6, colour it **red.**

 12, colour it **orange.**

 16, colour it **blue.**

 27, colour it **brown.**

 8, colour it **yellow.**

 15, colour it **green.**

 18, colour it **purple.**

$4 \times 2 =$ $\begin{array}{r} 4 \\ \times 2 \\ \hline \end{array}$

$5 \times 3 =$ $\begin{array}{r} 5 \\ \times 3 \\ \hline \end{array}$

$3 \times 2 =$ $\begin{array}{r} 3 \\ \times 2 \\ \hline \end{array}$

$3 \times 6 =$ $\begin{array}{r} 3 \\ \times 6 \\ \hline \end{array}$

$4 \times 3 =$ $\begin{array}{r} 4 \\ \times 3 \\ \hline \end{array}$

$2 \times 8 =$ $\begin{array}{r} 2 \\ \times 8 \\ \hline \end{array}$

$9 \times 3 =$ $\begin{array}{r} 9 \\ \times 3 \\ \hline \end{array}$

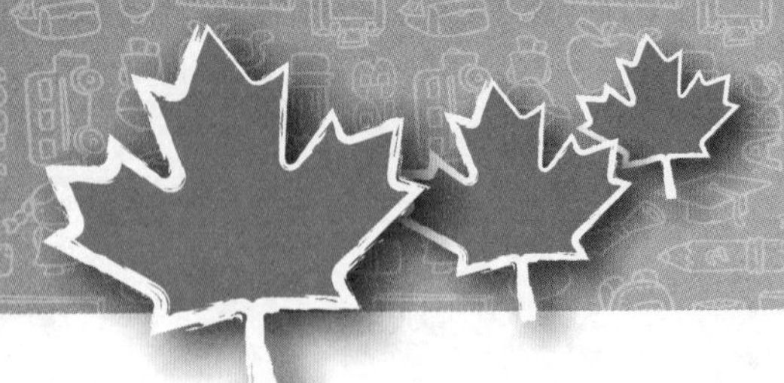

Name ______________________________

Multiplication

Directions: Use the code to colour the rainbow.

If the answer is:

6, colour it **green.** 16, colour it **pink.** 25, colour it **orange.**

8, colour it **purple.** 18, colour it **white** 27, colour it **blue.**

9, colour it **red.** 21, colour it **brown.**

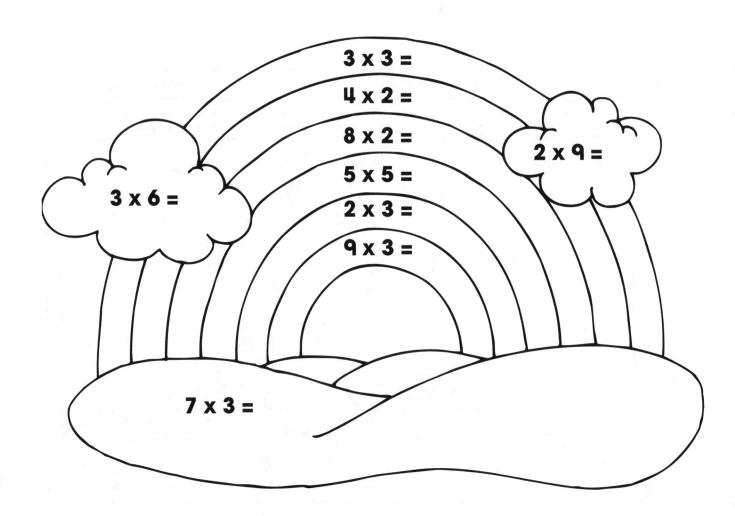

3 x 3 =

4 x 2 =

8 x 2 =

5 x 5 =

2 x 3 =

9 x 3 =

3 x 6 =

2 x 9 =

7 x 3 =

Name ______________________

Problem Solving

Directions: Tell if you add, subtract, or multiply. Then, write the answers. Hints: "In all" means to add. "Left" means to subtract. Groups with the same number in each means to multiply.

Example:

There are 6 red birds and 7 blue birds.
How many birds in all?

___add___ ___13___ birds

The pet store had 25 goldfish, but 10 were sold.
How many goldfish are left?

__________ _______ goldfish

There are 5 cages of bunnies. There are two bunnies in each cage.
How many bunnies are there in the store?

__________ _______ bunnies

The store had 18 puppies this morning. It sold 7 puppies today.
How many puppies are left?

__________ _______ puppies

Name ____________________

Problem Solving

Directions: Tell if you add, subtract, or multiply. Then, write the answers.

There were 12 frogs sitting on a log by a pond, but 3 frogs hopped away. How many frogs were left?

________________ ________ frogs

There are 9 flowers growing by the pond. Each flower has 2 leaves. How many leaves are there?

________________ ________ leaves

A tree had 7 squirrels playing in it. Then, 8 more came along. How many squirrels are there in all?

________________ ________ squirrels

There were 27 birds living in the trees around the pond, but 9 flew away. How many birds are left?

________________ ________ birds

Name ______________________________

Circle

A **circle** is a shape that is round. This is a circle: ◯

Directions: Find the circles and draw squares around them.

Directions: Trace the word. Then, write the word.

Name 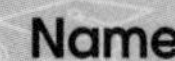

Square

A **square** is a shape with four corners and four sides of the same length. This is a square: □

Directions: Find the squares and draw circles around them.

Directions: Trace the word. Then, write the word.

Name ____________________

Rectangle

A **rectangle** is a shape with four corners and four sides. The sides opposite each other are the same length. This is a rectangle: ▭

Directions: Find the rectangles and draw circles around them.

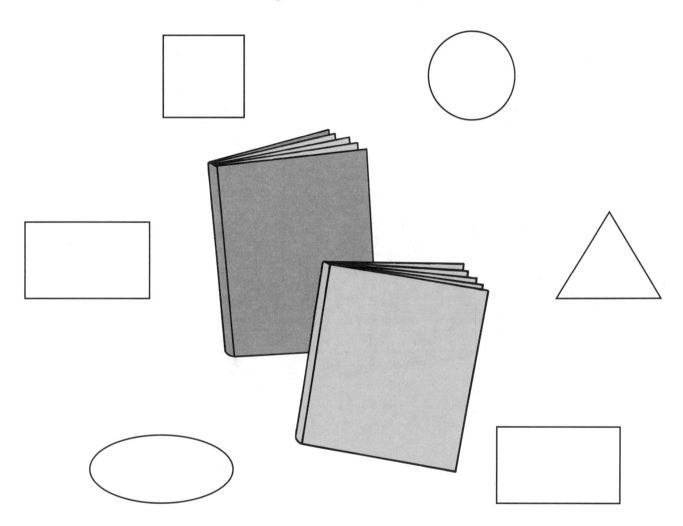

Directions: Trace the word. Then, write the word.

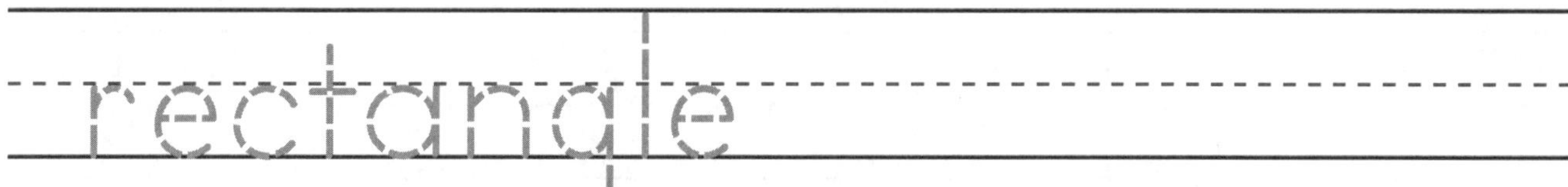

Name ______________________

Triangle

A **triangle** is a shape with three corners and three sides.
This is a triangle: △

Directions: Find the triangles and draw circles around them.

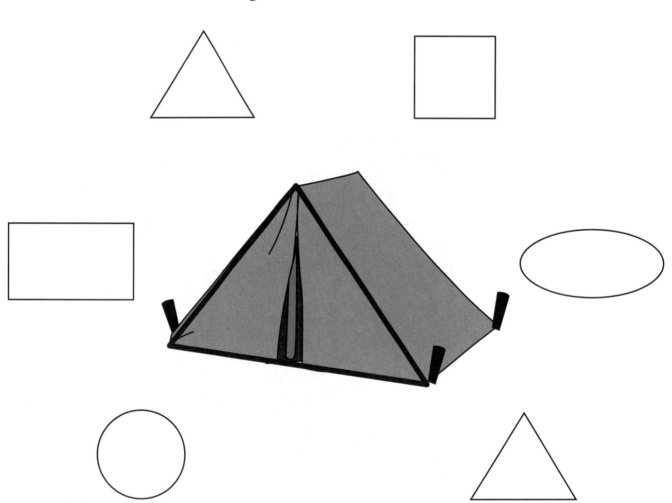

Directions: Trace the word. Then, write the word.

triangle

Name ______________________

Oval and Rhombus

An **oval** is egg-shaped. This is an oval: ⬭

A **rhombus** is a shape with four sides of the same length. Its corners form points at the top, sides, and bottom. This is a rhombus: ◇

Directions: Find the ovals. Colour them **red.**
Find the rhombuses. Colour them **blue.**

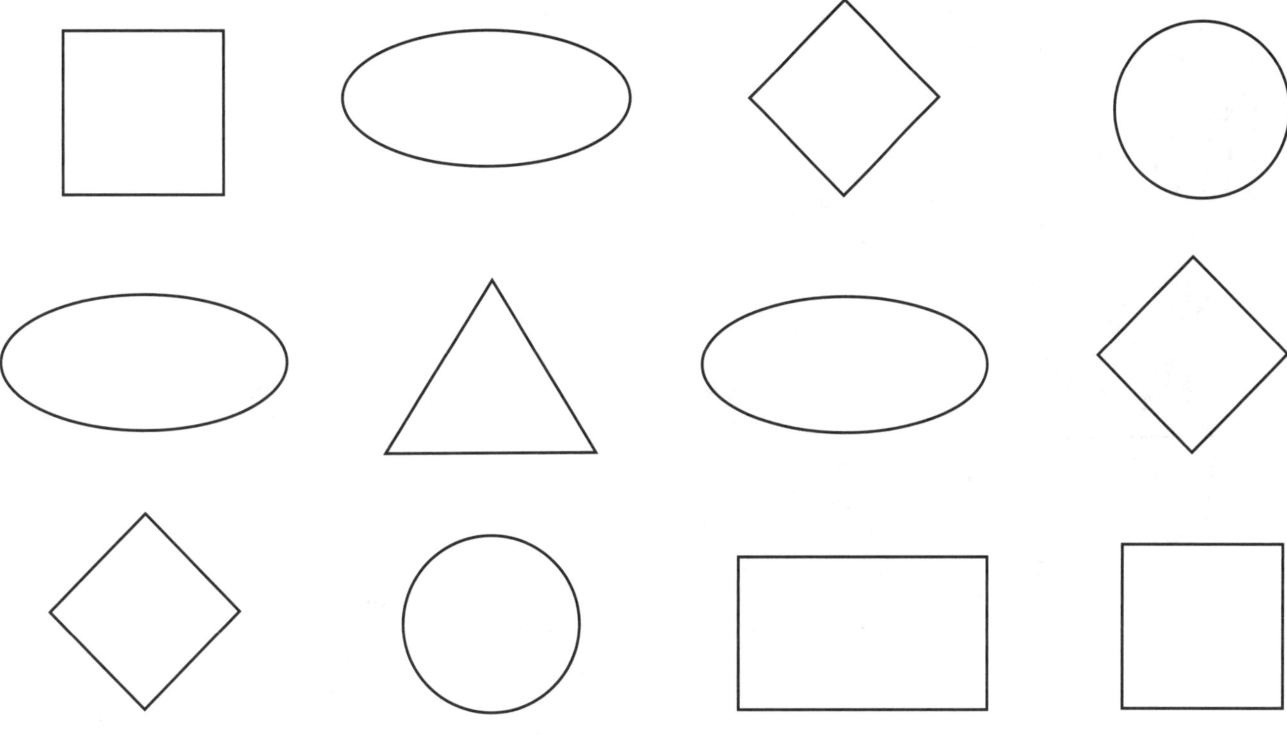

Directions: Trace the words. Then, write the words.

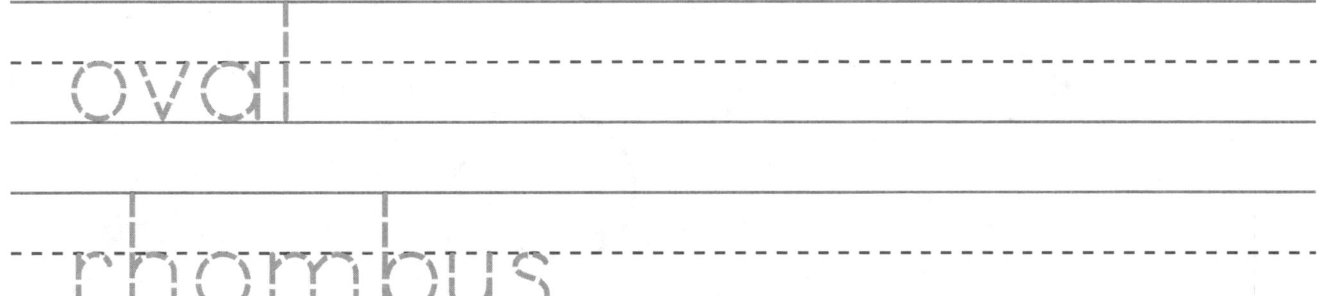

Name 

Geometry

Geometry is mathematics that has to do with lines and shapes.

Directions: Colour the shapes.

Colour the triangles **blue.**
Colour the circles **red.**
Colour the squares **green.**
Colour the rectangles **pink.**

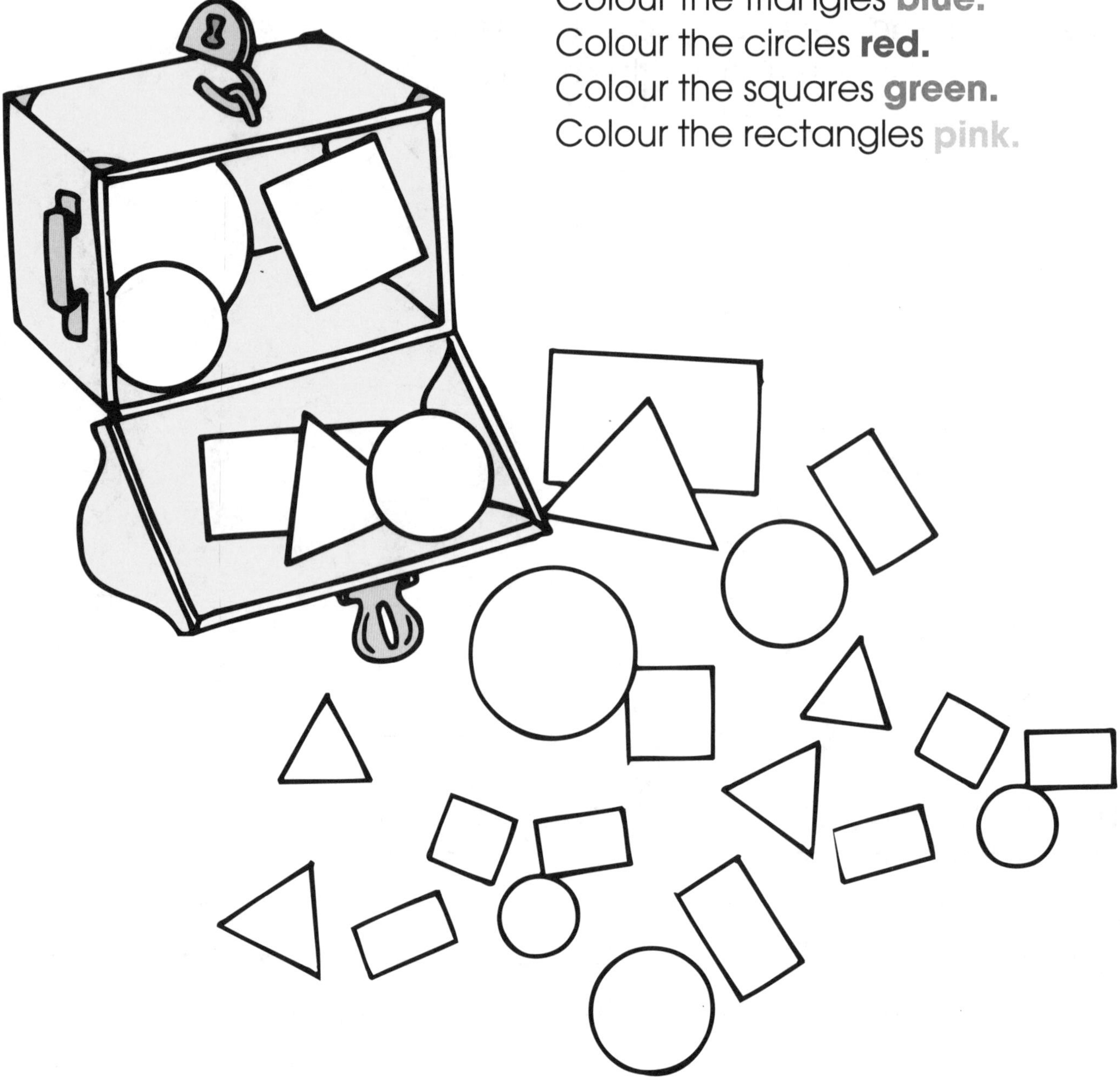

Name ____________________

Geometry

Directions: Draw a line from the word to the shape.

Use a **red** line for circles.
Use a **blue** line for squares.
Use a **yellow** line for rectangles.
Use a **green** line for triangles.

Circle **Square** **Triangle** **Rectangle**

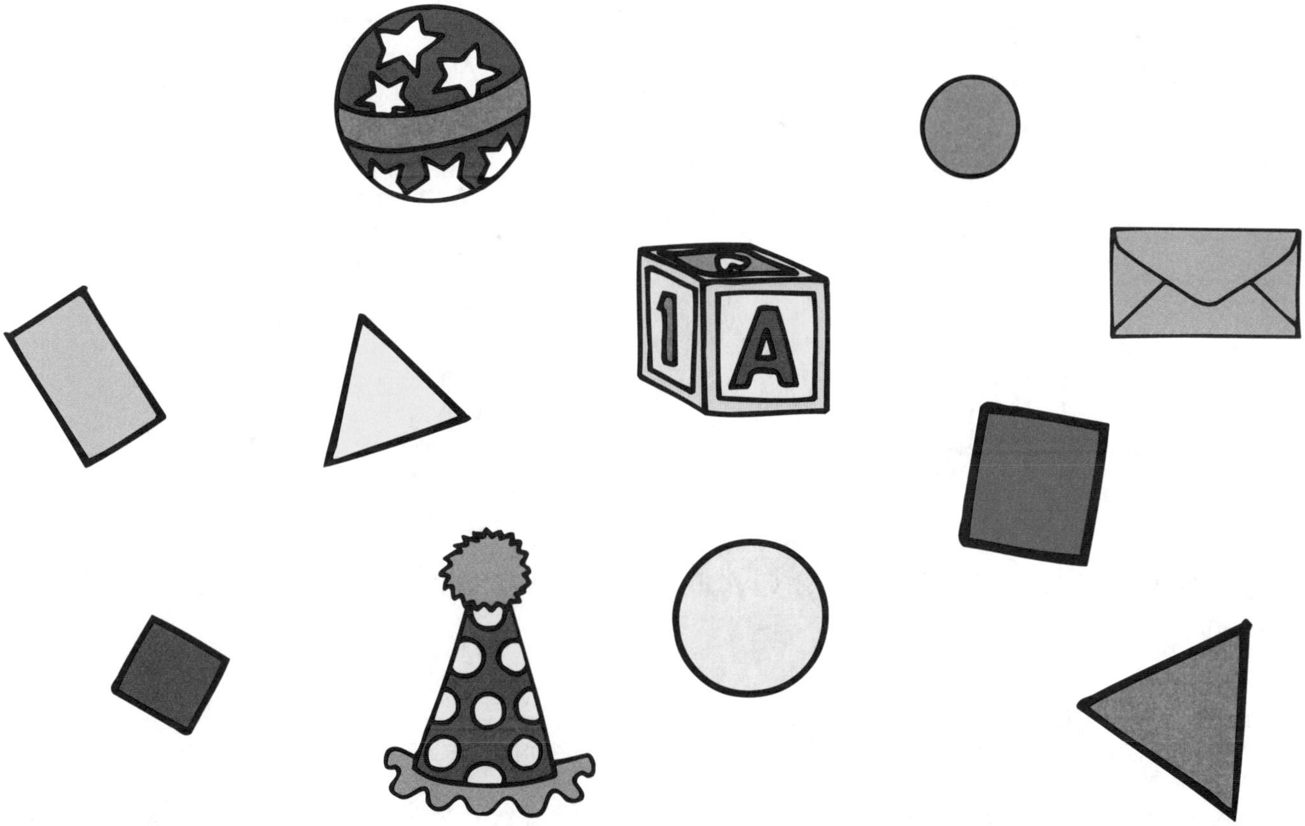

Name ______________________________

Shapes

Robbie the robot and his pal Roger are made of many different-shaped objects. Look at all the shapes on their bodies. Then, follow the directions below.

Directions: Use a **green** crayon to colour all the circles on their bodies.

This is a circle:

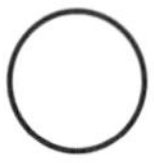

Use an **orange** crayon to colour all the ovals on their bodies.

This is an oval:

Colour the other shapes any way you like.

Name ______________________________

Shapes

Directions: Some shapes have sides. How many sides does each shape below have? Write the number of sides inside each shape.

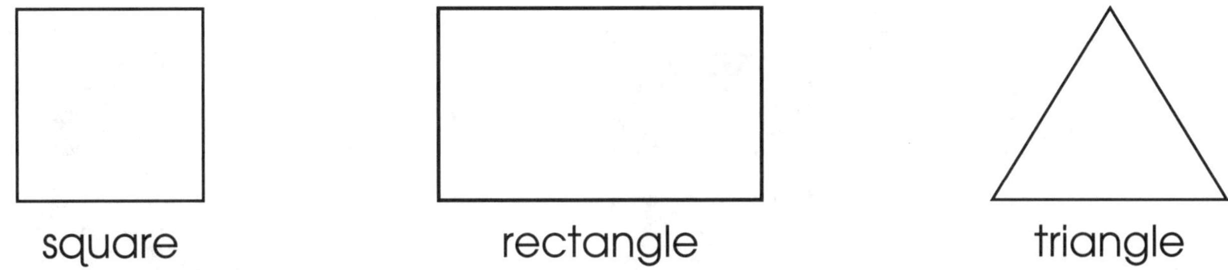

Directions: Help Robbie get to his space car by tracing the path that has only squares, rectangles, and triangles.

Hint: You may want to draw an **X** on all the other shapes. This will help you see the path more clearly.

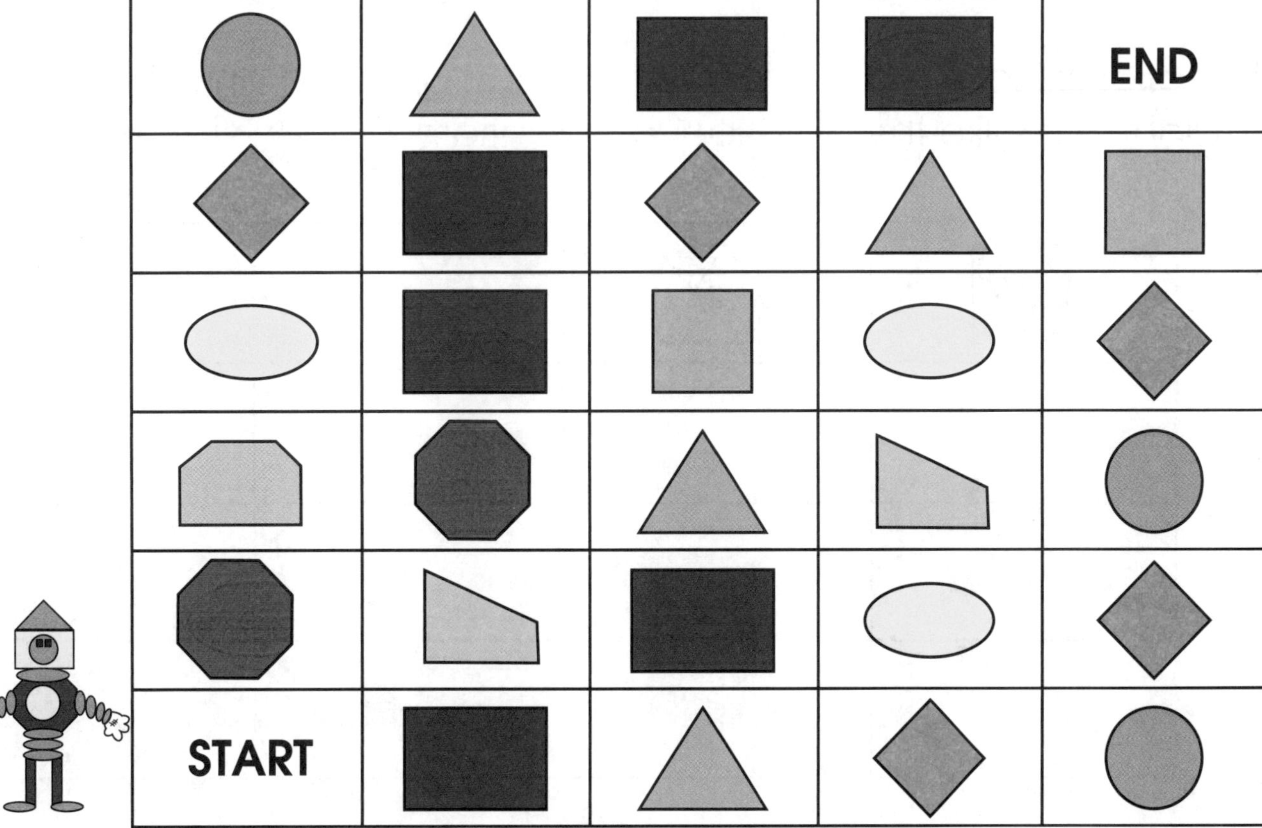

Name ____________________

Shapes

Directions: Look at the grid below. All the shapes have straight sides, like a square.

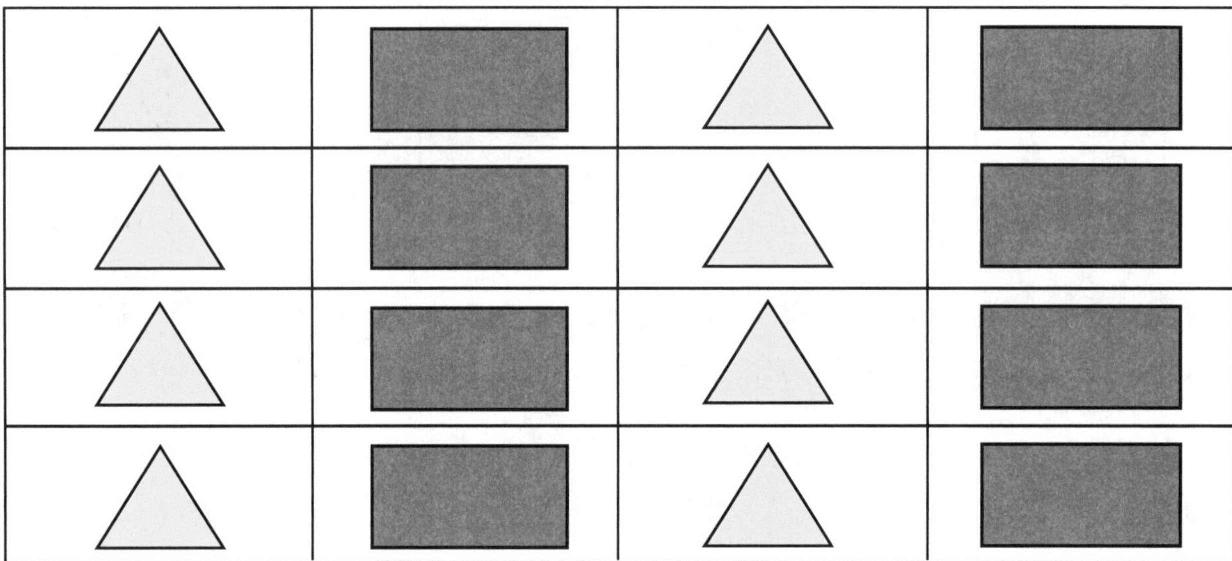

Directions: Now, make your own pattern grid. Use only shapes with straight sides like the grid above. The grid has been started for you.

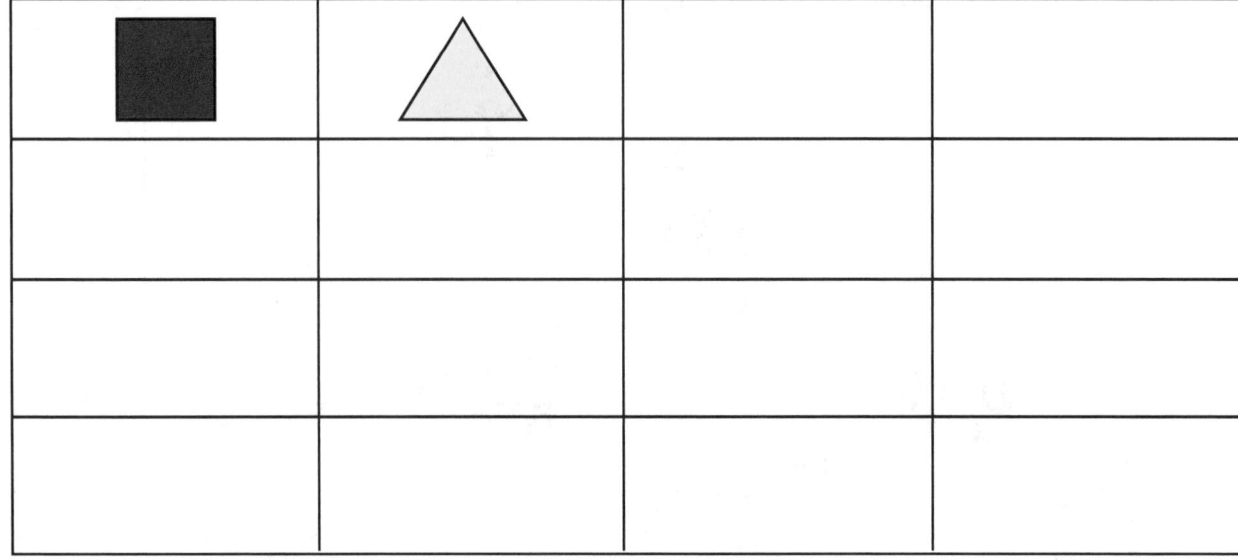

Name ___________________________

Measurement: Centimetres

A **centimetre** is a unit of length.

Directions: Use a centimetre ruler to measure the crayons to the nearest centimetre.

Example: The first crayon is about 7 centimetres long.

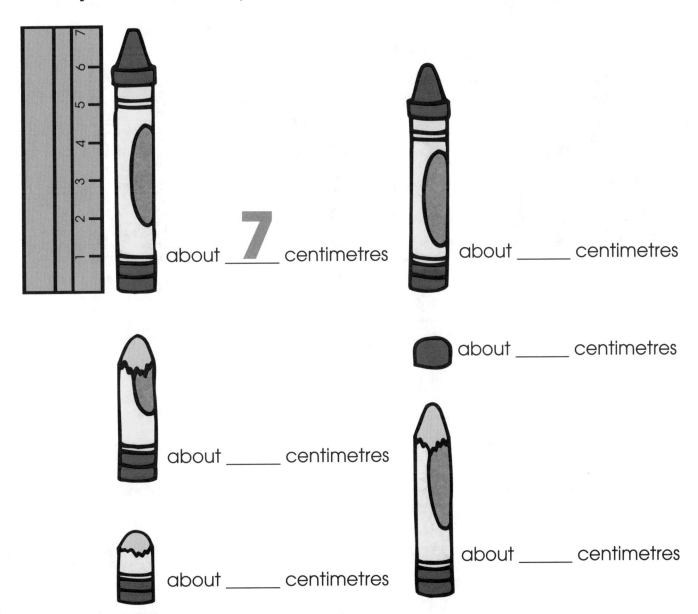

about **7** centimetres

about ______ centimetres

about ______ centimetres

about ______ centimetres

about ______ centimetres

about ______ centimetres

Name ______________________

Measurement: Centimetres

Directions: The moose is about 8 centimetres high. How many centimetres (cm) high are the trees? Write your answer in the blanks.

1. _____cm 2. _____cm 3. _____cm

4. _____cm 5. _____cm 6. _____cm 7. _____cm

Name ______________________________

Measuring in Centimetres

Directions: Use a centimetre ruler to find the height or the length of the objects below. Write the answer in each blank.

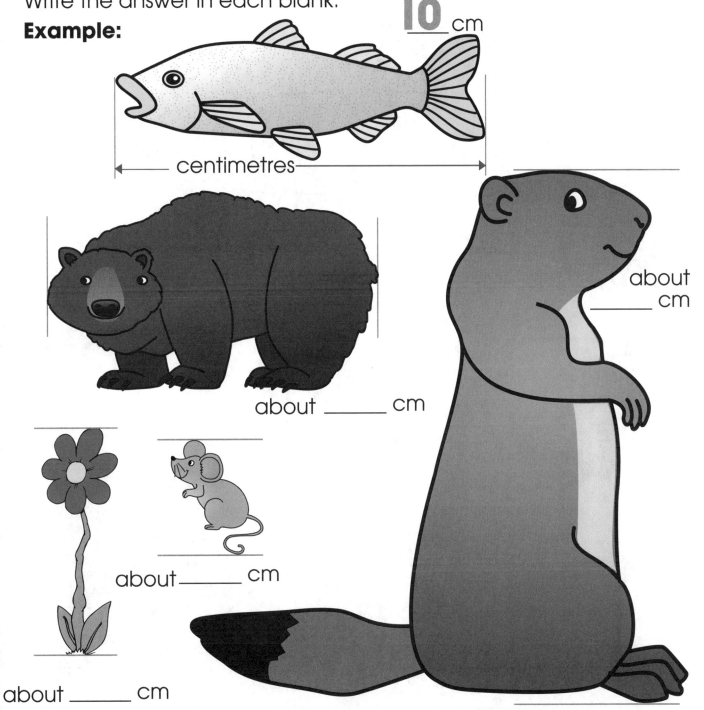

Example:

10 cm

centimetres

about ______ cm

about ______ cm

about ______ cm

about ______ cm

Name ______________________

Trip to the Watering Hole

Directions: Use a centimetre ruler to measure the distance each animal has to travel to reach the watering hole. Write the answer in each blank.

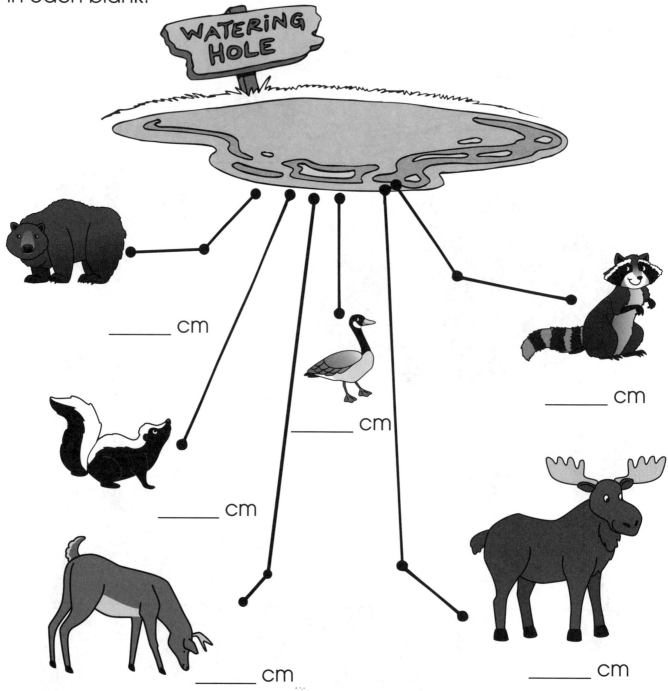

______ cm

______ cm

______ cm

______ cm

______ cm

______ cm

Name ____________________

Centimetre Sharpening

Directions: Use a centimetre ruler to measure each pencil. Subtract to find how many centimetres were lost when sharpening each pencil.

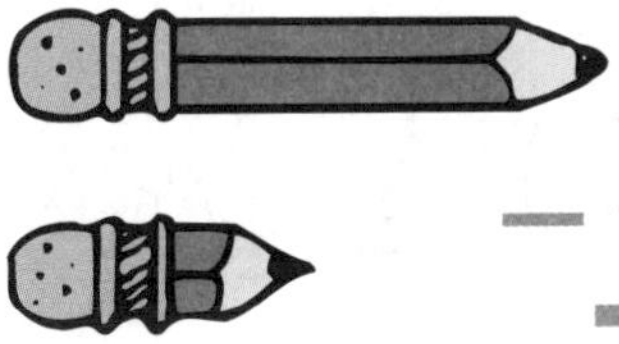

4 cm
− 2 cm
2 cm

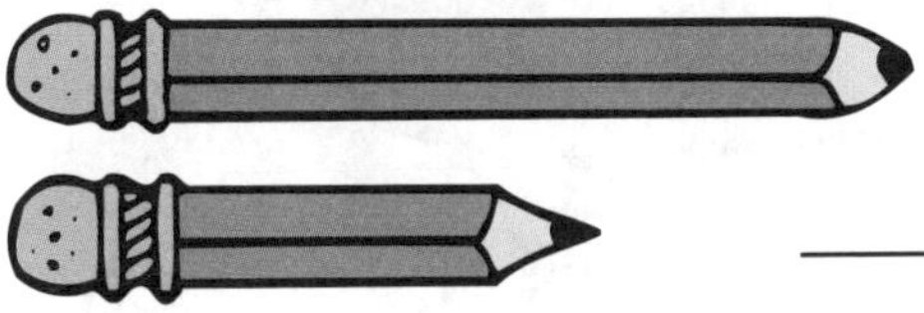

_____ cm
− _____ cm
_____ cm

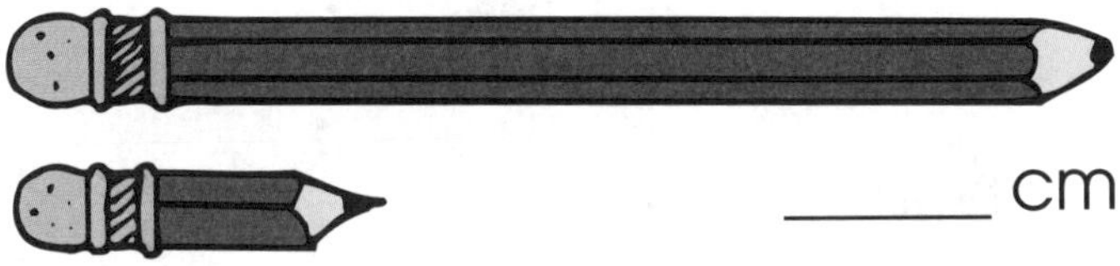

_____ cm
− _____ cm
_____ cm

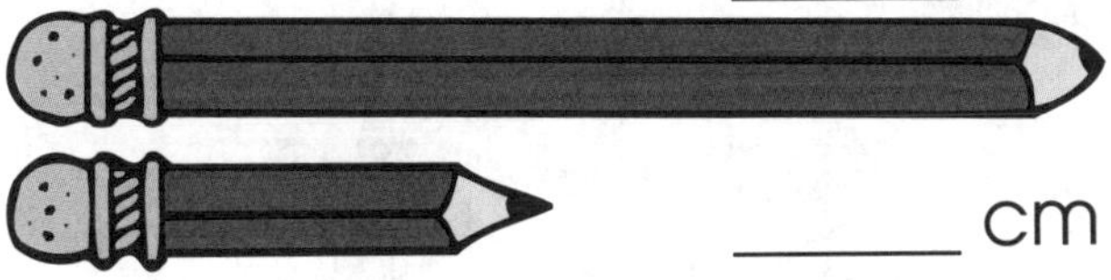

_____ cm
− _____ cm
_____ cm

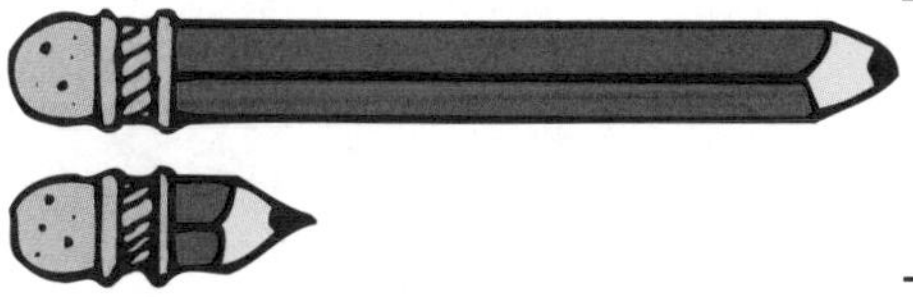

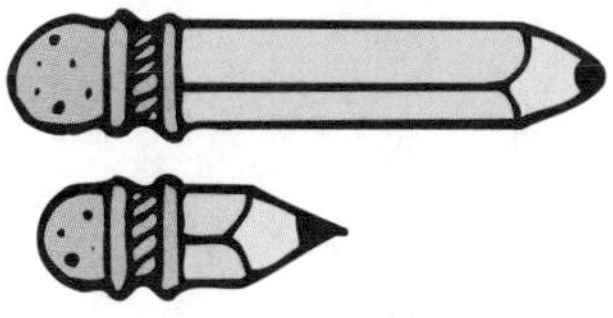

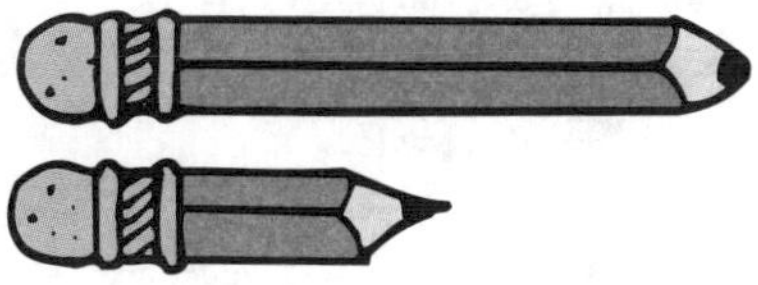

_____ cm
− _____ cm
_____ cm

_____ cm
− _____ cm
_____ cm

_____ cm
− _____ cm
_____ cm

Name ____________________

Measurement: cm

Directions: Use the ruler from pg. 209 to measure the fish to the nearest cm.

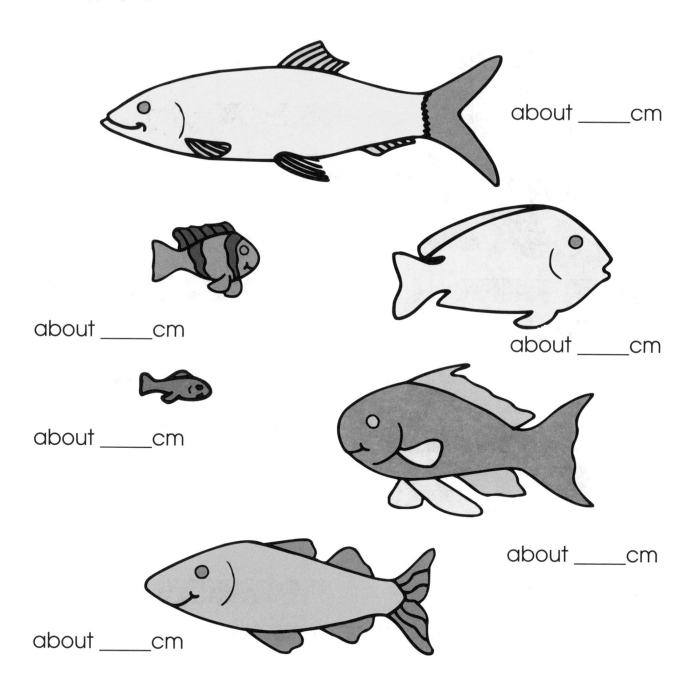

about _____cm

about _____cm

about _____cm

about _____cm

about _____cm

about _____cm

Name ____________________

Measurement: cm

Directions: Cut out the ruler. Measure each object to the nearest cm.

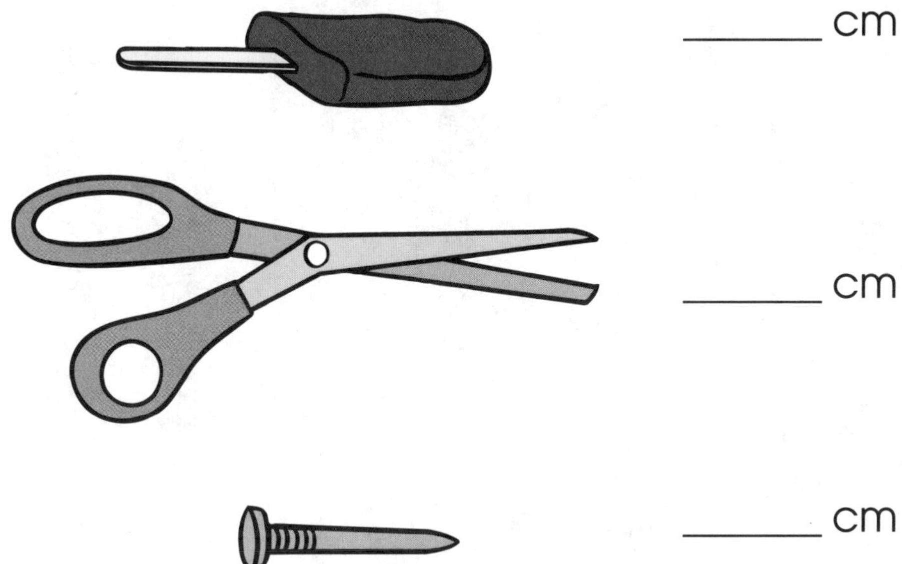

_______ cm

_______ cm

_______ cm

Directions: Measure objects around your house. Write the measurement to the nearest cm.

can of soup _______ cm

pen _______ cm

toothbrush _______ cm

paper clip _______ cm

small toy _______ cm

cut out

0 cm 1 2 3 4 5 6 7 8 9 10 11 12 13 14 15 16 17 18 19 20

This page was left intentionally blank for cutting activity on previous page.

Name ______________________________

How Big Are You?

Directions: How big are you? **Estimate,** or guess, how long some of your body parts are. Write your estimates below. Then, have a friend use a centimetre ruler to measure you. Write the numbers below. How close were your estimates?

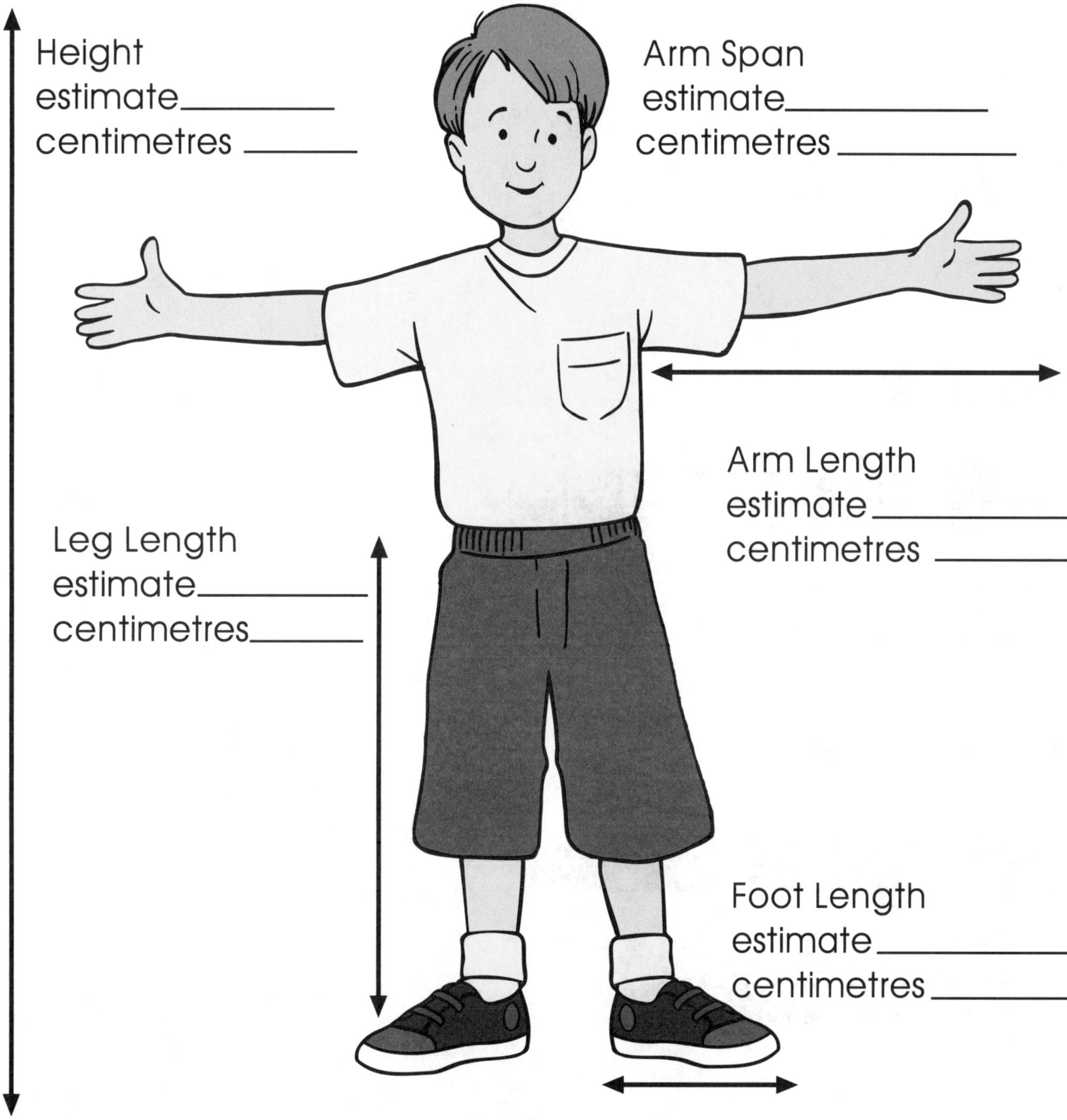

Height
estimate__________
centimetres ________

Arm Span
estimate______________
centimetres ____________

Arm Length
estimate ______________
centimetres ____________

Leg Length
estimate____________
centimetres________

Foot Length
estimate______________
centimetres____________

Name ______________________

Measurement: Centimetres

Directions: Use the ruler on pg. 209 to measure each object to the nearest cm.

Example: The paper clip is about 2 cm long.

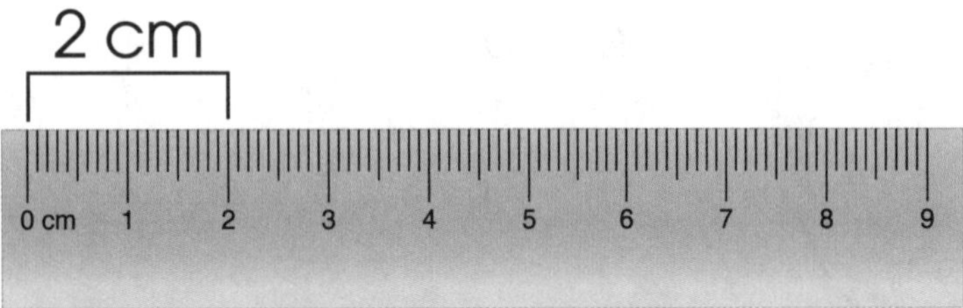

about 2 cm

about _____ cm

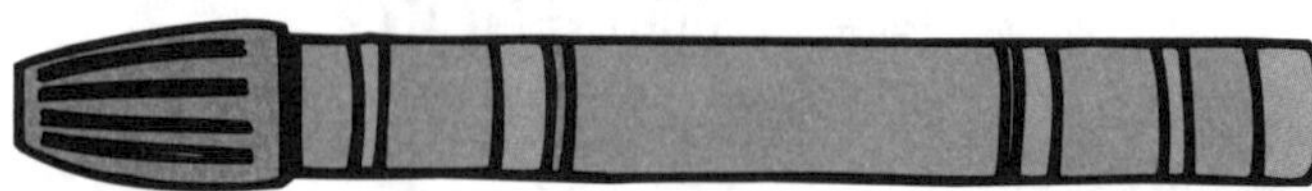

about _____ cm

about _____ cm

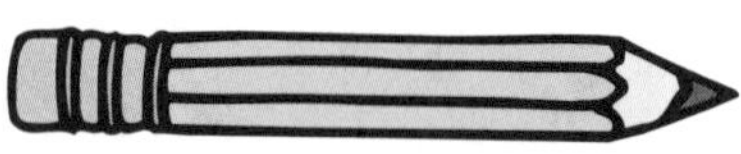

about _____ cm

about _____ cm

about _____ cm

Name ______________________

Measuring Monkeys

Directions: Use the cm ruler on pg. 209 to measure the length of each rope. Write the answer in each blank.

______

______

______

______

______

______

Name ______________________

Good Morning

Directions: Make your own bar graph. List 5 kinds of cereal below. Ask 5 people to vote for one cereal. Record the graph by colouring in 1 space for each vote. Use the information to ask and answer the questions.

Favourite Cereal

Cereals	1	2	3	4	5

Number of People

1. Which cereal was the favourite? ______________________

2. Which cereal had the fewest votes? ______________________

3. How many more voted for ______________________ (name of cereal) than for ______________________ (name of cereal)? ______

4. How many people chose ______________________ (name of cereal) and ______________________ (name of cereal) altogether? ______

Name ______________________________

Jungle Weather

Directions: The pictures show the weather for one month. Count the number of sunny, cloudy, and rainy days.

Directions: Complete the pictograph using the tallies above.

Weather for 1 Month

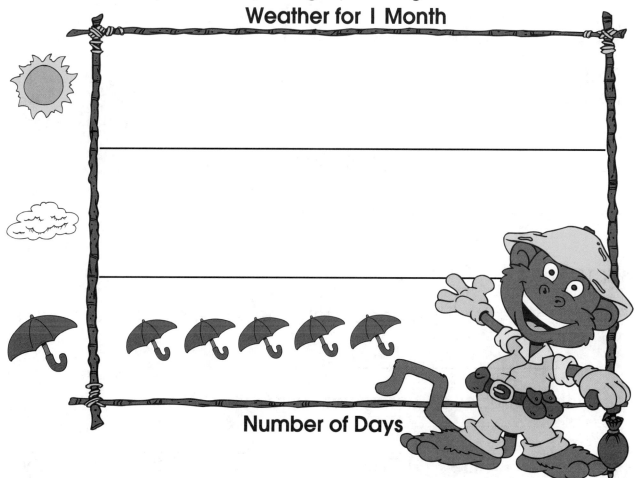

Number of Days

Name ____________________

What a Meal!

Directions: Use the pictograph to complete each sentence below.

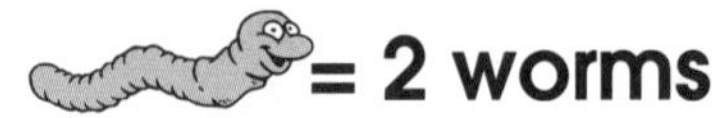

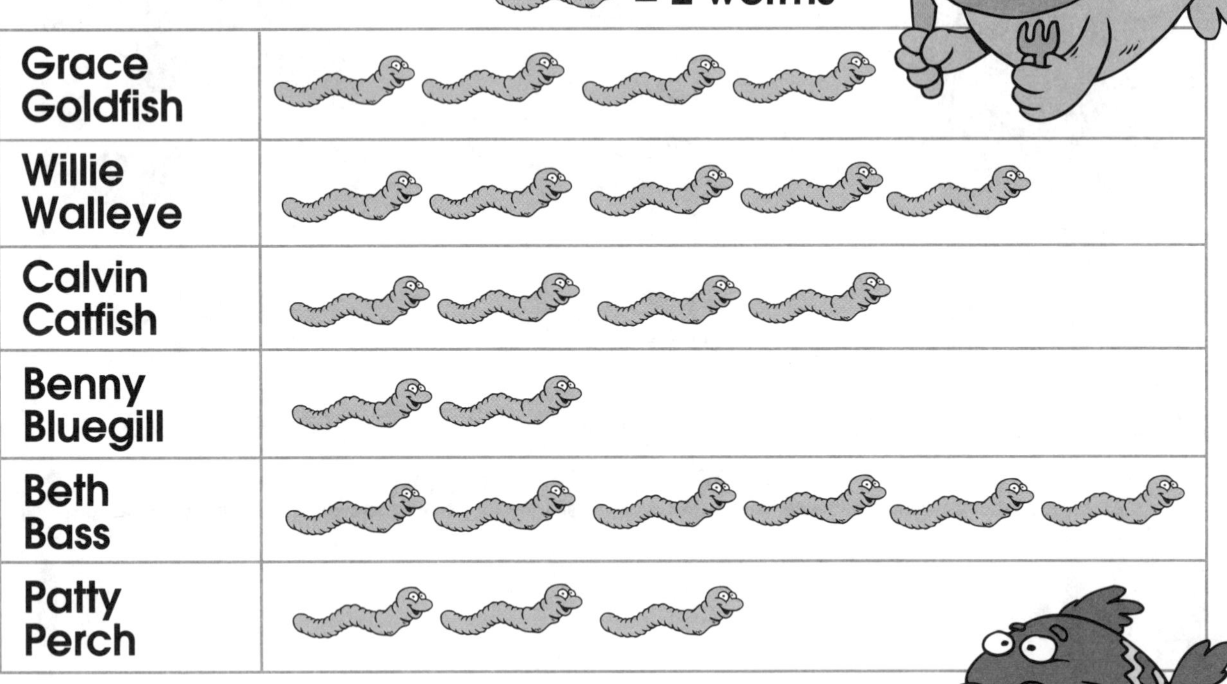

Grace Goldfish
Willie Walleye
Calvin Catfish
Benny Bluegill
Beth Bass
Patty Perch

1. ____________________ got the fewest worms.
2. ____________________ got the most worms.
3. ____________________ and ____________________ got the same number of worms.
4. Benny and Patty together caught the same number of worms as ____________________ .
5. Write the number of worms that each fish ate.

______	______	______	______	______	______
Grace	**Willie**	**Calvin**	**Benny**	**Beth**	**Patty**

Name ______________________

"Hockey Season"

Directions: Eight hockey teams have just completed their season Each team played eight games. Use this pictograph to answer the questions below.

(puck) = 1 win

Wiggle Worms	●●●●●●●
Jaguars	●●●●●●●●
Pandas	●●●●●●
Toucans	●●●
Centipedes	●●●●
Lightning Bugs	●
Hornets	●●
Monkeys	●

1. How many games did the Monkeys lose? ______

2. Which teams tied for last place?

   ______________________ and ______________________

3. Which team won the most games? ______________________

4. How many more games did the Wiggle Worms win than the Toucans? ______

5. Which four teams' total number of games won equal the Jaguars' number of games won? ______________________

Name ________________________________

Graphs

A **graph** is a drawing that shows information about numbers.

Directions: Count the apples in each row. Colour the boxes to show how many apples have bites taken out of them.

Example:

1	2	3	4	5	6	7	8
■	■	■					

Name ____________________________

Graphs

Directions: Count the banana peels in each column. Colour the boxes to show how many bananas have been eaten by the monkeys.

Example:

10	10	10	10	10
9	9	9	9	9
8	8	8	8	8
7	7	7	7	7
6	6	6	6	6
5	5	5	5	5
4	4	4	4	4
3	3	3	3	3
2	2	2	2	2
1	1	1	1	1

Name ______________________

Graphs

Directions: Count the fish. Colour the bowls to make a graph that shows the number of fish.

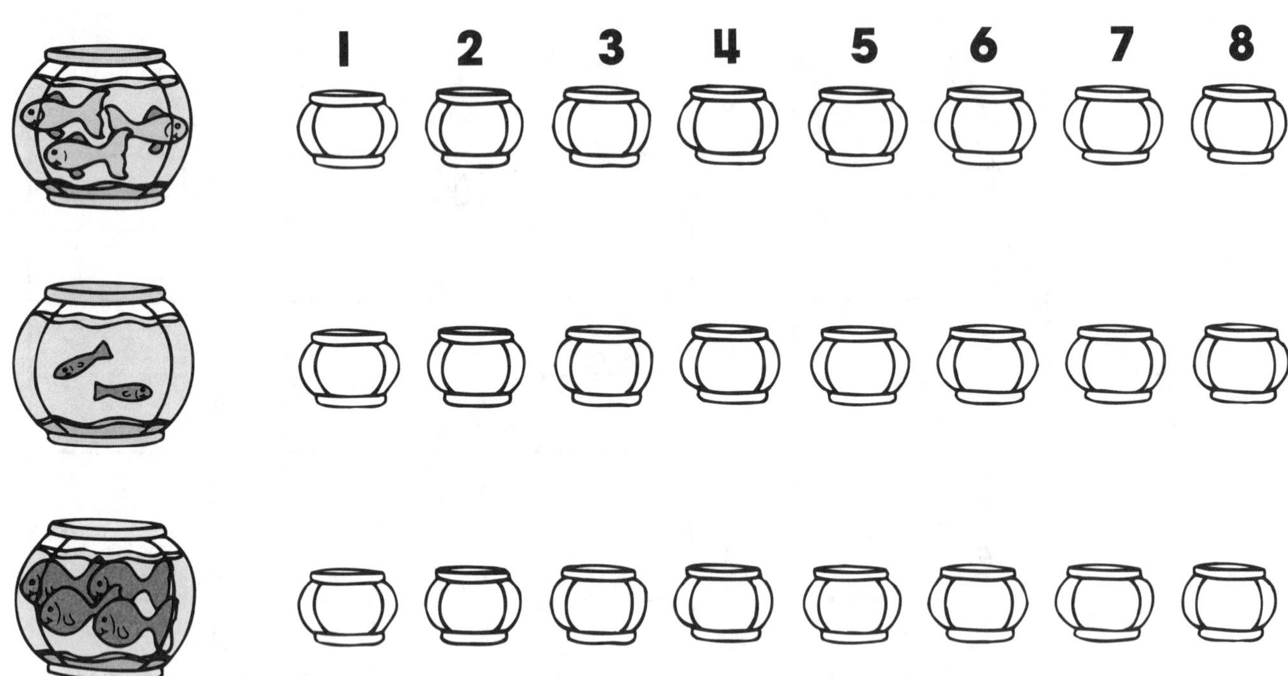

Directions: Use your fishbowl graphs to find the answers to the following questions. Draw a line to the correct bowl.

The most fish

The fewest fish

Name ____________________

Treasure Quest

Directions: Read the directions. Draw the pictures where they belong on the grid. Start at 0 and go . . .

over 2, up 5. Draw a 

over 9, up 3. Draw a 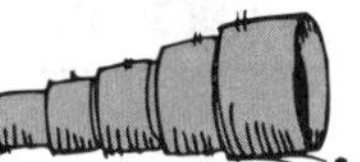

over 8, up 6. Draw a 

over 5, up 2. Draw a 

over 1, up 7. Draw a

over 7, up 1. Draw a 

over 6, up 4. Draw a 

over 2, up 3. Draw a 

over 3, up 1. Draw a 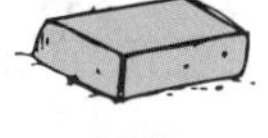

over 4, up 6. Draw a 

8										
7										
6										
5										
4										
3										
2										
1										
0	1	2	3	4	5	6	7	8	9	10

Name ____________________

Let's Get Things in Order!

Directions: Help Mrs. Brown pick flowers in her garden. The flowers she wants are listed in the chart. Use the descriptions to colour the flowers in her garden.

↓	⟶	Colour it:
1st row	6th flower	red
2nd row	4th flower	blue
3rd row	1st flower	yellow
4th row	9th flower	pink
5th row	10th flower	orange
6th row	2nd flower	green
7th row	5th flower	black
8th row	7th flower	grey
9th row	8th flower	purple
10th row	3rd flower	brown

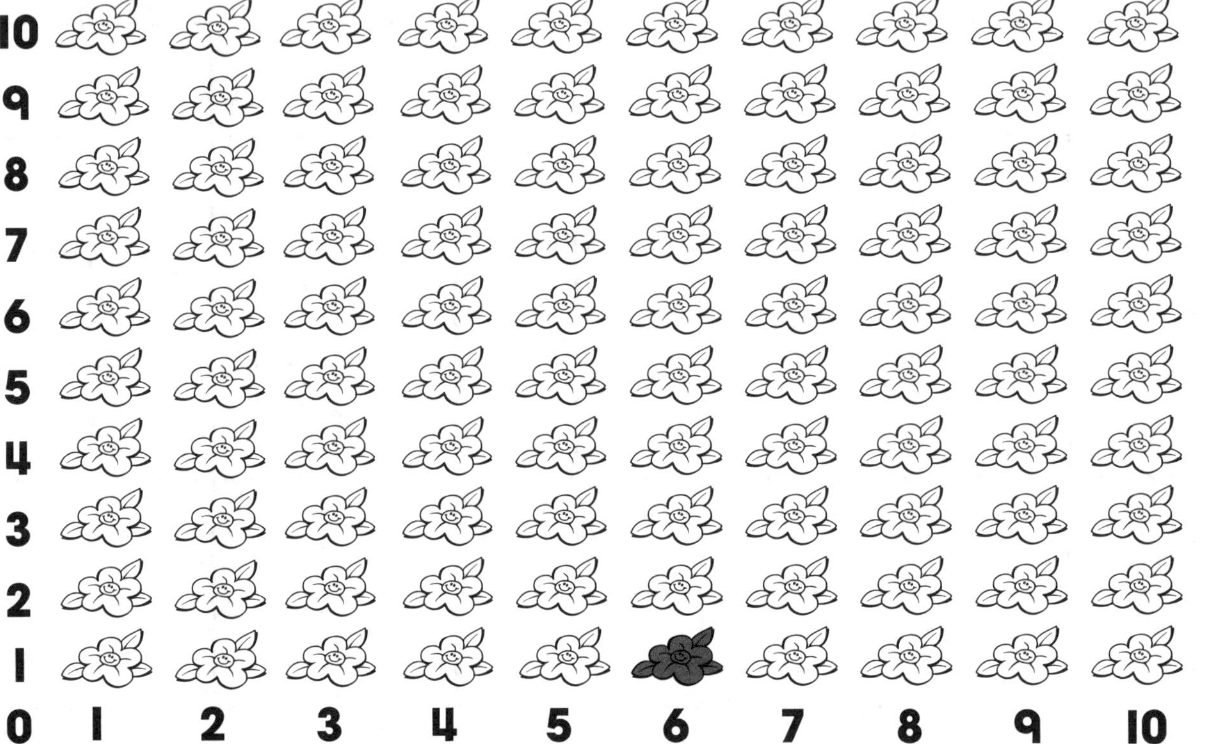

Whole and Half

A **fraction** is a number that names part of a whole, such as $\frac{1}{2}$.

Directions: Colour half of each thing.

Example: whole apple

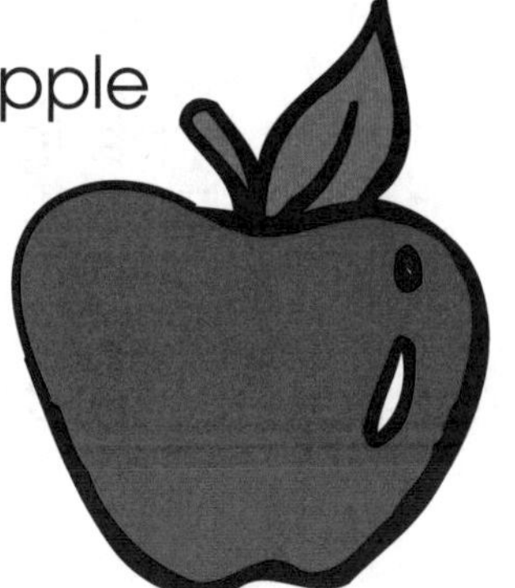

half an apple

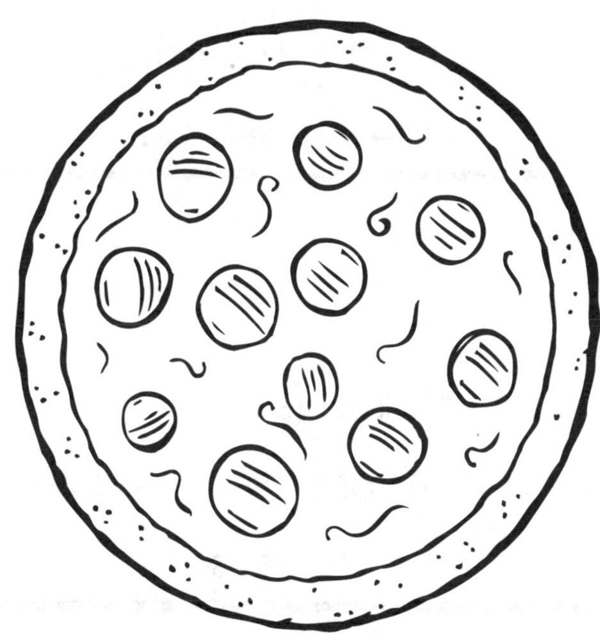

Name ______________________

One Third

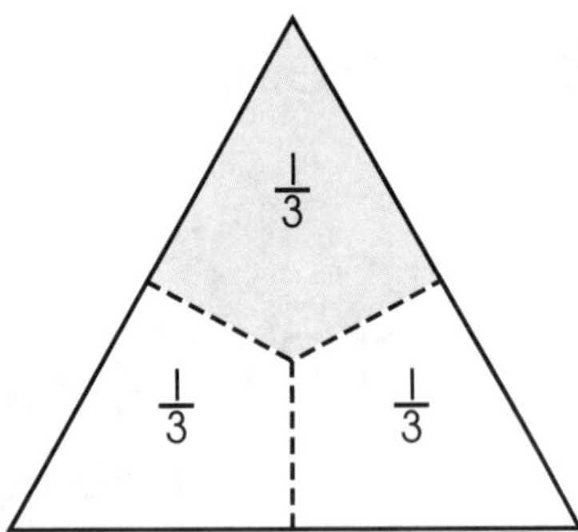

1 part is blue.

The 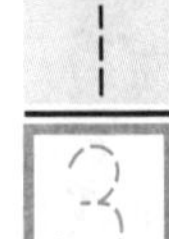 parts are the same size.

$\frac{1}{3}$ of the inside is blue.

Directions: Complete the fraction statements.

Example: 

1 part is blue.

3 parts are the same size.

$\frac{1}{3}$ of the inside is blue.

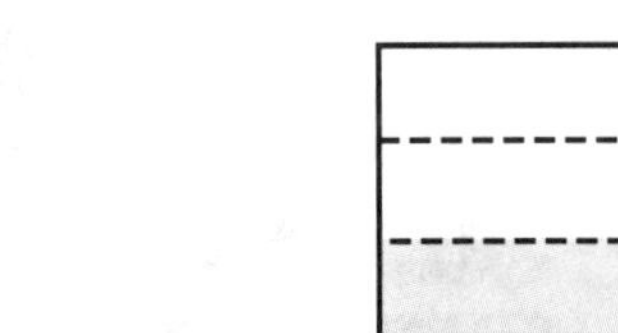

____ part is blue.

____ parts are the same size.

____ of the inside is blue.

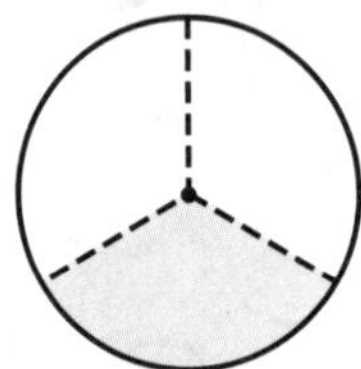

____ part is blue.

____ parts are the same size.

____ of the inside is blue.

____ part is blue.

____ parts are the same size.

____ of the inside is blue.

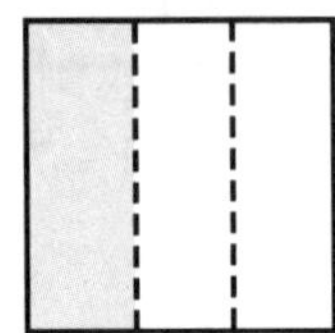

____ of the inside is blue.

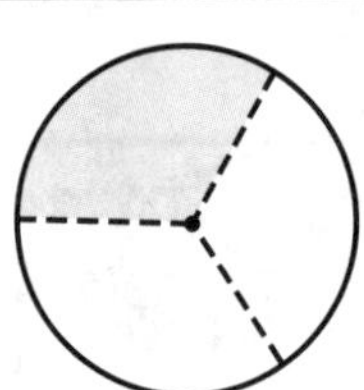

____ of the inside is blue.

Name ____________________

One Fourth

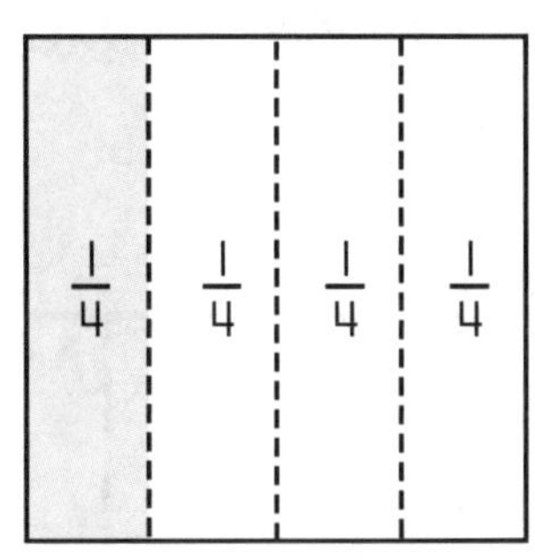

1 part is blue.

The 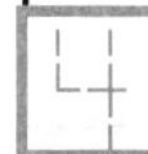 4 parts are the same size.

$\frac{1}{4}$ of the inside is blue.

Directions: Complete the fraction statements.

Example:

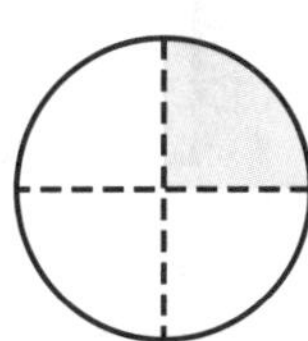
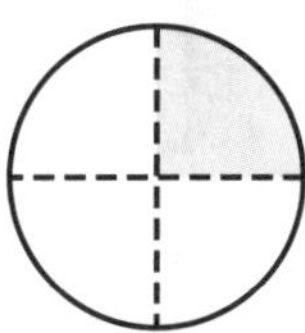

1 part is blue.

4 parts are the same size.

$\frac{1}{4}$ of the inside is blue.

_____ part is blue.

_____ parts are the same size.

_____ of the inside is blue.

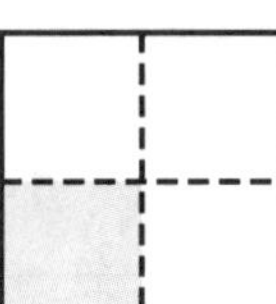

_____ part is blue.

_____ parts are the same size.

_____ of the inside is blue.

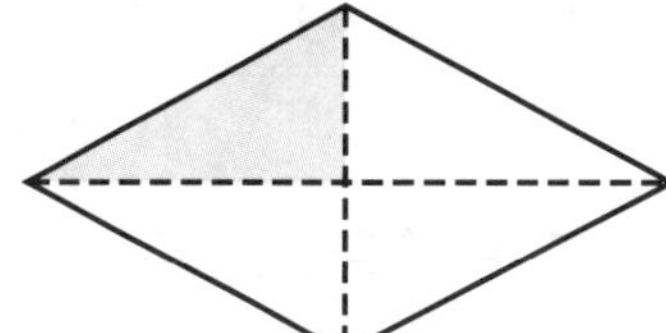

_____ part is blue.

_____ parts are the same size.

_____ of the inside is blue.

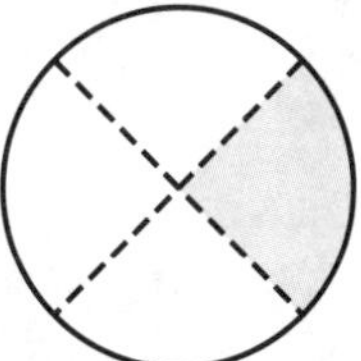

_____ of the inside is blue.

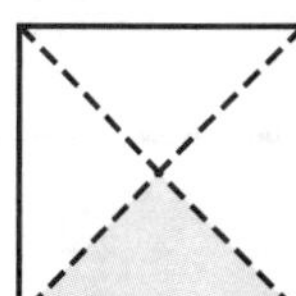

_____ of the inside is blue.

Name ____________________

Thirds and Fourths

Directions: Each shape has 3 equal parts. Colour one section, or $\frac{1}{3}$, of each shape.

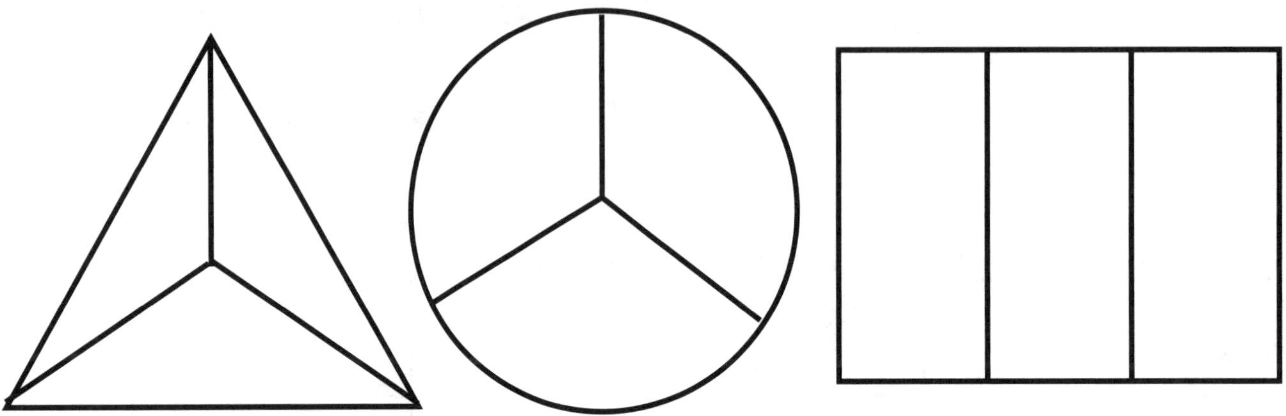

Directions: Each shape has 4 equal parts. Colour one section, or $\frac{1}{4}$, of each shape.

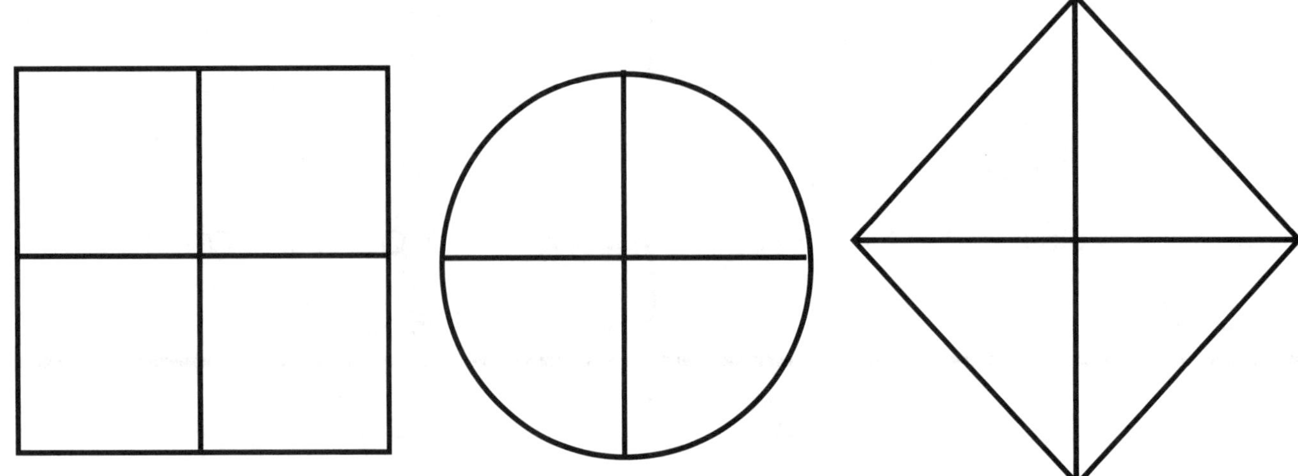

Name ______________________________

Fractions: Half, Third, Fourth

Directions: Colour the correct fraction of each shape.

Examples:

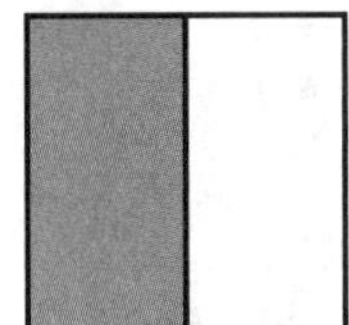

shaded part 1
equal parts 2
$\frac{1}{2}$ (one-half)

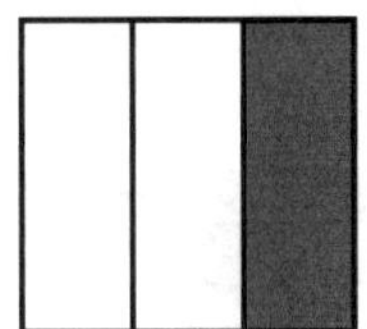

shaded part 1
equal parts 3
$\frac{1}{3}$ (one-third)

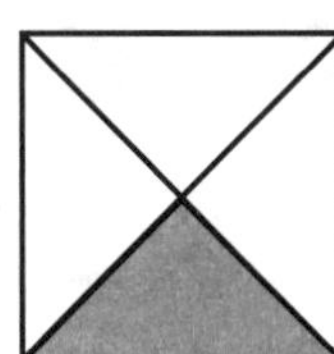

shaded part 1
equal parts 4
$\frac{1}{4}$ (one-fourth)

Colour $\frac{1}{3}$ **red**	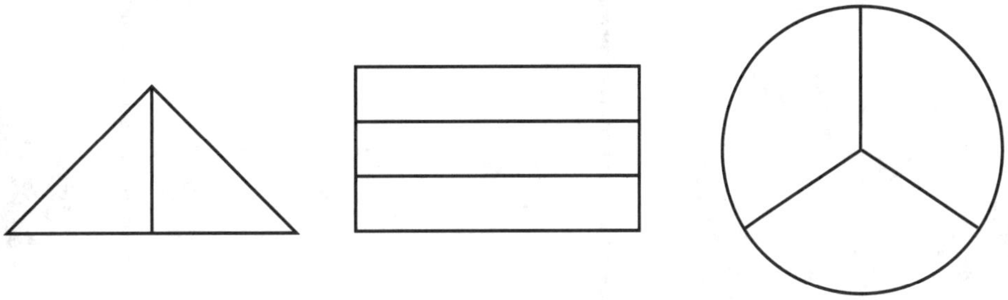
Colour $\frac{1}{4}$ **blue**	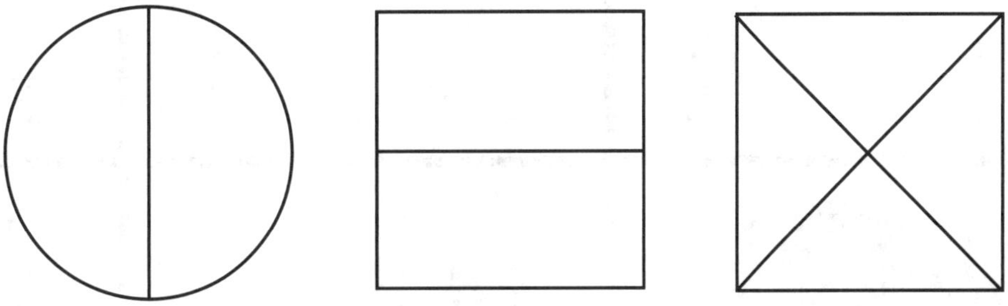
Colour $\frac{1}{2}$ **orange**	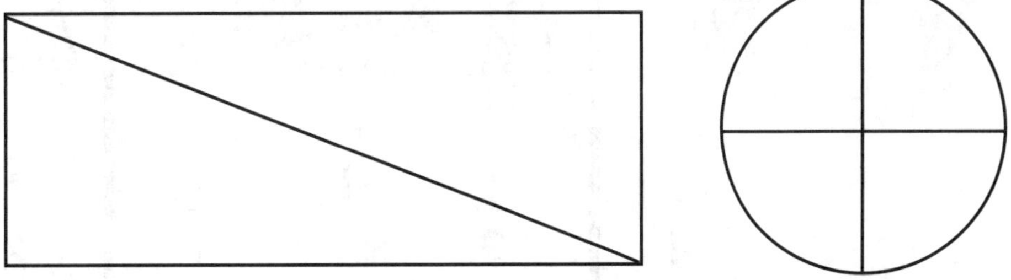

Name ____________________

Fraction Food

Directions: Count the equal parts. Circle the fraction that names one of the parts.

$\frac{1}{2}$ $\frac{1}{3}$ $\frac{1}{4}$

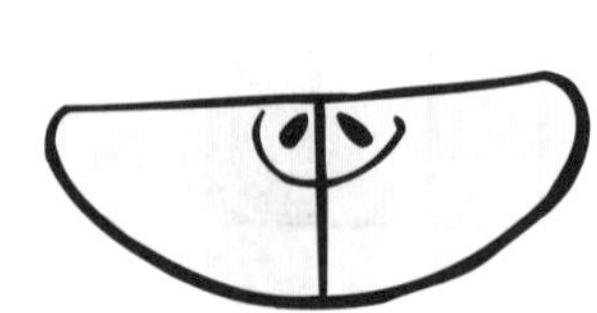

$\frac{1}{2}$ $\frac{1}{3}$ $\frac{1}{4}$

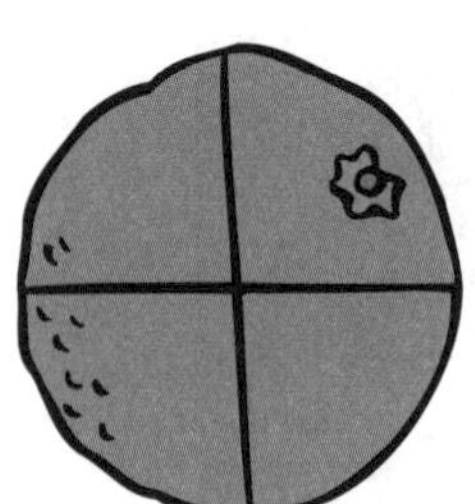

$\frac{1}{2}$ $\frac{1}{3}$ $\frac{1}{4}$

$\frac{1}{2}$ $\frac{1}{3}$ $\frac{1}{4}$

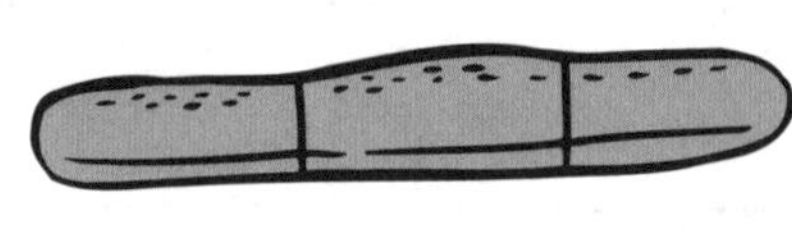

$\frac{1}{2}$ $\frac{1}{3}$ $\frac{1}{4}$

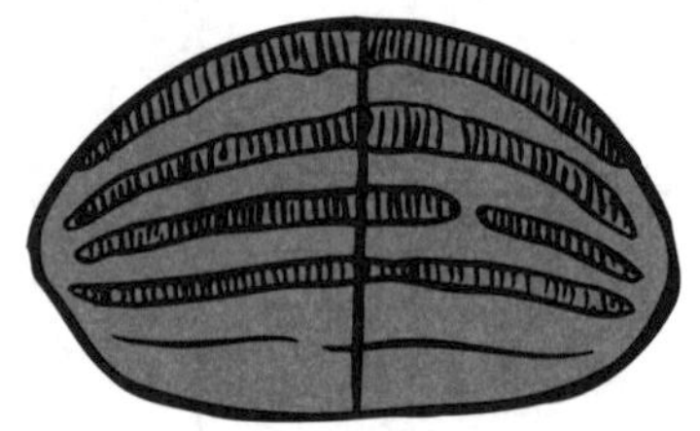

$\frac{1}{2}$ $\frac{1}{3}$ $\frac{1}{4}$

$\frac{1}{2}$ $\frac{1}{3}$ $\frac{1}{4}$

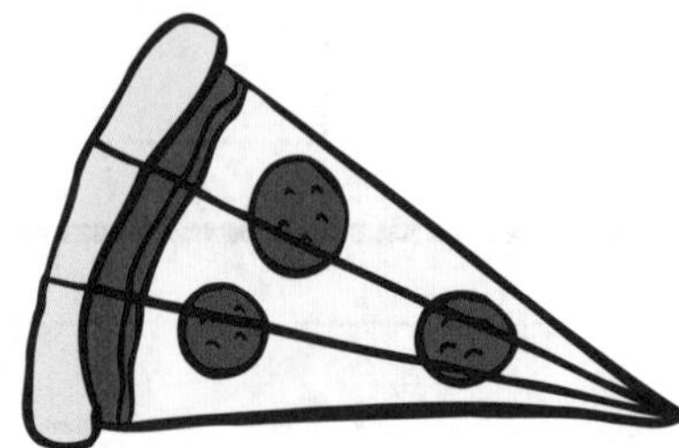

$\frac{1}{2}$ $\frac{1}{3}$ $\frac{1}{4}$

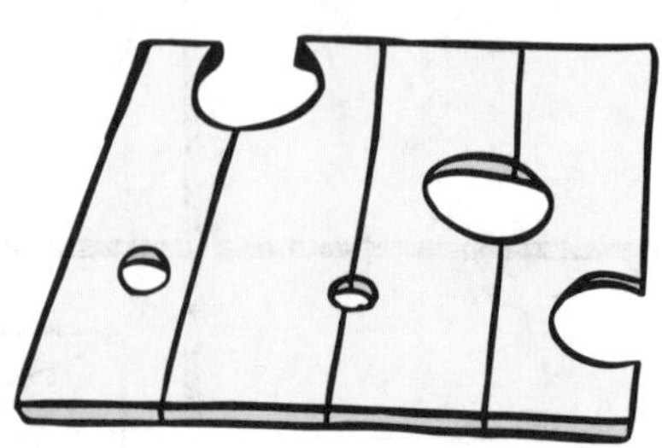

$\frac{1}{2}$ $\frac{1}{3}$ $\frac{1}{4}$

Name ____________________

Shaded Shapes

Directions: Draw a line to match each fraction with its correct shape.

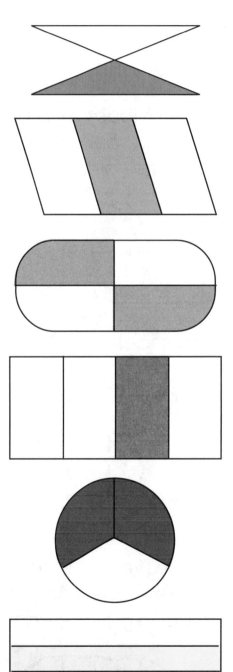

$\frac{1}{3}$ shaded

$\frac{2}{4}$ shaded

$\frac{1}{4}$ shaded

$\frac{1}{2}$ shaded

$\frac{3}{4}$ shaded

$\frac{2}{3}$ shaded

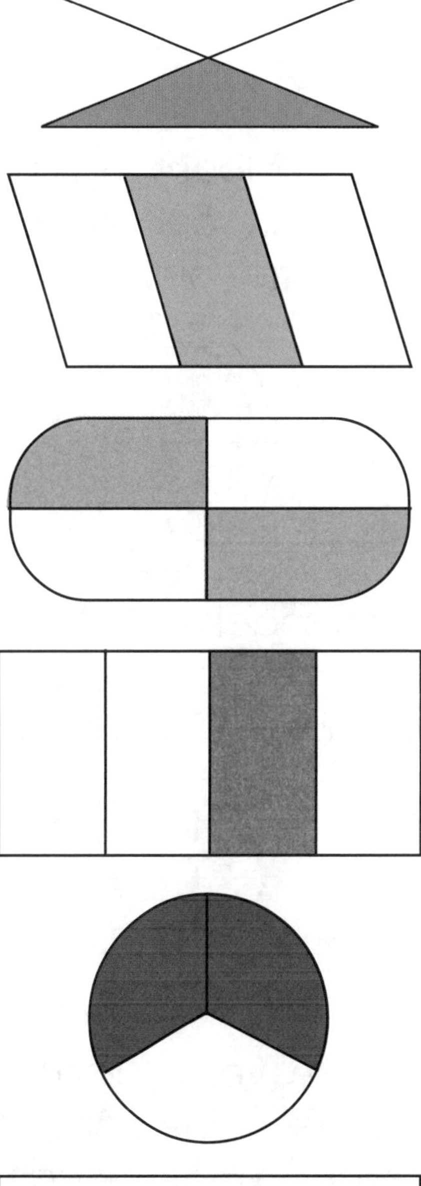

Name ______________________

Martha Moose's Diet

Directions: Help Martha Moose choose the right piece of food.

1. Martha Moose may have $\frac{1}{4}$ of this chocolate pie. Colour in $\frac{1}{4}$ of the pie.

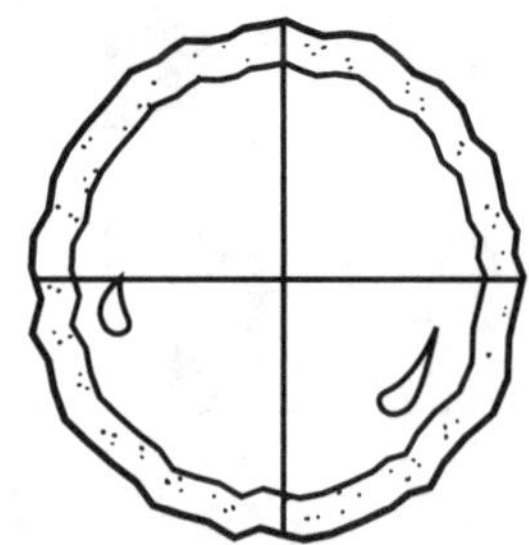

2. For a snack, she wants $\frac{1}{3}$ of this chocolate cake. Colour in $\frac{1}{3}$ of the cake.

3. For an evening snack, she can have $\frac{1}{4}$ of the candy bar. Colour in $\frac{1}{4}$ of the candy bar.

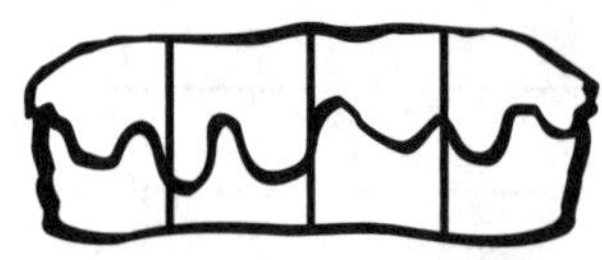

4. Martha Moose may eat $\frac{1}{3}$ of this pizza. Colour in $\frac{1}{3}$ the pizza.

5. For lunch, Martha Moose gets $\frac{1}{2}$ of the sandwich. Colour in $\frac{1}{2}$ of the sandwich.

6. She ate $\frac{1}{2}$ of the apple for lunch. Colour in $\frac{1}{2}$ of apple.

Name ____________________

Fractions: Half, Third, Fourth

Directions: Study the examples. Circle the fraction that shows the shaded part. Then, circle the fraction that shows the white part.

Examples:

shaded $\frac{1}{4}$ $\frac{1}{3}$ $\frac{1}{2}$ (circled: $\frac{1}{2}$)

white $\frac{1}{3}$ $\frac{1}{2}$ $\frac{1}{4}$ (circled: $\frac{1}{2}$)

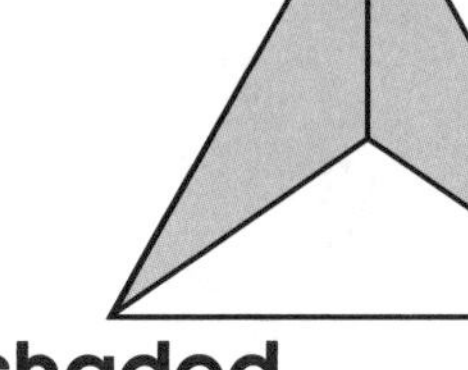

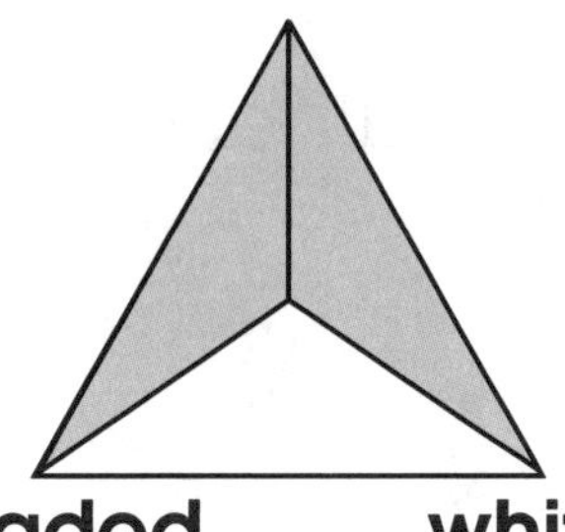

shaded $\frac{1}{2}$ $\frac{2}{3}$ $\frac{3}{4}$ (circled: $\frac{2}{3}$)

white $\frac{2}{3}$ $\frac{1}{2}$ $\frac{1}{3}$ (circled: $\frac{1}{3}$)

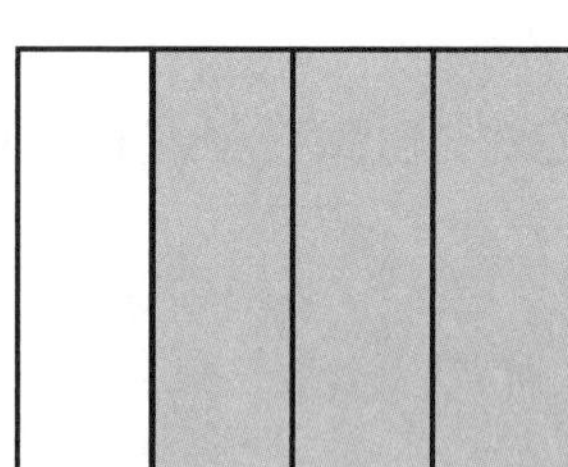

shaded $\frac{1}{4}$ $\frac{1}{2}$ $\frac{3}{4}$ (circled: $\frac{3}{4}$)

white $\frac{1}{4}$ $\frac{2}{3}$ $\frac{1}{2}$ (circled: $\frac{1}{4}$)

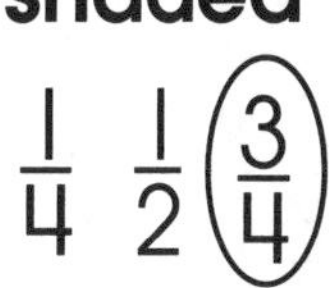

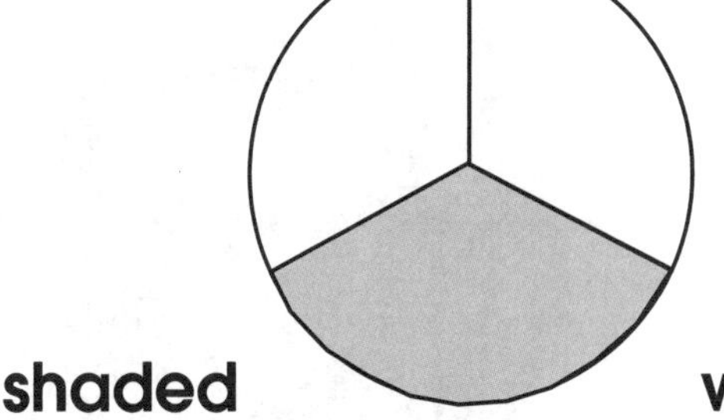

shaded $\frac{1}{4}$ $\frac{1}{3}$ $\frac{1}{2}$

white $\frac{2}{4}$ $\frac{2}{3}$ $\frac{2}{2}$

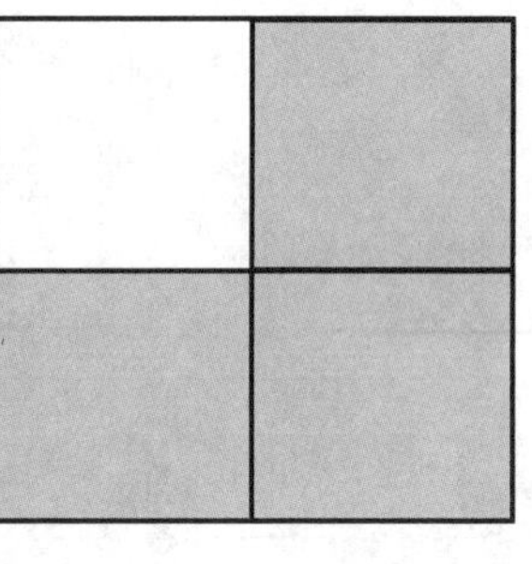

shaded $\frac{3}{4}$ $\frac{1}{3}$ $\frac{3}{2}$

white $\frac{1}{2}$ $\frac{1}{4}$ $\frac{1}{3}$

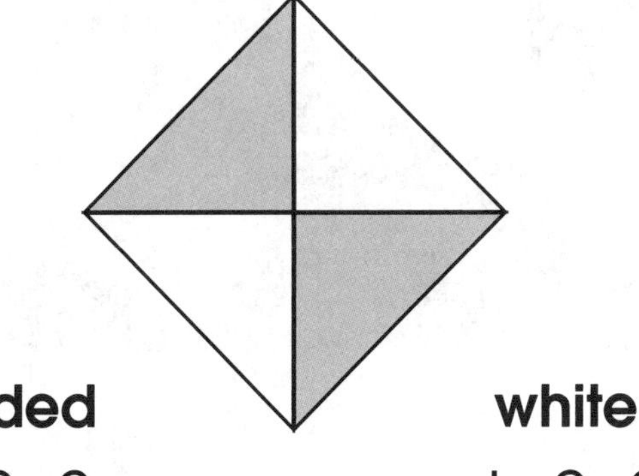

shaded $\frac{2}{3}$ $\frac{2}{4}$ $\frac{2}{2}$

white $\frac{1}{3}$ $\frac{2}{4}$ $\frac{2}{2}$

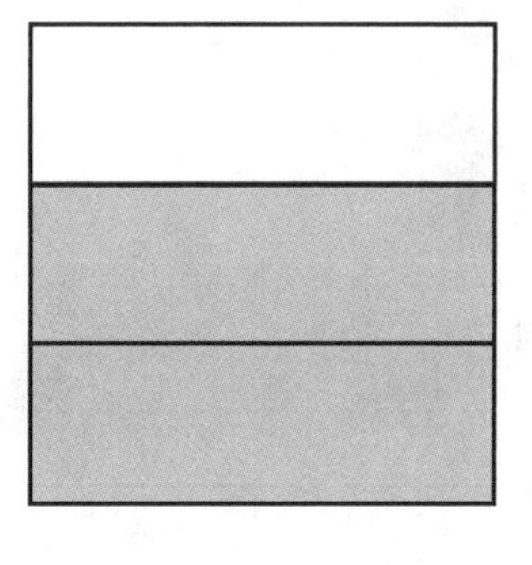

shaded $\frac{1}{3}$ $\frac{2}{3}$ $\frac{2}{2}$

white $\frac{1}{2}$ $\frac{1}{4}$ $\frac{1}{3}$

Name 

Fractions

One morning, Mrs. Murky asks her class:

"Which would you rather have, $\frac{1}{2}$ of a candy bar or $\frac{2}{4}$ of a candy bar?"

Directions: Which would you rather have? Explain your answer.

Name ______________________

Fractions

Directions: Rodney, Jed, and Ursula had a pizza party. They ordered 1 large fish-eye pizza and 1 large toadstool pizza. Draw lines through the pizzas to divide them equally into slices. Colour the pizza slices in 3 colours, 1 for each frog, to show how many slices each frog gets.

How many slices will each frog get? ______________________

Name ______________________

Clocks: Identifying Parts

Directions: A clock face has numbers. Trace the numbers on the clock.

Tick

Tock

12 11 10 9 8 7 6 5 4 3 2 1

Name ______________________

Writing the Time

An hour is sixty minutes long. It takes an hour for the BIG HAND to goaround the clock. When the BIG HAND is on 12, and the little hand points to a number, that is the hour!

Directions: The **BIG HAND** is on the 12. Colour it **red**. The **little hand** is on the 8. Colour it **blue**.

The **BIG HAND** is on __________ .

The **little hand** is on __________ .

It is __________ o'clock.

Name ____________________

Writing the Time

Directions: Colour the little hour hand **red**. Fill in the blanks.

The **BIG HAND** is on ________ .

The **little hand** is on ________ .

It is ________ o'clock.

The **BIG HAND** is on ________ .

The **little hand** is on ________ .

It is ________ o'clock.

The **BIG HAND** is on ________ .

The **little hand** is on ________ .

It is ________ o'clock.

The **BIG HAND** is on ________ .

The **little hand** is on ________ .

It is ________ o'clock.

Name ______________________

Practice

Directions: What is the time?

______ o'clock

______ o'clock

______ o'clock

______ o'clock

______ o'clock

______ o'clock

______ o'clock

______ o'clock

______ o'clock

______ o'clock

______ o'clock

______ o'clock

Name ____________________

Matching Digital and Face Clocks

Long ago, there were only wind-up clocks. Today, we also have electric and battery clocks. We may soon have solar clocks!

Directions: Match the digital and face clocks that show the same time.

Name ____________________

Writing Time on the Half-Hour

Directions: Write the times.

____

______ minutes past

____

______ o'clock

____

______ minutes past

____

______ o'clock

What is your dinner time?

Directions: Circle the time you eat.

Name  ______________________

Writing Time on the Half-Hour

Directions: What time is it?

half past ________

half past ________

half past ________

half past ________

half past ________

half past ________

Name ______________________

Time to the Quarter-Hour: Introduction

Each **hour** has **60** minutes. An **hour** has **4 quarter-hours**. A **quarter-hour** is **15 minutes**.

This clock face shows a quarter of an hour.

From the **12** to the **3** is **15 minutes**.

From the 12 to the 3 is 15 minutes.

___15___ minutes after ___8___ o'clock

is ___8:15___

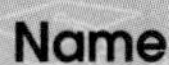

Name ______________________________

Writing Time on the Half-Hour

Directions: Draw the hands. Write the times.

5:15

15 minutes after

5 o'clock

10:15

______ minutes after

______ o'clock

2:15

______ minutes after

______ o'clock

9:15

______ minutes after

______ o'clock

Name ______________________

Time to the Minute Intervals: Introduction

Each **number** on the clock face stands for **5** minutes.

Directions: Count by **5s** beginning at the **12**.
Write the numbers here:

00 _05_ _10_ _15_ _20_ _25_

It is _25_ minutes after _8_ o'clock. It is written 8:25.

Directions: Count by **5s.**

00 ____ ____ ____ ____ ____ ____ ____

It is ____ minutes after ____ o'clock.

____ : ____

Name ______________________

Drawing the Minute Hand

Directions: Draw the hands on these fish clocks.

7:45

8:05

11:15

3:20

5:55

1:50

12:10

10:25

4:40

Name ______________________________

Counting Pennies

Note: Although pennies are no longer in circulation, they are useful as counters.

Directions: Count the pennies.
How many cents?

Example:

        = 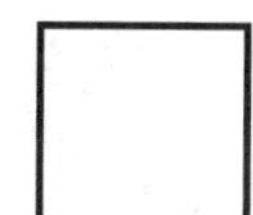

     = 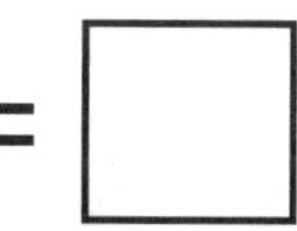

         = 

   = 

      = 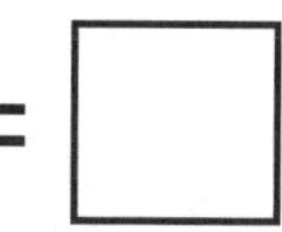

       = 

  = 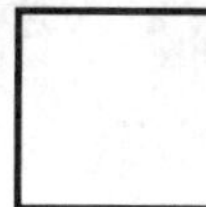

          = ☐

Name ______________________

Counting Pennies

Note: Although pennies are no longer in circulation, they are useful as counters.

Directions: Count the pennies in each triangle.

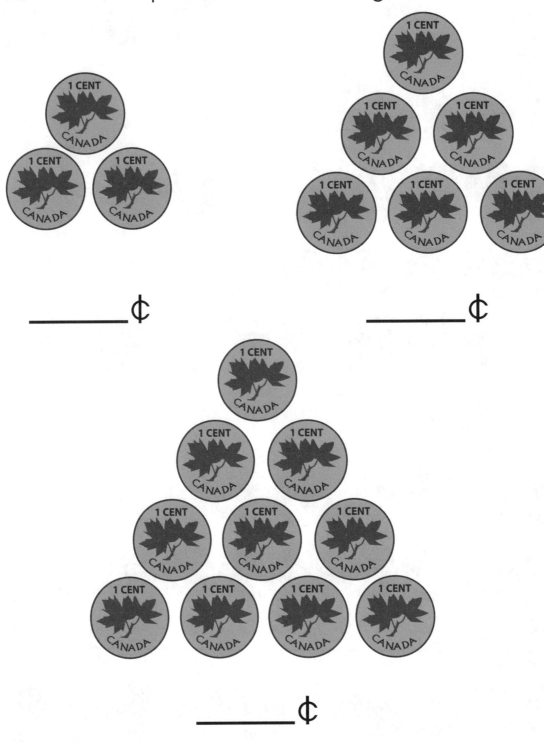

1 CENT CANADA 1 CENT CANADA 1 CENT CANADA

______¢

1 CENT CANADA 1 CENT CANADA 1 CENT CANADA 1 CENT CANADA 1 CENT CANADA 1 CENT CANADA

______¢

1 CENT CANADA 1 CENT CANADA 1 CENT CANADA 1 CENT CANADA 1 CENT CANADA 1 CENT CANADA 1 CENT CANADA 1 CENT CANADA 1 CENT CANADA 1 CENT CANADA

______¢

Name ______________________________

Nickels: Introduction

Note: Although pennies are no longer in circulation, they are useful as counters.

Directions: Look at the two sides of a nickel. Colour the nickels **silver**.

front

back

___1___ nickel = ___5___ pennies

___1___ nickel = ___5___ cents

___1___ nickel = ___5___ ¢

Directions: Write the number of cents in a nickel.

5¢ = _____¢ + _____¢ + _____¢ + _____¢ + _____¢

=

Name ______________________

Nickels: Counting by Fives

Directions: Count the nickels by 5s. Write the amount.

Example:

5 cents = 1 nickel

Count 

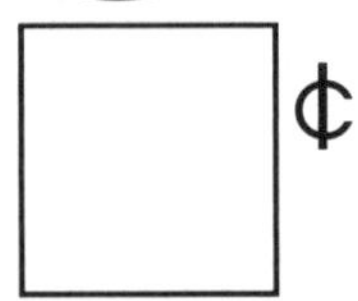

Count

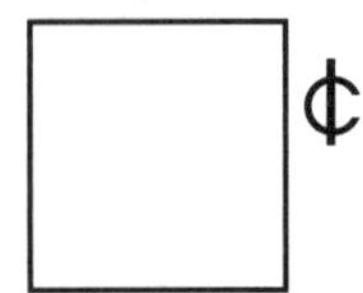

Count 

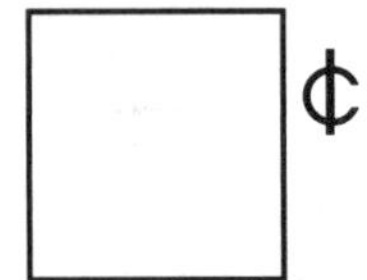

Count 

Count ____, ____, ____,

Name ______________________

Dimes: Introduction

Note: Although pennies are no longer in circulation, they are useful as counters.

A dime is small, but quite strong. It can buy more than a penny or a nickel.

front

back

Each side of a dime is different. It has ridges on its edge.

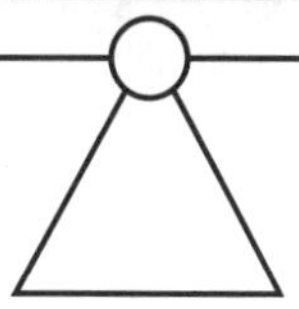

Directions: Write the number of cents in a dime.

__________ dime = __________ pennies

__________ dime = __________ cents

__________ dime = __________ ¢

Name ____________________

Dimes: Counting by Tens

Directions: Count by 10s. Write the number. Circle the group with more.

_________ ¢ or _________ ¢

_________ ¢ or _________ ¢

_________ ¢ or _________ ¢

Name ____________________

Counting With Dimes, Nickels, and Pennies

Note: Although pennies are no longer in circulation, they are useful as counters.

Directions: Count the money. Start with the dime. Write the amount.

1. 

__________ ¢

2. 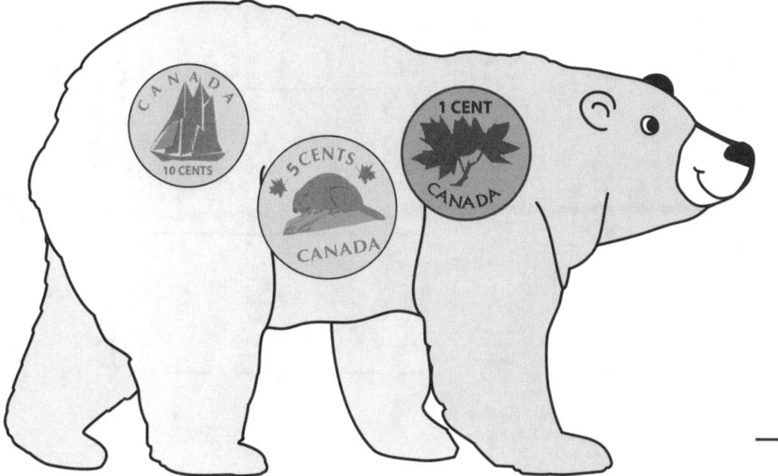

__________ ¢

3. Circle the answer.
Who has more money?

Name ______________________________

Quarters: Introduction

A quarter is larger than dimes, nickles, and pennies. It can also buy more.

front

back

Directions: Write the number of cents in a quarter.

__________ quarter = __________ pennies

__________ quarter = __________ cents

__________ quarter = __________ ¢

Directions: Count these nickels by 5s. Is this another way to make 25¢?

yes no

Name ____________________

Counting With Quarters

These are some machines that use quarters.

Directions: Colour each machine you have to put quarters into. Circle the number of quarters you need.

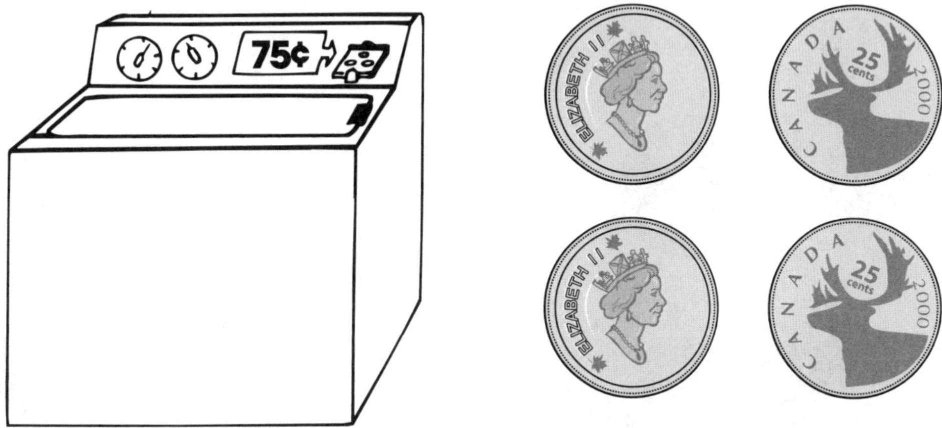

I need __________ quarters to wash clothes.

I need __________ quarter(s) to make a phone call.

Name ______________________________

Counting With Quarters, Dimes, Nickels, and Pennies

Note: Although pennies are no longer in circulation, they are useful as counters.

Directions: Match the money with the amount.

35 ¢

36 ¢

40 ¢

27 ¢

15 ¢

21 ¢

8 ¢

Name ____________________

Counting With Quarters, Dimes, Nickels, and Pennies

Here are things to buy for your hair.

Directions: How many of each coin do you need?
Write 1, 2, 3, or 4.

	Quarters	Dimes	Nickels	Pennies

Name ______________________

Subtracting for Change

Adam wanted to know how much change he would have left when he bought things. He made this picture to help him subtract.

4 dimes
— 1 dime
3 dimes

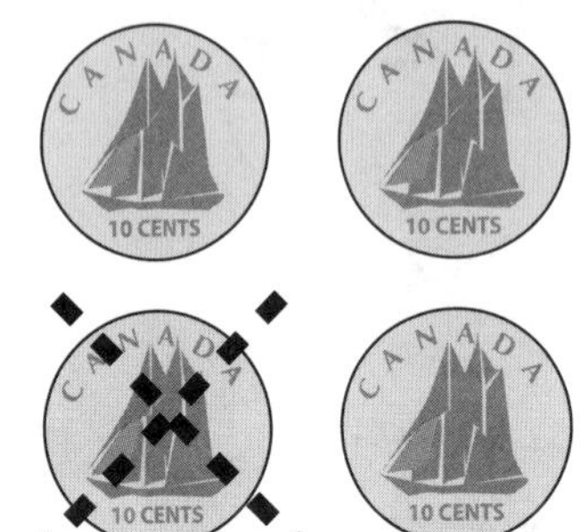

40¢
— 10¢
30¢

Directions: Cross out and subtract.

6 dimes
— 4 dimes
_____ dimes

60¢
— 40¢
_____ ¢

Name ______________________________

Problem-Solving With Money

Directions: Draw the coins you use. Write the number of coins on each blank.

1.

5 1 1 1 1

__________ dimes

__________ nickels

__________ pennies

2.

__________ dimes

__________ nickels

__________ pennies

3.

__________ dimes

__________ nickels

__________ pennies

4. Find another way to pay for the

__________ dimes

__________ nickels

__________ pennies

Name ____________________

Problem-Solving With Money

Directions: Draw the fewest coins you use to buy each item. Write the number of coins on each blank.

1.

35¢

________ quarters

________ dimes

________ nickels

________ pennies

2.

29¢

________ quarters

________ dimes

________ nickels

________ pennies

3.

43¢

________ quarters

________ dimes

________ nickels

________ pennies

4. Find another way to pay for the

________ quarters

________ dimes

________ nickels

________ pennies

Name ______________________

Making Exact Amounts of Money: Two Ways to Pay

Directions: Find two ways to pay. Show what coins you use.

1.

______ quarters
______ dimes
______ nickels
______ pennies

2.

______ quarters
______ dimes
______ nickels
______ pennies

3.

______ quarters
______ dimes
______ nickels
______ pennies

4.

______ quarters
______ dimes
______ nickels
______ pennies

Name ______________________

Making Exact Amounts of Money: Two Ways to Pay

Directions: Find two ways to pay. Show what coins you use.

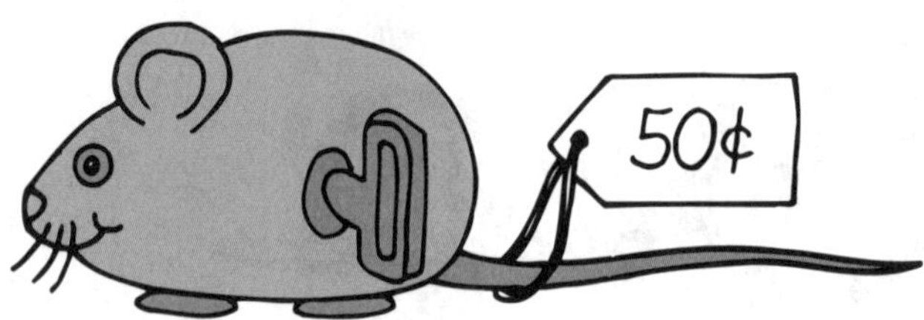

1.

______ quarters
______ dimes
______ nickels
______ pennies

2.

______ quarters
______ dimes
______ nickels
______ pennies

3.

______ quarters
______ dimes
______ nickels
______ pennies

4.

______ quarters
______ dimes
______ nickels
______ pennies

Name ______________________________

Making Exact Amounts of Money: How Much More?

Note: Although pennies are no longer in circulation, they are useful as counters.

Directions: Count the coins. Find out how much more money you need to pay the exact amount.

YARD SALE

50¢

How much money do you have? __________ ¢

How much more money do you need? __________ ¢

60¢

How much money do you have? __________ ¢

How much more money do you need? __________ ¢

Solve this puzzle.

How much more money does Chipmunk need?

__________ ¢

I have I quarter and 4 dimes. I need one more coin to pay for the nut mobile.
75¢

Name ____________________

Geometry - Transformations

A flip is a tranformation where an image is turned over a line. The flipped image has the same angle, length, and size as the original image, but is flipped in another direction. Example:

Directions: Draw the flip to show the other position.

Name ____________________

A **slide** is a tranformation that moves an image in a straight line to make a copy of the image in another location.

Example: 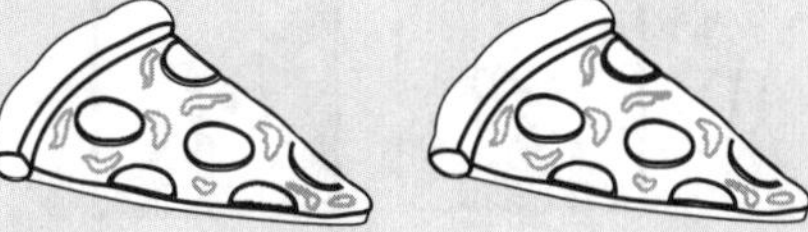

Directions: Draw a slide of each image to the right of the original.

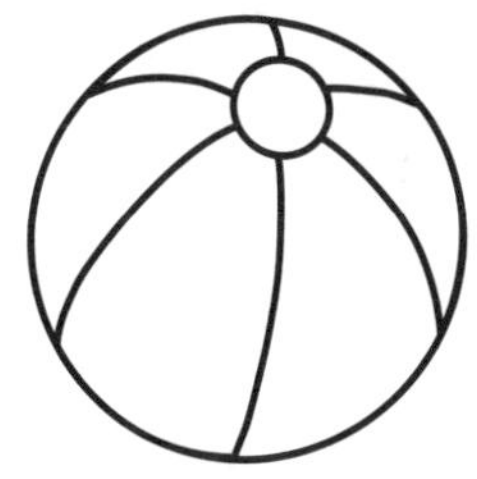

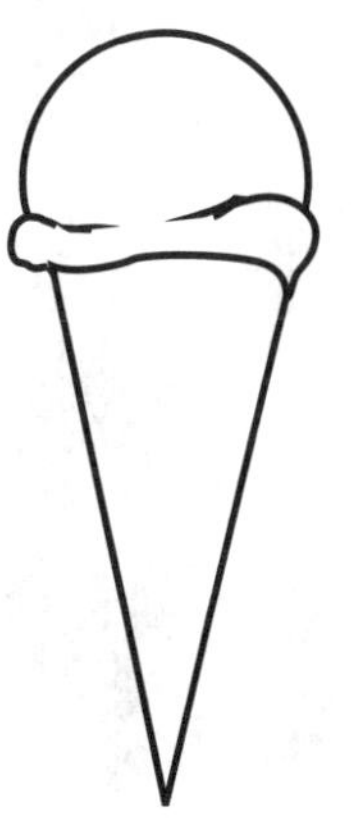

Name ______________________

Symmetry is shown when one side of an object is the mirror image of the other side.

Examples:

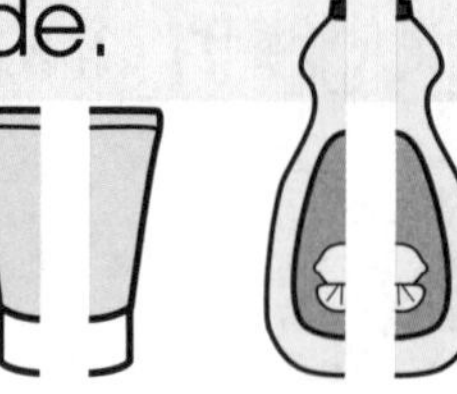

Directions: In these pictures, half the object is missing. Draw the missing half so that the shape is symemetrical. Colour the picture.

Name ____________________

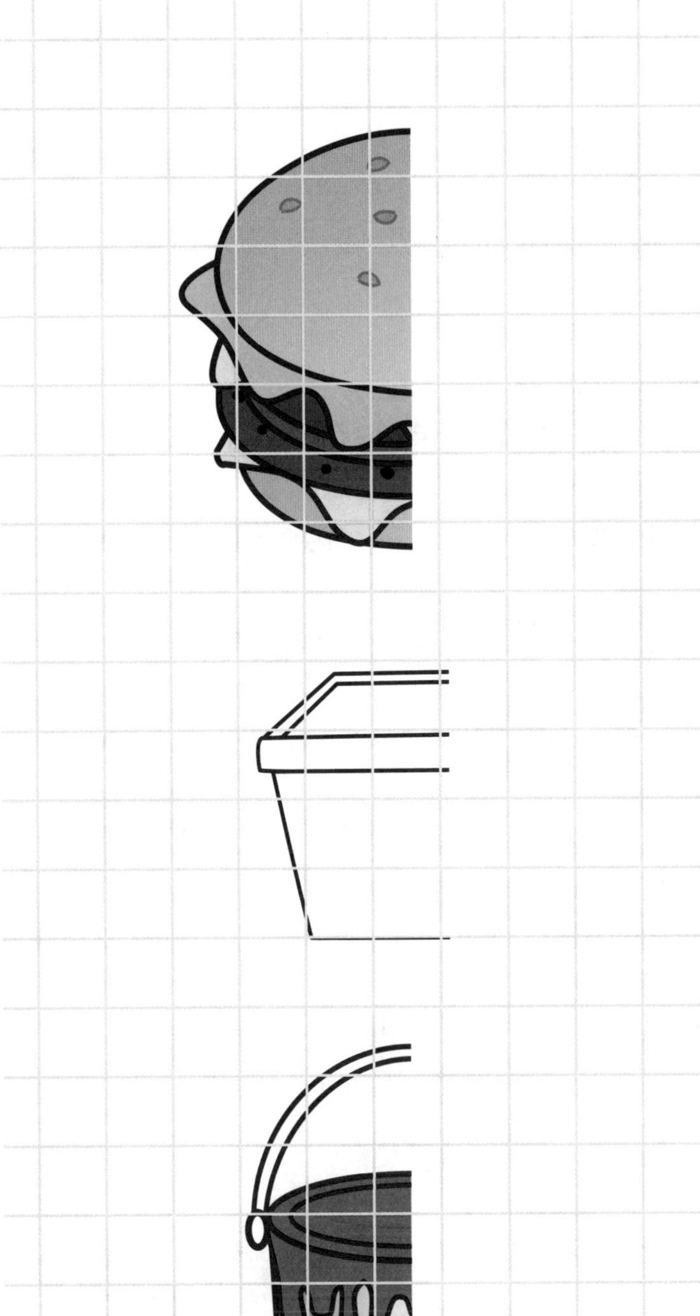

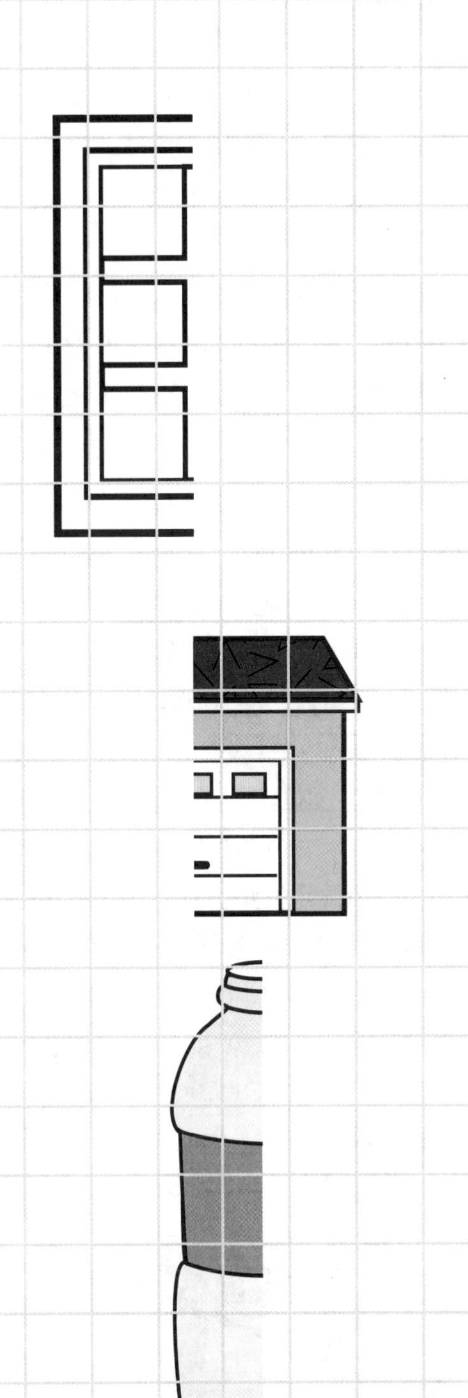

Glossary

Addition: "Putting together," or adding, two or more numbers to find the sum. For example: 3 + 5 = 8.

Circle: A figure that is round.

Classifying: Putting similar things into groups or categories.

Comparing: Looking at two numbers to determine which is larger and which is smaller.

Counting: Naming or writing numbers in sequence.

Difference: The answer in a subtraction problem.

Digit: The symbols used to write numbers: 0, 1, 2, 3, 4, 5, 6, 7, 8, and 9.

Dime: A coin which is worth ten cents. It is written 10¢ or $.10.

Dollar: A coin which is worth one hundred cents. It is written $1.00. We also call it a loonie.

Estimate: Determining an approximate number or amount before counting or measuring to find the actual number or amount.

Fact Family: A group of three numbers in which the two smaller numbers are the addends.

Fractions: Equal parts of a whole designated by symbols like $\frac{1}{2}$ and $\frac{3}{4}$.

Geometry: The study of lines and shapes in mathematics.

Graph: A diagram that shows the relationship between two or more sets of objects with a series of lines, bars, or pictures.

Measurement: The process of determining size, quantity, or amount.

Multiplication: A short way to find the sum of adding the same number a certain number of times.

Nickel: A coin which is worth five cents.
It is written 5¢ or $.05.

Ordinal Numbers: Numbers that show place or order in a series, such as first, second, third, etc.
Oval: A figure that is egg-shaped.
Pattern: A repeated arrangement of numbers, shapes, or pictures.
Penny: A coin that is no longer in circulation which is worth one cent. It is written 1¢ or $.01.
Place Value: Where a digit or numeral is in the number.
In the number 23, 2 has the place value of tens and 3 is ones.
Quarter: A coin which is worth twenty-five cents. It is written 25¢ or $.25.
Rectangle: A figure with four corners and four sides. The sides opposite each other are the same length.
Rhombus: A figure with four sides of the same length.
Sequencing: Putting numbers in the correct order.
Sorting: To organize or arrange objects in groups by similar properties.
Square: A figure with four corners and four sides of the same length.
Subtraction: "Taking away," or subtracting, one number from another.
Sum: The answer in an addition problem.
Telling Time: The ability to look at a clock and read or write the time in minutes before or after the hour.
Triangle: A figure with three corners and three sides.

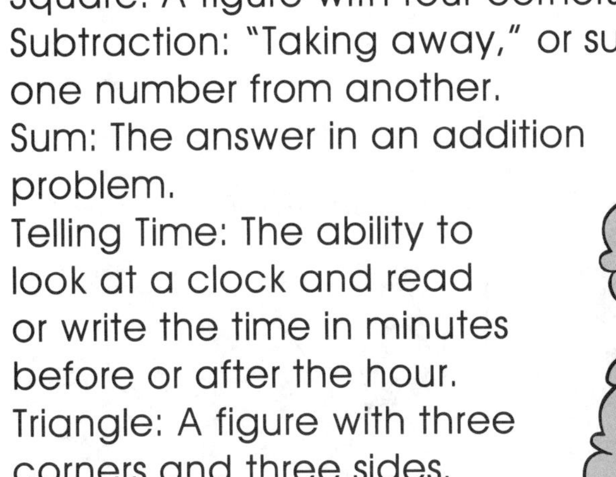

Answer Key

Page 4

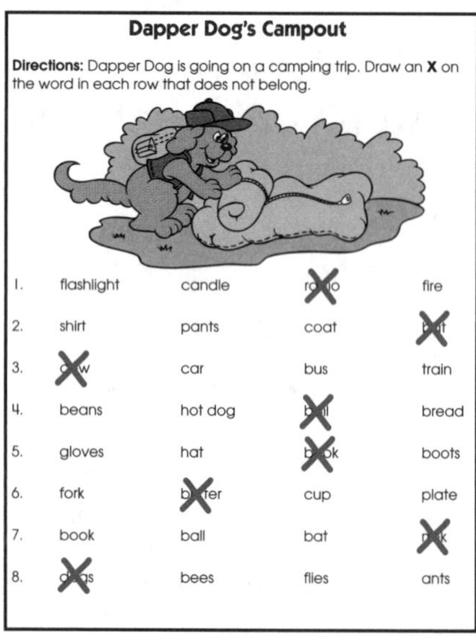

Dapper Dog's Campout

Directions: Dapper Dog is going on a camping trip. Draw an **X** on the word in each row that does not belong.

1.	flashlight	candle	X radio	fire
2.	shirt	pants	coat	X bat
3.	X saw	car	bus	train
4.	beans	hot dog	X ball	bread
5.	gloves	hat	X book	boots
6.	fork	X butter	cup	plate
7.	book	ball	bat	X rock
8.	X dogs	bees	flies	ants

Page 5

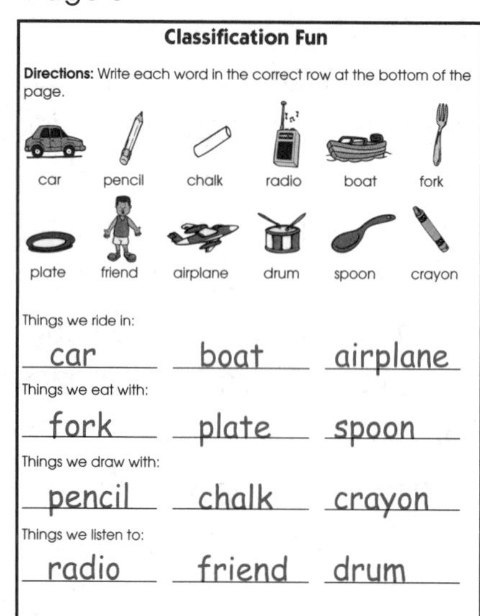

Classification Fun

Directions: Write each word in the correct row at the bottom of the page.

car, pencil, chalk, radio, boat, fork, plate, friend, airplane, drum, spoon, crayon

Things we ride in: car, boat, airplane

Things we eat with: fork, plate, spoon

Things we draw with: pencil, chalk, crayon

Things we listen to: radio, friend, drum

Page 6

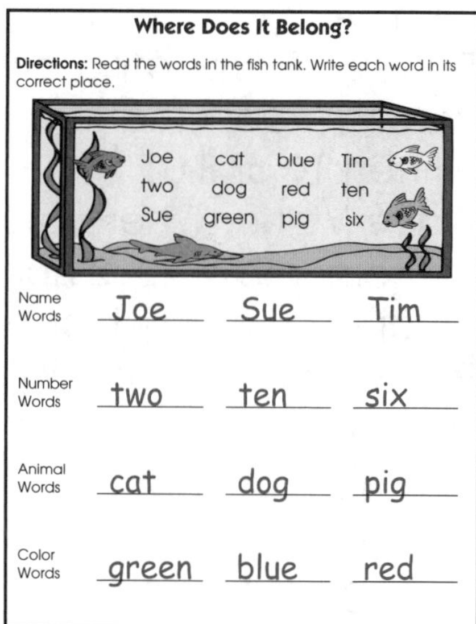

Where Does It Belong?

Directions: Read the words in the fish tank. Write each word in its correct place.

Joe, cat, blue, Tim, two, dog, red, ten, Sue, green, pig, six

Name Words: Joe, Sue, Tim

Number Words: two, ten, six

Animal Words: cat, dog, pig

Color Words: green, blue, red

Page 7

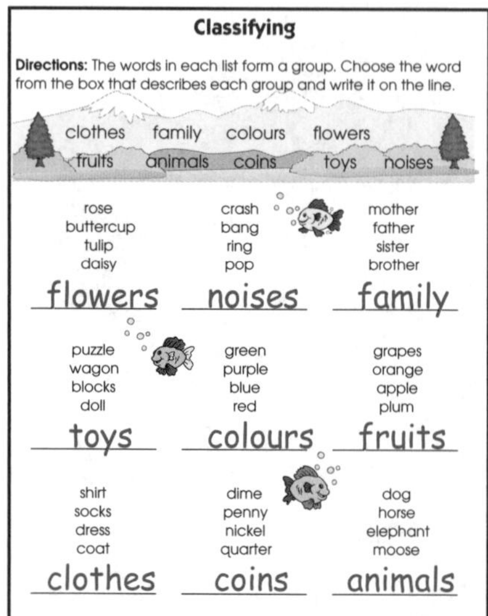

Classifying

Directions: The words in each list form a group. Choose the word from the box that describes each group and write it on the line.

clothes, family, colours, flowers, fruits, animals, coins, toys, noises

rose, buttercup, tulip, daisy — flowers

crash, bang, ring, pop — noises

mother, father, sister, brother — family

puzzle, wagon, blocks, doll — toys

green, purple, blue, red — colours

grapes, orange, apple, plum — fruits

shirt, socks, dress, coat — clothes

dime, penny, nickel, quarter — coins

dog, horse, elephant, moose — animals

Page 8

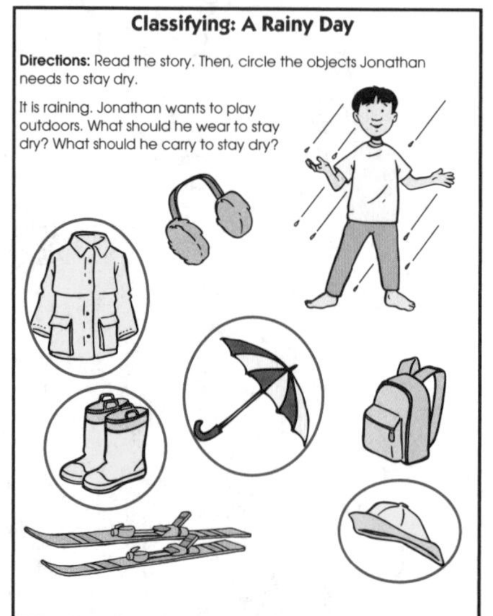

Classifying: A Rainy Day

Directions: Read the story. Then, circle the objects Jonathan needs to stay dry.

It is raining. Jonathan wants to play outdoors. What should he wear to stay dry? What should he carry to stay dry?

Page 9

Classifying: Outdoor/Indoor Games

Classifying is putting things that are alike into groups.

Directions: Read about games. Draw an **X** on the games you can play indoors. Circle the objects used for outdoor games.

Some games are outdoor games. Some games are indoor games. Outdoor games are active. Indoor games are quiet.

Which do you like best? Answers Will Vary.

Page 10

Classifying: Art Tools

Directions: Read about art tools. Then, color only the art tools.

Andrea uses different art tools to help her design her masterpieces. To cut, she needs scissors. To draw, she needs a pencil. To color, she needs crayons. To paint, she needs a brush.

Write which tools are needed to:

draw	color	cut
pencil	crayon	scissors

Page 11

Classifying: Foods

Darcy likes fruit and things made from fruit. She also likes bread.

Directions: Circle the things on the menu that Darcy will eat.

MENU

apple pie	corn
peas	rolls
beans	banana bread
oranges	grape juice
chicken	

Page 12

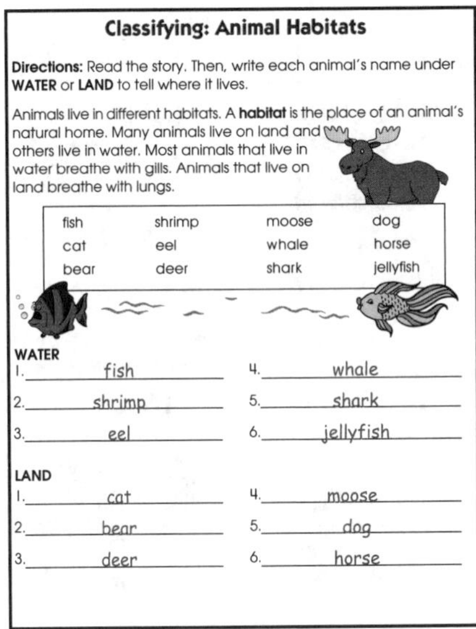

Classifying: Animal Habitats

Directions: Read the story. Then, write each animal's name under **WATER** or **LAND** to tell where it lives.

Animals live in different habitats. A **habitat** is the place of an animal's natural home. Many animals live on land and others live in water. Most animals that live in water breathe with gills. Animals that live on land breathe with lungs.

fish	shrimp	moose	dog
cat	eel	whale	horse
bear	deer	shark	jellyfish

WATER

1. fish
2. shrimp
3. eel
4. whale
5. shark
6. jellyfish

LAND

1. cat
2. bear
3. deer
4. moose
5. dog
6. horse

Page 13

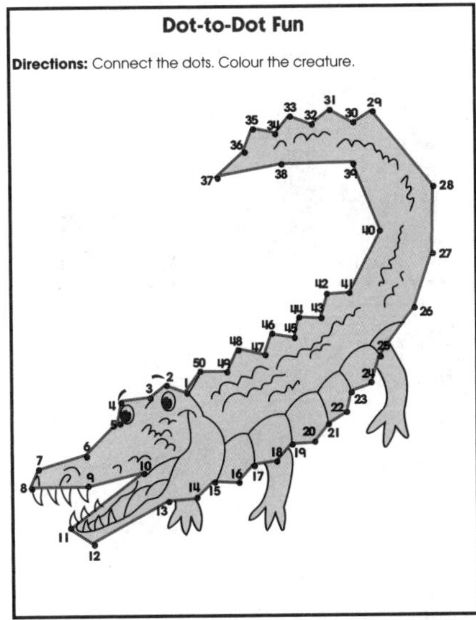

Dot-to-Dot Fun

Directions: Connect the dots. Colour the creature.

Page 14

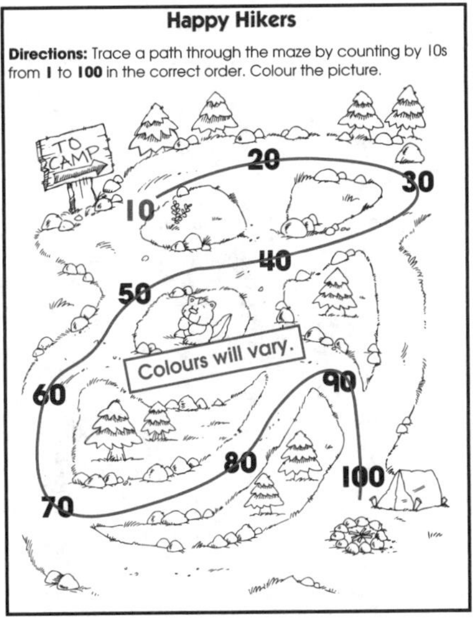

Happy Hikers

Directions: Trace a path through the maze by counting by 10s from **1** to **100** in the correct order. Colour the picture.

Page 15

Rainbow-Coloured Numbers

Directions: Colour the spaces: **1 = red**, **2 = blue**, **3 = yellow**, **4 = green**, and **5 = orange**

Page 16

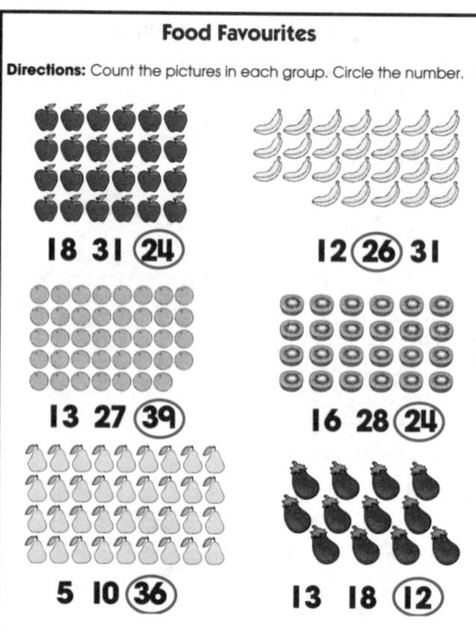

Food Favourites
Directions: Count the pictures in each group. Circle the number.
18 31 (24)
12 (26) 31
13 27 (39)
16 28 (24)
5 10 (36)
13 18 (12)

Page 17

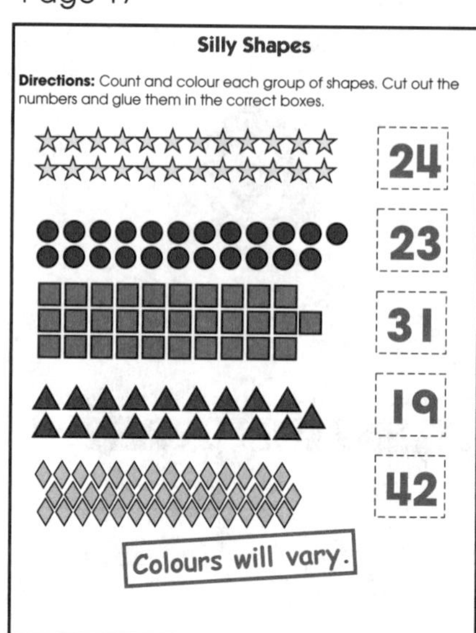

Silly Shapes
Directions: Count and colour each group of shapes. Cut out the numbers and glue them in the correct boxes.
24
23
31
19
42
Colours will vary.

Page 19

Clown Capers
Directions: Count the number of each thing in the picture. Write the number on the line.
1
2
3
4
5
6
7
8
9
10

Page 20

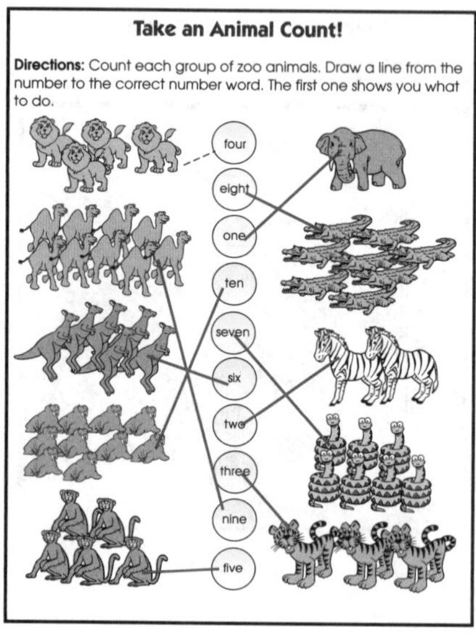

Page 21

Sheepish Shepherd
Directions: Count the sheep on the hill. Then, write that number on each tree.
3
9
2
8
7
5
4
1
10
6

Page 22

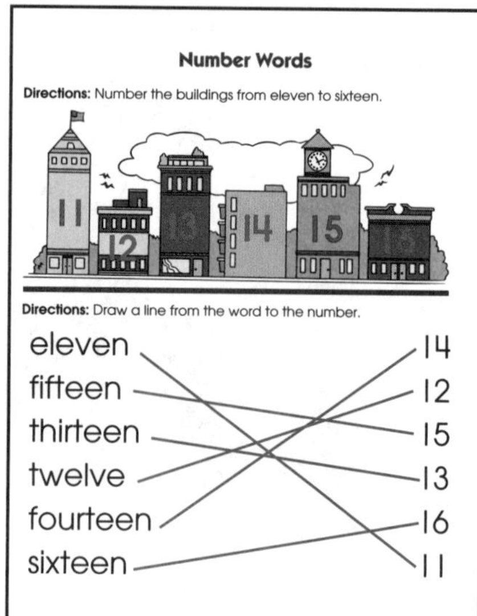

Number Words
Directions: Number the buildings from eleven to sixteen.
11
12
13
14
15
16
Directions: Draw a line from the word to the number.
eleven
fifteen
thirteen
twelve
fourteen
sixteen
14
12
15
13
16
11

Page 23

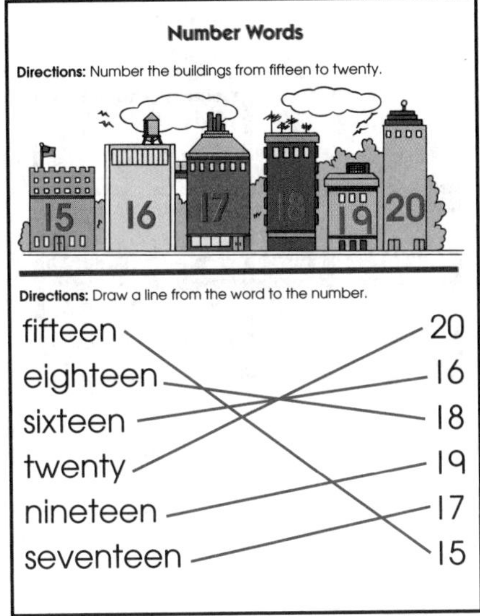

Number Words
Directions: Number the buildings from fifteen to twenty.
15
16
17
18
19
20
Directions: Draw a line from the word to the number.
fifteen
eighteen
sixteen
twenty
nineteen
seventeen
20
16
18
19
17
15

Page 24

Number Words

Directions: Write each number beside the correct picture. Then, write it again.

one two three four five six seven eight nine ten

Example:

six six
three three
two two
nine nine
four four
seven seven
five five
one one
eight eight

Page 25

Sequencing Numbers

Sequencing is putting numbers in the correct order.

Directions: Write the missing numbers.

Example: 14, 15, 16

23, 24, 25	17, 18, 19	18, 19, 20
16, 17, 18	32, 33, 34	34, 35, 36
35, 36, 37	45, 46, 47	42, 43, 44
28, 29, 30	26, 27, 28	22, 23, 24
42, 43, 44	11, 12, 13	47, 48, 49
32, 33, 34	36, 37, 38	34, 35, 36
16, 17, 18	42, 43, 44	21, 22, 23
47, 48, 49	22, 23, 24	28, 29, 30

Page 26

Counting

Directions: Write the numbers that are:

next in order	one less	one greater
22, 23, 24, 25	15, 16	6, 7
674, 675, 676	246, 247	125, 126
227, 228, 229	549, 550	499, 500
199, 200, 201	332, 333	750, 751
329, 330, 331	861, 862	933, 934

Directions: Write the missing numbers.

13 14 15 16 17 18

163 164 165 166 167 168

821 822 823 824 825 826

Page 27

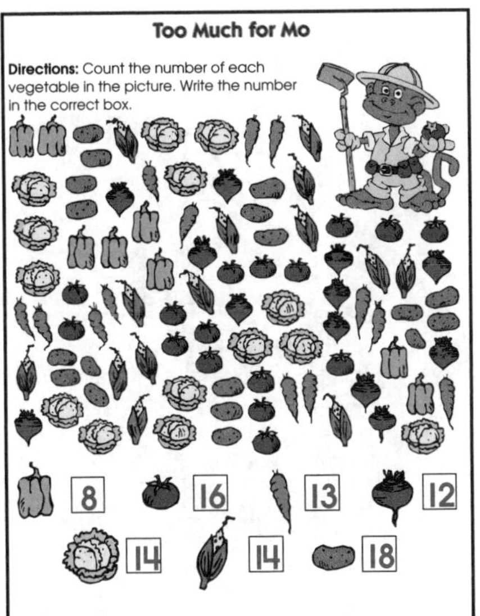

Too Much for Mo
Directions: Count the number of each vegetable in the picture. Write the number in the correct box.
8
16
13
12
14
14
18

Page 28

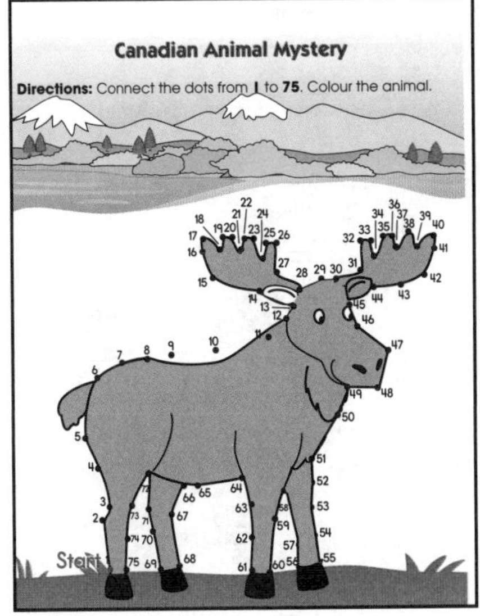

Canadian Animal Mystery
Directions: Connect the dots from 1 to 75. Colour the animal.
Start

Page 29

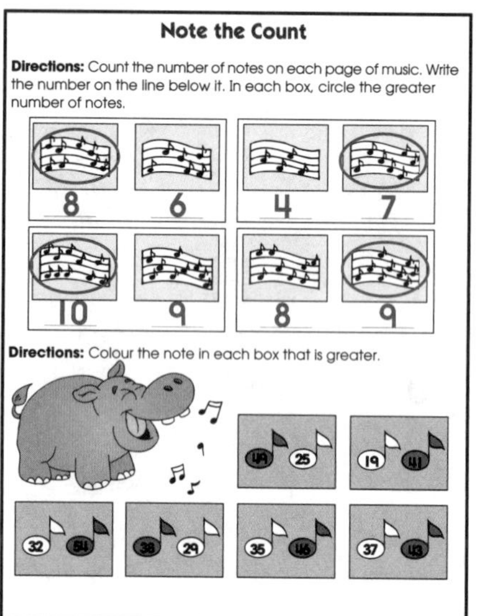

Page 30

Plump Piglets
Directions: Read the clues to find out how many ears of corn each pig ate. Write the number on the line below each pig.
I ate the number that comes before 26.
Patsy
25
I ate the number that comes between 87 and 89.
Horace
88
I ate the number that comes after 92.
Pinky
93
I ate the number that comes before 57.
Hilda
56
I ate the number that comes between 39 and 41.
Porky
40
Who ate the most? Pinky Who ate the least? Patsy

Page 31

Page 33

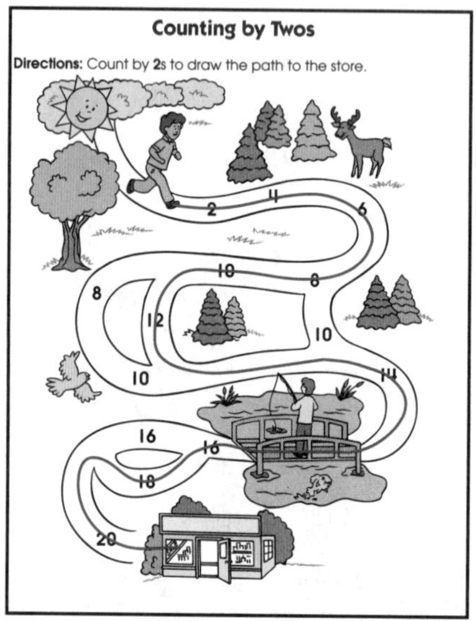

Counting by Twos
Directions: Count by 2s to draw the path to the store.

Page 34

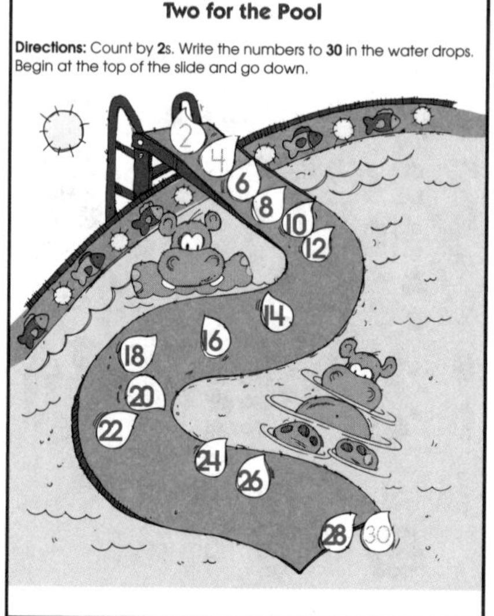

Two for the Pool
Directions: Count by 2s. Write the numbers to 30 in the water drops. Begin at the top of the slide and go down.
2
4
6
8
10
12
14
16
18
20
22
24
26
28
30

Page 35

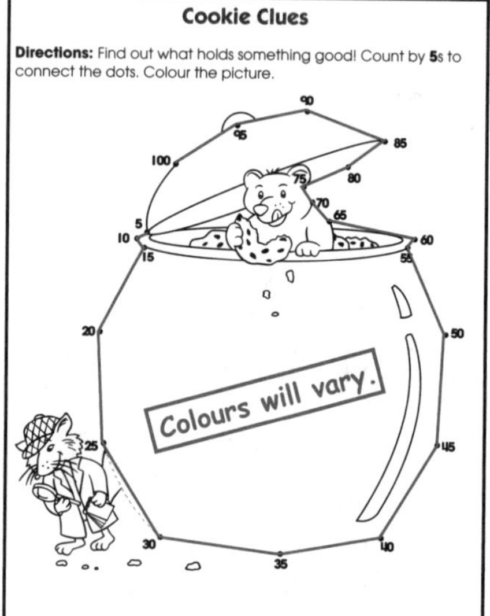

Cookie Clues
Directions: Find out what holds something good! Count by 5s to connect the dots. Colour the picture.
Colours will vary.

Page 36

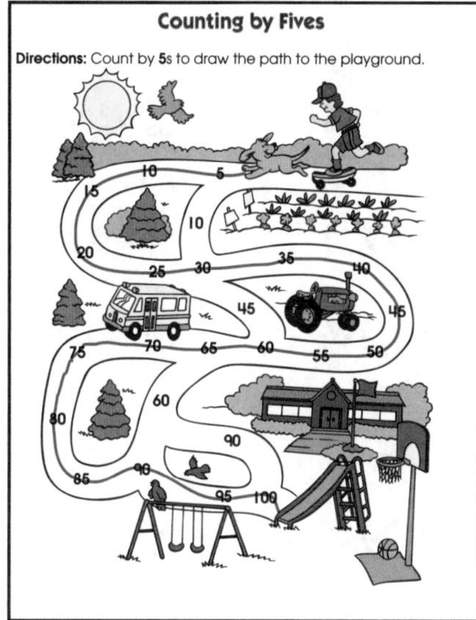

Counting by Fives

Directions: Count by **5**s to draw the path to the playground.

Page 37

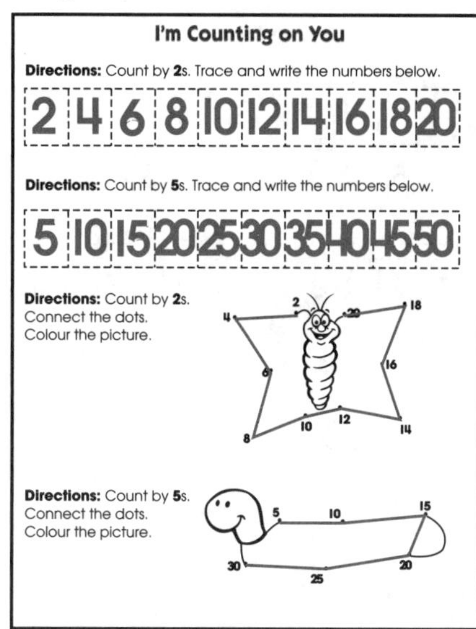

I'm Counting on You

Directions: Count by **2**s. Trace and write the numbers below.

2 4 6 8 10 12 14 16 18 20

Directions: Count by **5**s. Trace and write the numbers below.

5 10 15 20 25 30 35 40 45 50

Directions: Count by **2**s.
Connect the dots.
Colour the picture.

Directions: Count by **5**s.
Connect the dots.
Colour the picture.

Page 38

Desert Trek

Directions: Count by **10**s. Colour each canteen with a **10** to lead the camel to the watering hole.

Page 39

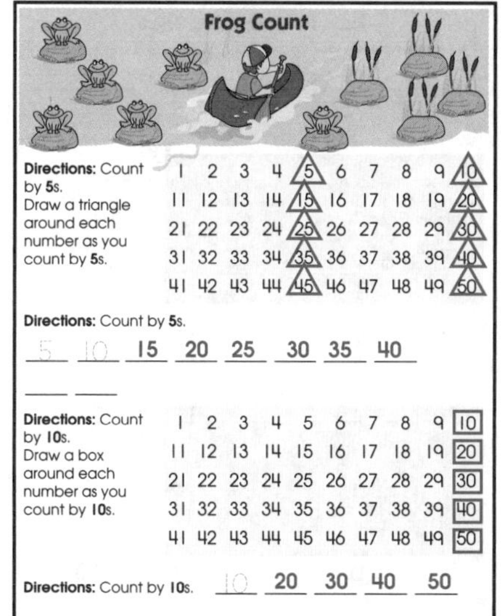

Frog Count

Directions: Count by **5**s.
Draw a triangle around each number as you count by **5**s.

1 2 3 4 5 6 7 8 9 10
11 12 13 14 15 16 17 18 19 20
21 22 23 24 25 26 27 28 29 30
31 32 33 34 35 36 37 38 39 40
41 42 43 44 45 46 47 48 49 50

Directions: Count by **5**s.

5 10 15 20 25 30 35 40

Directions: Count by **10**s.
Draw a box around each number as you count by **10**s.

1 2 3 4 5 6 7 8 9 10
11 12 13 14 15 16 17 18 19 20
21 22 23 24 25 26 27 28 29 30
31 32 33 34 35 36 37 38 39 40
41 42 43 44 45 46 47 48 49 50

Directions: Count by **10**s. 10 20 30 40 50

Page 40

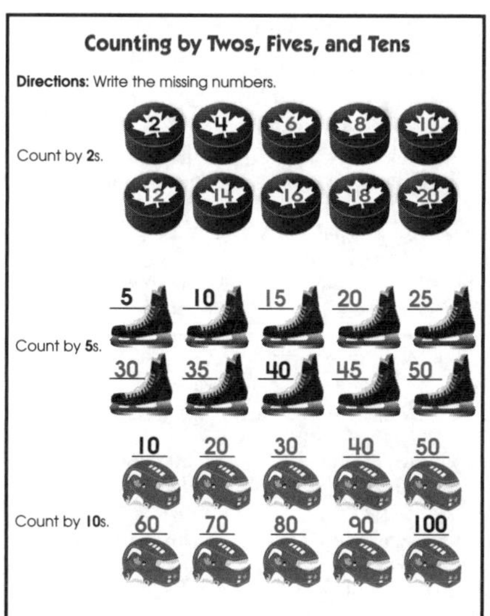

Counting by Twos, Fives, and Tens

Directions: Write the missing numbers.

Count by **2**s. 2 4 6 8 10 12 14 16 18 20

Count by **5**s. 5 10 15 20 25 30 35 40 45 50

Count by **10**s. 10 20 30 40 50 60 70 80 90 100

Page 41

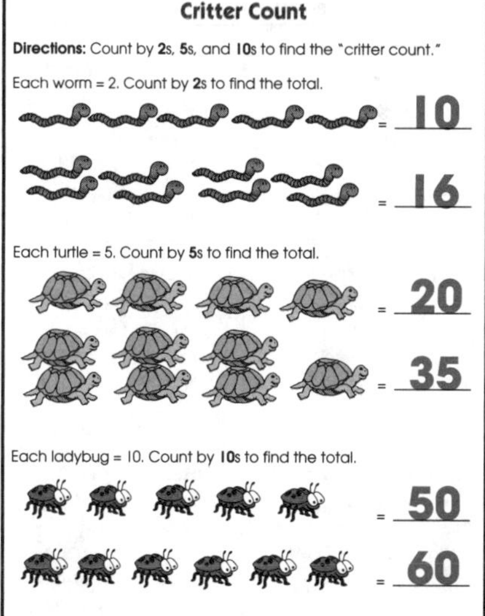

Critter Count

Directions: Count by **2**s, **5**s, and **10**s to find the "critter count."

Each worm = 2. Count by **2**s to find the total.

= 10

= 16

Each turtle = 5. Count by **5**s to find the total.

= 20

= 35

Each ladybug = 10. Count by **10**s to find the total.

= 50

= 60

Page 43

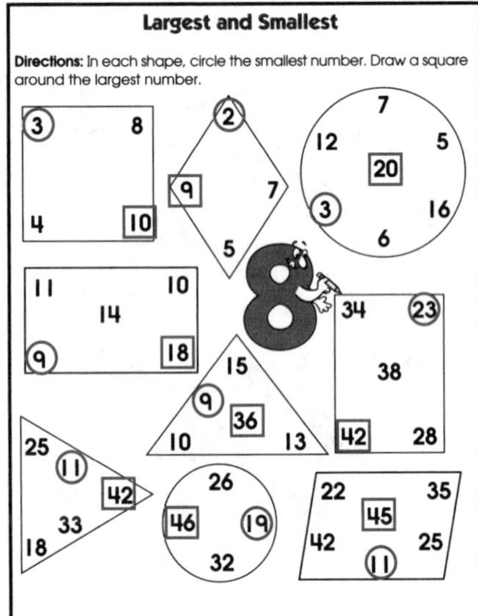

Largest and Smallest

Directions: In each shape, circle the smallest number. Draw a square around the largest number.

3 8 4 10

2 9 7 5

7 12 5 20 3 16 6

11 10 14 9 18

34 23 38 42 28

15 9 36 10 13

25 11 42 33 18

26 46 19 32

22 35 45 42 25 11

Page 44

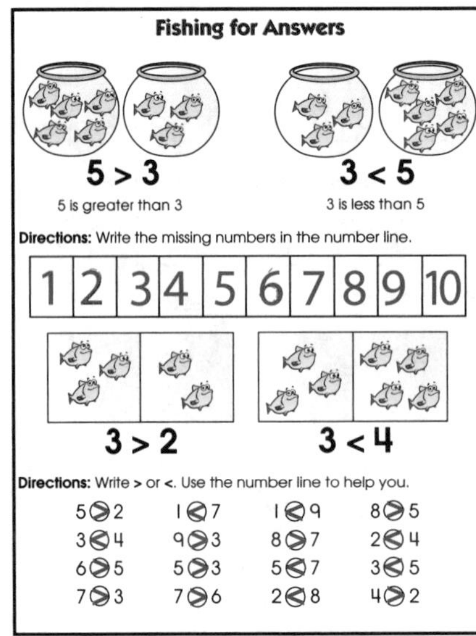

Fishing for Answers

5 > 3

5 is greater than 3

3 < 5

3 is less than 5

Directions: Write the missing numbers in the number line.

1 2 3 4 5 6 7 8 9 10

3 > 2

3 < 4

Directions: Write > or <. Use the number line to help you.

5 > 2	1 < 7	1 < 9	8 > 5
3 < 4	9 > 3	8 > 7	2 < 4
6 > 5	5 > 3	5 < 7	3 < 5
7 > 3	7 > 6	2 < 8	4 > 2

Page 45

"Mouth" Math

Directions: Write < or > in each circle. Make sure the "mouth" is open toward the greater number!

36 < 49	35 < 53
20 > 18	74 > 21
53 < 76	68 < 80
29 > 26	45 > 19
90 > 89	70 > 67

Page 46

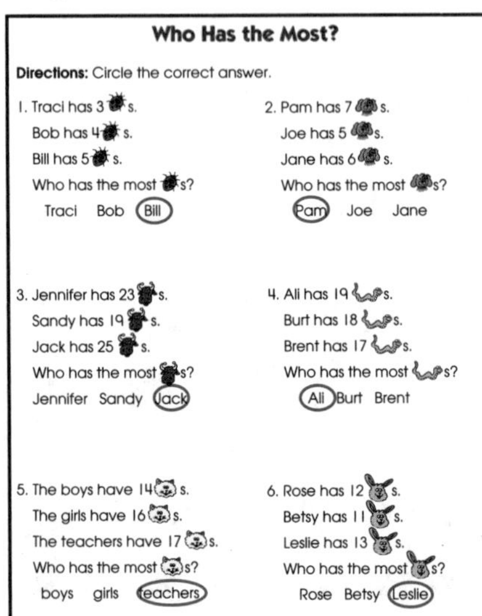

Who Has the Most?

Directions: Circle the correct answer.

1. Traci has 3 s.
   Bob has 4 s.
   Bill has 5 s.
   Who has the most s?
   Traci Bob **(Bill)**

2. Pam has 7 s.
   Joe has 5 s.
   Jane has 6 s.
   Who has the most s?
   (Pam) Joe Jane

3. Jennifer has 23 s.
   Sandy has 19 s.
   Jack has 25 s.
   Who has the most s?
   Jennifer Sandy **(Jack)**

4. Ali has 19 s.
   Burt has 18 s.
   Brent has 17 s.
   Who has the most s?
   (Ali) Burt Brent

5. The boys have 14 s.
   The girls have 16 s.
   The teachers have 17 s.
   Who has the most s?
   boys girls **(teachers)**

6. Rose has 12 s.
   Betsy has 11 s.
   Leslie has 13 s.
   Who has the most s?
   Rose Betsy **(Leslie)**

Page 47

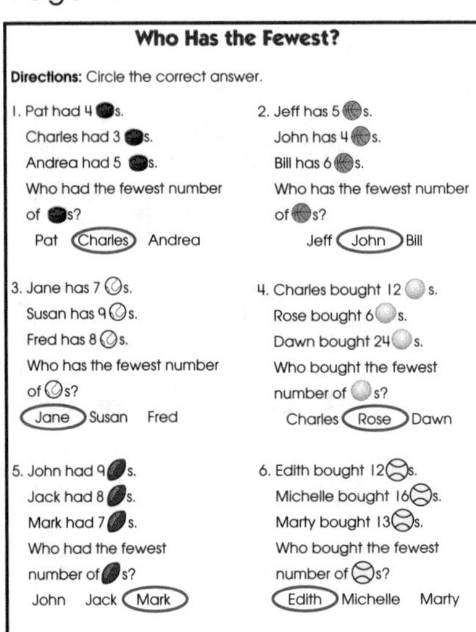

Who Has the Fewest?

Directions: Circle the correct answer.

1. Pat had 4 s.
   Charles had 3 s.
   Andrea had 5 s.
   Who had the fewest number of s?
   Pat **(Charles)** Andrea

2. Jeff has 5 s.
   John has 4 s.
   Bill has 6 s.
   Who has the fewest number of s?
   Jeff **(John)** Bill

3. Jane has 7 s.
   Susan has 9 s.
   Fred has 8 s.
   Who has the fewest number of s?
   (Jane) Susan Fred

4. Charles bought 12 s.
   Rose bought 6 s.
   Dawn bought 24 s.
   Who bought the fewest number of s?
   Charles **(Rose)** Dawn

5. John had 9 s.
   Jack had 8 s.
   Mark had 7 s.
   Who had the fewest number of s?
   John Jack **(Mark)**

6. Edith bought 12 s.
   Michelle bought 16 s.
   Marty bought 13 s.
   Who bought the fewest number of s?
   (Edith) Michelle Marty

Page 48

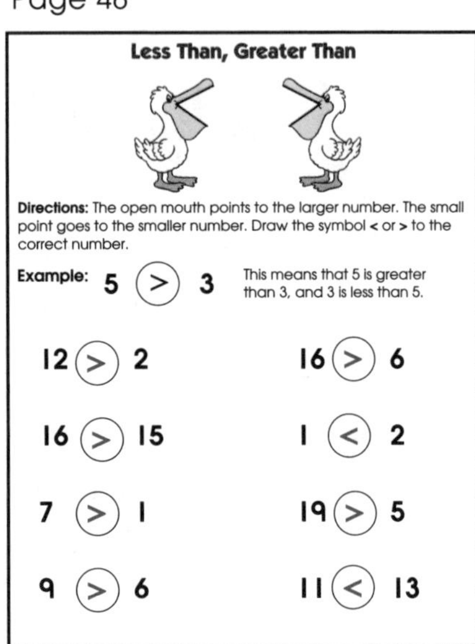

Less Than, Greater Than

Directions: The open mouth points to the larger number. The small point goes to the smaller number. Draw the symbol < or > to the correct number.

Example: 5 > 3 This means that 5 is greater than 3, and 3 is less than 5.

12 > 2	16 > 6
16 > 15	1 < 2
7 > 1	19 > 5
9 > 6	11 < 13

Page 49

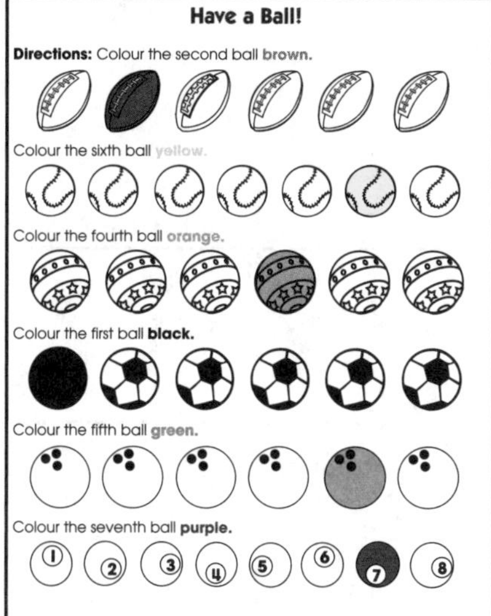

Have a Ball!

Directions: Colour the second ball **brown.**

Colour the sixth ball **yellow.**

Colour the fourth ball **orange.**

Colour the first ball **black.**

Colour the fifth ball **green.**

Colour the seventh ball **purple.**

1 2 3 4 5 6 7 8

Page 50

Swimming in Style!

Directions: Colour the swimsuits. The first person is wearing a **yellow** mask.

Colour the fourth suit **brown.**
Colour the second suit **purple.**
Colour the first suit **red.**
Colour the seventh suit **pink.**
Colour the third suit **blue.**
Colour the eighth suit **green.**
Colour the fifth suit **orange.**
Colour the sixth suit **yellow.**

Page 51

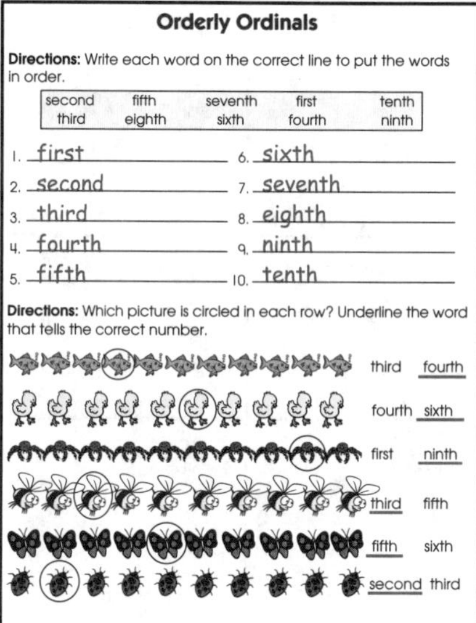

Orderly Ordinals

Directions: Write each word on the correct line to put the words in order.

second	fifth	seventh	first	tenth
third	eighth	sixth	fourth	ninth

1. first
2. second
3. third
4. fourth
5. fifth
6. sixth
7. seventh
8. eighth
9. ninth
10. tenth

Directions: Which picture is circled in each row? Underline the word that tells the correct number.

third <u>fourth</u>
fourth <u>sixth</u>
first <u>ninth</u>
<u>third</u> fifth
<u>fifth</u> sixth
<u>second</u> third

Page 52

Which Place in the Race?

Directions: Write the correct word to tell each runner's place in the race.

fifth
first
fourth
third
seventh
second
sixth

Page 53

Flags First

Directions:
Colour the ninth flag **red.**
Write **O** on the second flag.
Colour the eighth flag **blue.**
Write **D** on the first flag.
Colour the sixth flag **yellow.**
Write **G** on the fourth flag.
Colour the tenth flag **purple.**
Write **O** on the third flag.
Colour the seventh flag **green.**
Colour the fifth flag **orange.**
What word did you spell? Good

Page 54

How Many Robots in All?

Directions: Look at the pictures. Complete the addition sentences.

Example:
How many s are there in all?
2 + 4 = 6

How many s are there in all?
3 + 5 = 8

How many s are there in all?
4 + 3 = 7

How many s are there in all?
4 + 5 = 9

How many s are there in all?
2 + 5 = 7

How many s are there in all?
4 + 4 = 8

Page 55

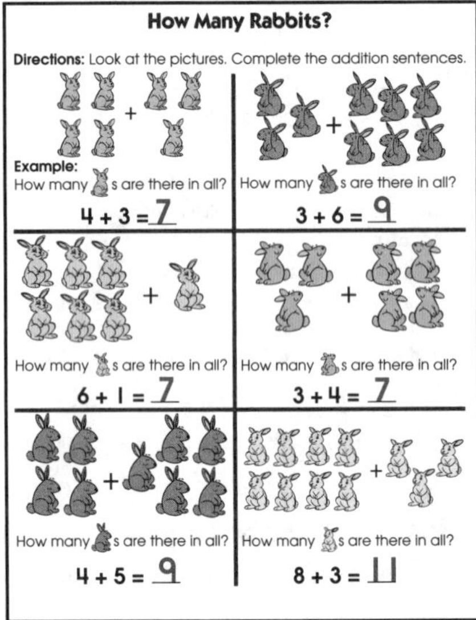

How Many Rabbits?

Directions: Look at the pictures. Complete the addition sentences.

Example:
How many s are there in all?
4 + 3 = 7

How many s are there in all?
3 + 6 = 9

How many s are there in all?
6 + 1 = 7

How many s are there in all?
3 + 4 = 7

How many s are there in all?
4 + 5 = 9

How many s are there in all?
8 + 3 = 11

Page 56

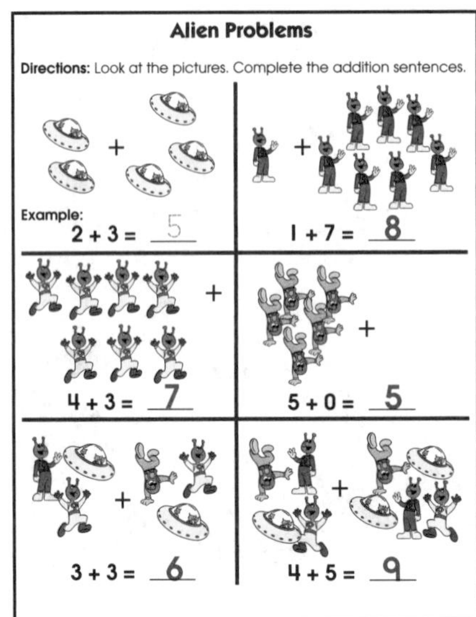

Alien Problems

Directions: Look at the pictures. Complete the addition sentences.

Example:
2 + 3 = 5

1 + 7 = 8

4 + 3 = 7

5 + 0 = 5

3 + 3 = 6

4 + 5 = 9

Page 57

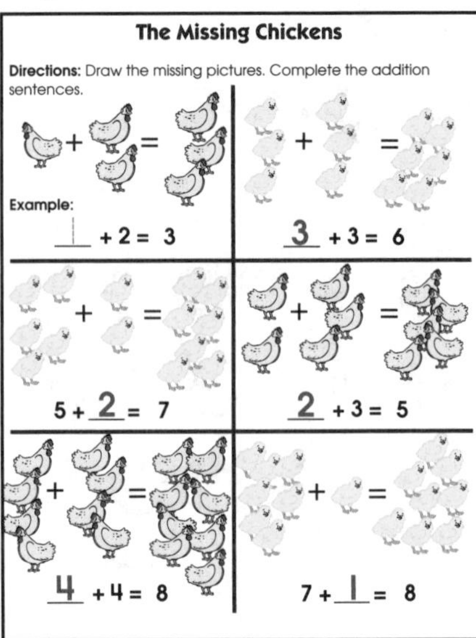

The Missing Chickens

Directions: Draw the missing pictures. Complete the addition sentences.

Example:
1 + 2 = 3

3 + 3 = 6

5 + 2 = 7

2 + 3 = 5

4 + 4 = 8

7 + 1 = 8

Page 58

Signs of Gain

Directions: Roll a die. Write the addend from the die in the top box. Add to find the sum. Roll again to make each sentence different.

5 + 1

Answers will vary.

Page 59

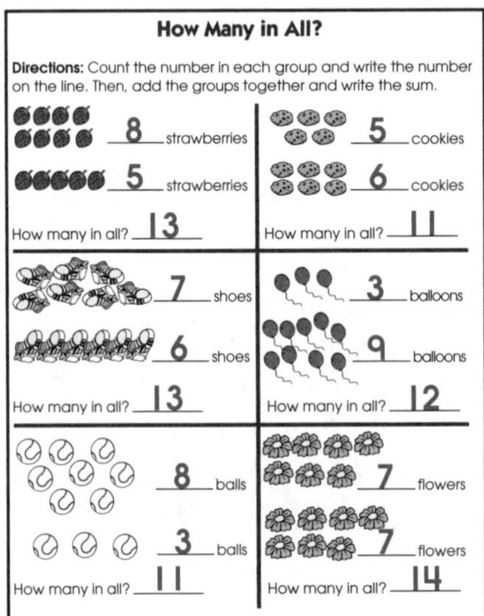

How Many in All?

Directions: Count the number in each group and write the number on the line. Then, add the groups together and write the sum.

8 strawberries
5 strawberries
How many in all? 13

5 cookies
6 cookies
How many in all? 11

7 shoes
6 shoes
How many in all? 13

3 balloons
9 balloons
How many in all? 12

8 balls
3 balls
How many in all? 11

7 flowers
7 flowers
How many in all? 14

Page 60

Adding 1

Directions: Write a number in the top box of each problem. Complete the problem. Make each problem different.

10 + 1 = 11

14 + 1

Answers will vary.

Page 61

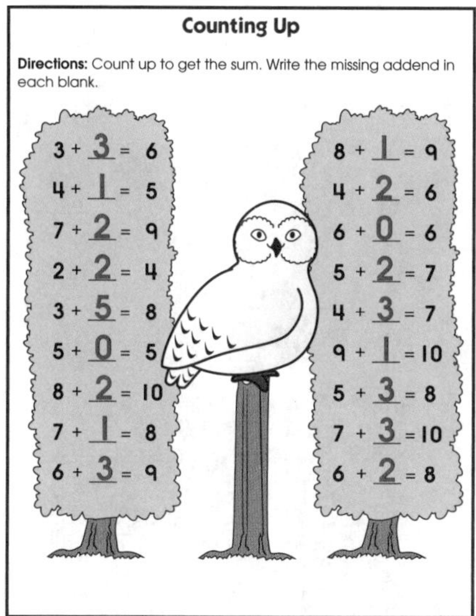

Counting Up

Directions: Count up to get the sum. Write the missing addend in each blank.

3 + 3 = 6
4 + 1 = 5
7 + 2 = 9
2 + 2 = 4
3 + 5 = 8
5 + 0 = 5
8 + 2 = 10
7 + 1 = 8
6 + 3 = 9

8 + 1 = 9
4 + 2 = 6
6 + 0 = 6
5 + 2 = 7
4 + 3 = 7
9 + 1 = 10
5 + 3 = 8
7 + 3 = 10
6 + 2 = 8

Page 62

Animal Addition

Directions: Add to find the sum. **Example:**

4 + 7 = 11

3 + 9 = 12
6 + 7 = 13
6 + 5 = 11
5 + 7 = 12
4 + 9 = 13
9 + 6 = 15
7 + 7 = 14
9 + 6 = 15
6 + 8 = 14

Page 63

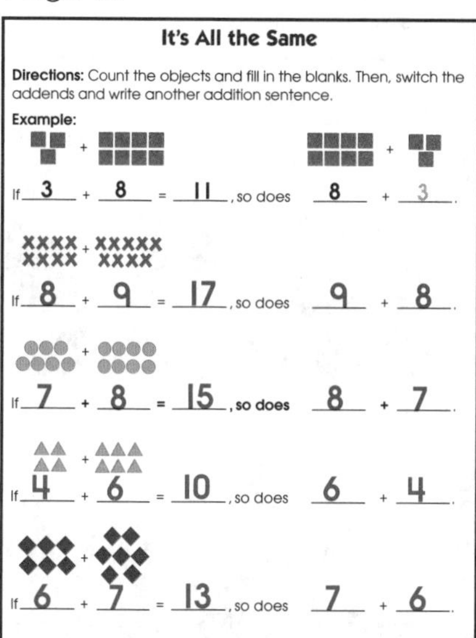

It's All the Same

Directions: Count the objects and fill in the blanks. Then, switch the addends and write another addition sentence.

Example:

If 3 + 8 = 11, so does 8 + 3.

If 8 + 9 = 17, so does 9 + 8.

If 7 + 8 = 15, so does 8 + 7.

If 4 + 6 = 10, so does 6 + 4.

If 6 + 7 = 13, so does 7 + 6.

Page 64

Add the Apples

Directions: Match the addition sentences with their sums.

8 + 2, 9 + 6, 2 + 2 — 15, 4, 10
1 + 2, 6 + 7, 5 + 6 — 11, 3, 13
3 + 2, 6 + 8, 5 + 5 — 10, 14, 5
6 + 6, 6 + 3, 3 + 4 — 12, 9, 7
6 + 2, 1 + 1, 1 + 5 — 8, 6, 2
7 + 2, 6 + 9, 12 + 1 — 15, 9, 13
10 + 4, 9 + 5, 7 + 1 — 14, 8, 11

Page 65

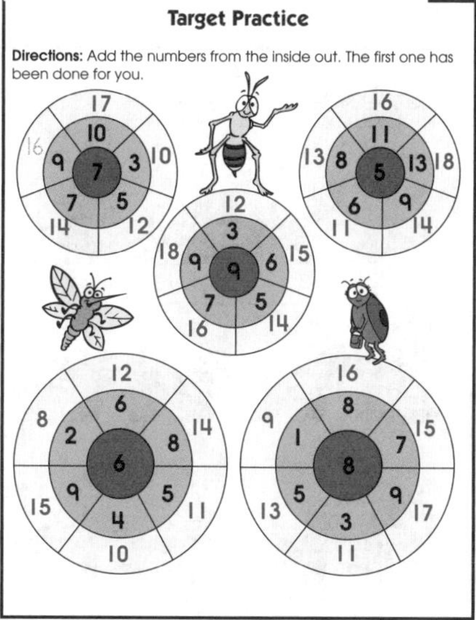

Target Practice

Directions: Add the numbers from the inside out. The first one has been done for you.

Page 66

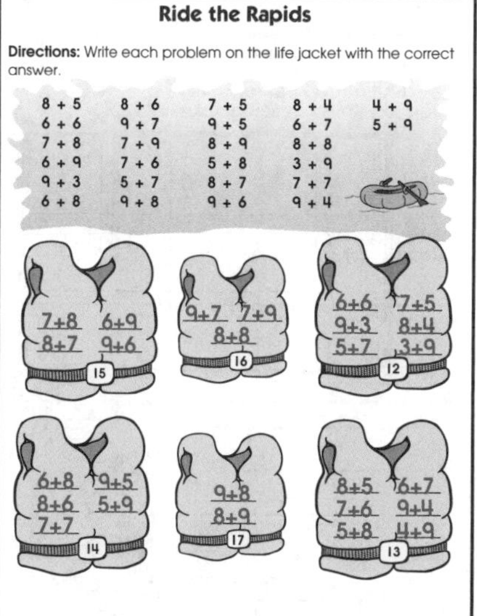

Ride the Rapids

Directions: Write each problem on the life jacket with the correct answer.

8 + 5, 6 + 6, 7 + 8, 6 + 9, 9 + 3, 6 + 8
8 + 6, 9 + 7, 7 + 9, 7 + 6, 5 + 7, 9 + 8
7 + 5, 9 + 5, 8 + 9, 5 + 8, 8 + 7, 9 + 6
8 + 4, 6 + 7, 8 + 8, 3 + 9, 7 + 7, 9 + 4
4 + 9, 5 + 9

15: 7+8, 8+7, 6+9, 9+6
16: 9+7, 7+9, 8+8
12: 6+6, 9+3, 5+7, 7+5, 8+4, 3+9
14: 6+8, 8+6, 7+7, 9+5, 5+9
17: 9+8, 8+9
13: 8+5, 7+6, 5+8, 6+7, 9+4, 4+9

Page 67

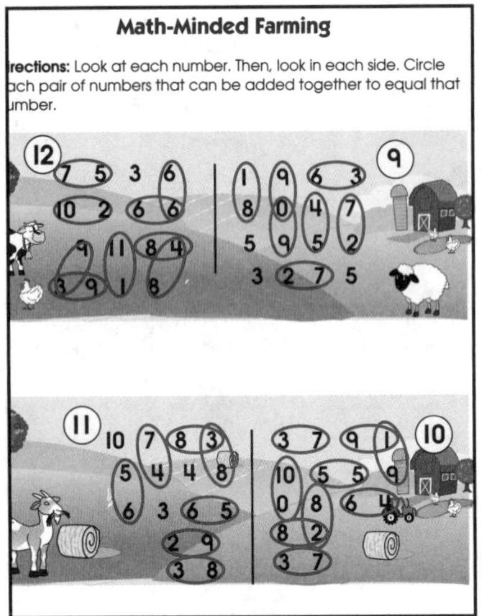

Math-Minded Farming

Directions: Look at each number. Then, look in each side. Circle each pair of numbers that can be added together to equal that number.

12: 7 5 3 6 / 10 2 6 6 / 9 11 8 4 / 3 9 1 8
9: 1 9 6 3 / 8 0 4 7 / 5 9 5 2 / 3 2 7 5
11: 10 7 8 3 / 5 4 4 8 / 6 3 6 5 / 2 9 / 3 8
10: 3 7 9 1 / 10 5 5 9 / 0 8 6 4 / 8 2 / 3 7

Page 68

Ancient Adding

Directions: Roll a pair of dice. Write the addend from each die on the lines below. Add to find the sum. Roll again to make each sentence different.

__ + __ = __

Answers will vary.

Page 69

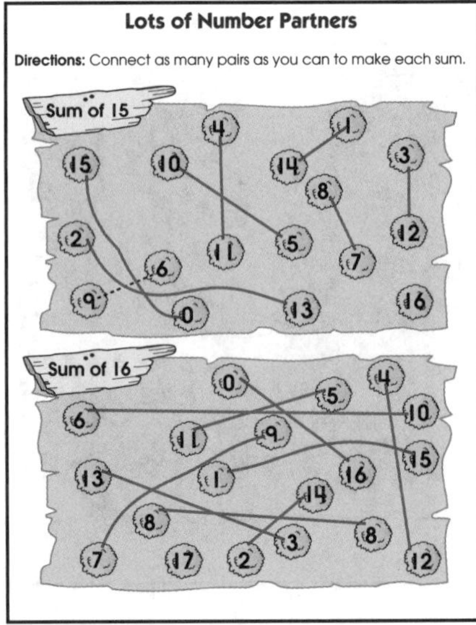

Lots of Number Partners

Directions: Connect as many pairs as you can to make each sum.

Sum of 15

Sum of 16

Page 70

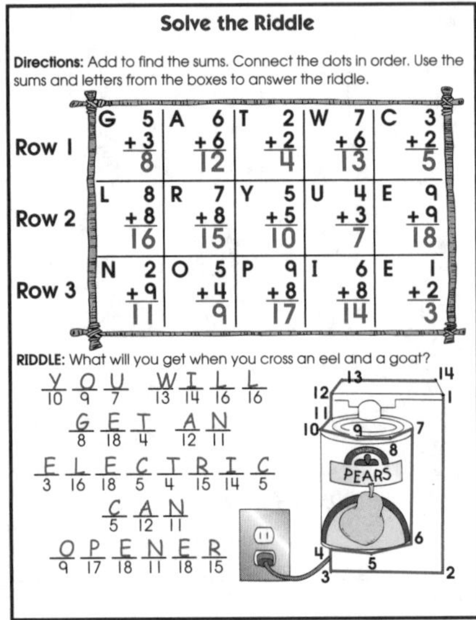

Solve the Riddle

Directions: Add to find the sums. Connect the dots in order. Use the sums and letters from the boxes to answer the riddle.

Row 1	G 5 + 3 = 8	A 6 + 6 = 12	T 2 + 2 = 4	W 7 + 6 = 13	C 3 + 2 = 5
Row 2	L 8 + 8 = 16	R 7 + 8 = 15	Y 5 + 5 = 10	U 4 + 3 = 7	E 9 + 9 = 18
Row 3	N 2 + 9 = 11	O 5 + 4 = 9	P 9 + 8 = 17	I 6 + 8 = 14	E 1 + 2 = 3

RIDDLE: What will you get when you cross an eel and a goat?

YOU WILL GET AN ELECTRIC CAN OPENER

Page 71

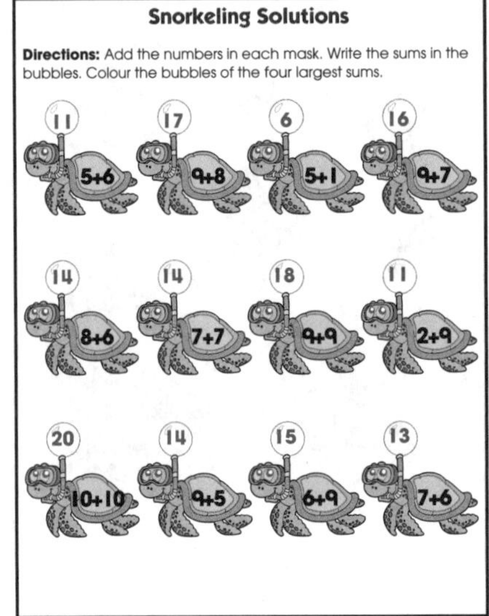

Snorkeling Solutions

Directions: Add the numbers in each mask. Write the sums in the bubbles. Colour the bubbles of the four largest sums.

5+6 = 11; 9+8 = 17; 5+1 = 6; 9+7 = 16
8+6 = 14; 7+7 = 14; 9+9 = 18; 2+9 = 11
10+10 = 20; 9+5 = 14; 6+9 = 15; 7+6 = 13

Page 72

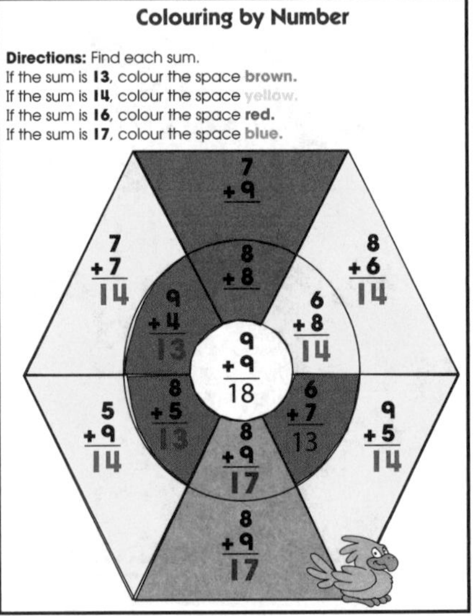

Colouring by Number

Directions: Find each sum.
If the sum is **13**, colour the space **brown.**
If the sum is **14**, colour the space **yellow.**
If the sum is **16**, colour the space **red.**
If the sum is **17**, colour the space **blue.**

7 + 9; 8 + 8; 7 + 7 = 14; 8 + 6 = 14; 9 + 4 = 13; 6 + 8 = 14; 9 + 9 = 18; 8 + 5 = 13; 6 + 7 = 13; 5 + 9 = 14; 9 + 5 = 14; 8 + 9 = 17; 8 + 9 = 17

Page 73

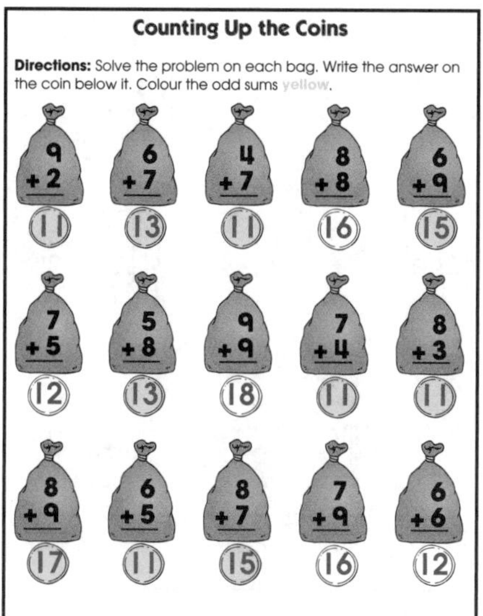

Counting Up the Coins

Directions: Solve the problem on each bag. Write the answer on the coin below it. Colour the odd sums yellow.

9 + 2 = 11, 6 + 7 = 13, 4 + 7 = 11, 8 + 8 = 16, 6 + 9 = 15

7 + 5 = 12, 5 + 8 = 13, 9 + 9 = 18, 7 + 4 = 11, 8 + 3 = 11

8 + 9 = 17, 6 + 5 = 11, 8 + 7 = 15, 7 + 9 = 16, 6 + 6 = 12

Page 74

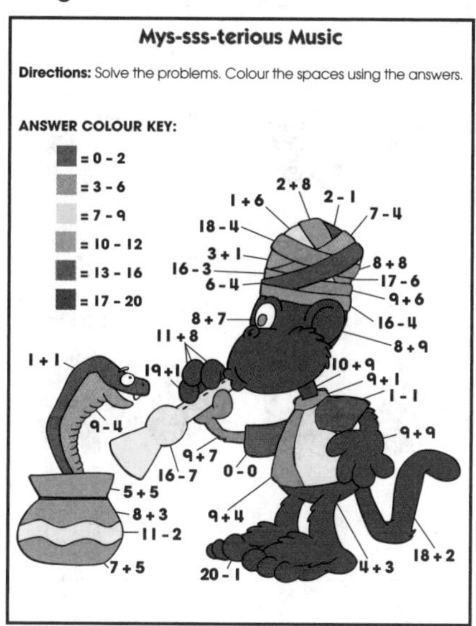

Mys-sss-terious Music

Directions: Solve the problems. Colour the spaces using the answers.

ANSWER COLOUR KEY:

= 0 - 2
= 3 - 6
= 7 - 9
= 10 - 12
= 13 - 16
= 17 - 20

Page 75

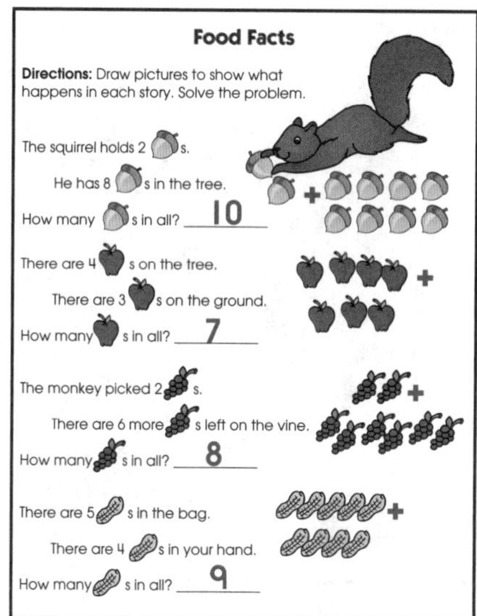

Food Facts

Directions: Draw pictures to show what happens in each story. Solve the problem.

The squirrel holds 2 s.
He has 8 s in the tree.
How many s in all? 10

There are 4 s on the tree.
There are 3 s on the ground.
How many s in all? 7

The monkey picked 2 s.
There are 6 more s left on the vine.
How many s in all? 8

There are 5 s in the bag.
There are 4 s in your hand.
How many s in all? 9

Page 76

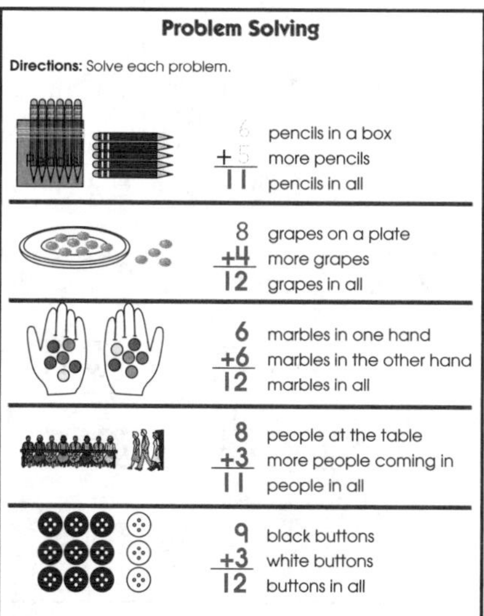

Problem Solving

Directions: Solve each problem.

6 pencils in a box
+5 more pencils
11 pencils in all

8 grapes on a plate
+4 more grapes
12 grapes in all

6 marbles in one hand
+6 marbles in the other hand
12 marbles in all

8 people at the table
+3 more people coming in
11 people in all

9 black buttons
+3 white buttons
12 buttons in all

Page 77

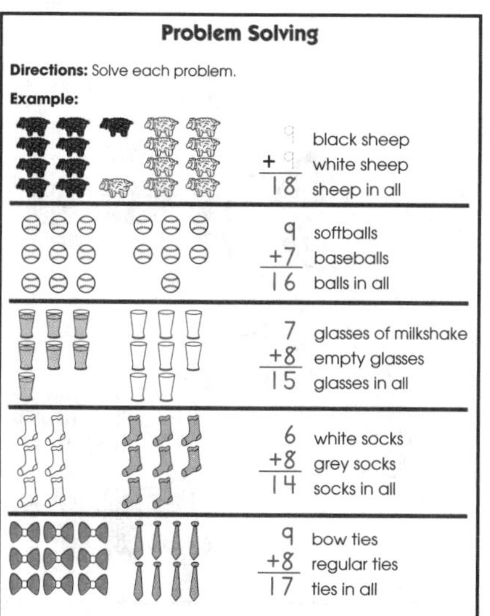

Problem Solving

Directions: Solve each problem.

Example:

9 black sheep
+9 white sheep
18 sheep in all

9 softballs
+7 baseballs
16 balls in all

7 glasses of milkshake
+8 empty glasses
15 glasses in all

6 white socks
+8 grey socks
14 socks in all

9 bow ties
+8 regular ties
17 ties in all

Page 78

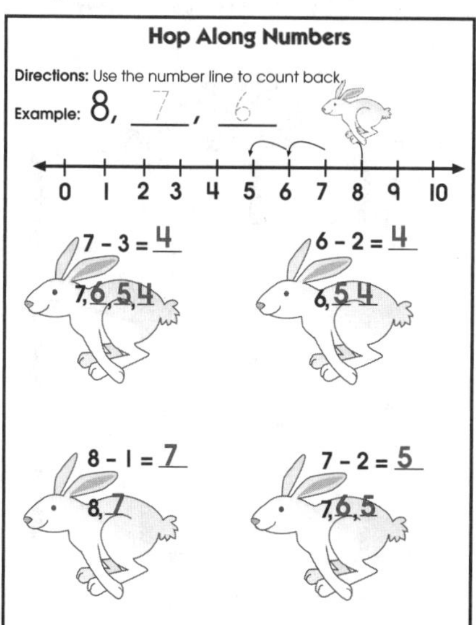

Hop Along Numbers

Directions: Use the number line to count back.

Example: 8, 7, 6

0 1 2 3 4 5 6 7 8 9 10

7 - 3 = 4 (7, 6, 5, 4)

6 - 2 = 4 (6, 5, 4)

8 - 1 = 7 (8, 7)

7 - 2 = 5 (7, 6, 5)

Page 79

Bubbly Baths

Directions: Solve the subtraction sentences below. Write each answer on a rubber duck.

Page 80

Leaves Leaving the Limb

Directions: Subtract to find the difference. Use the code to colour the leaves. Code: **0 = green** **1 = red** **2 = yellow** **3 = brown**

How many of each colour?

3 4 3 2

Page 81

Secrets of Subtraction

Directions: Solve the subtraction problems. Use the code to find the secret message.

Code:	7	5	2	6	4	3
	K	T	Y	E	W	A

PLEASE, DON'T EVER

8 -3	10 - 7	9 -2	10 - 4	9 -6	6 - 2	7 -4	8 -6
5	3	7	6	3	4	3	2
T	A	K	E	A	W	A	Y

MY MATH!

Page 82

Subtraction Makes Al Hungry

Directions: Write a different problem for each answer.

Example:

5 − 4 = 1 8 − 7 = 1 2 2

3 3 4 4

5 6 7 8

Answers will vary.

Page 83

Differences in Boxes

Directions: Colour the two numbers in each box that show the given difference.

Difference of 1

6	4	3	1	4	0
3	8	**5**	**6**	1	7

Difference of 1

3	**7**	**2**	**3**	6	3
1	**8**	5	7	9	7

Difference of 2

3	0	3	8	7	1
7	1	6	9	**4**	**6**

Difference of 2

3	**4**	7	4	**10**	**8**
8	**2**	10	5	5	4

Difference of 0

2	1	7	**3**	**5**	6
4	2	8	**3**	**5**	4

Page 84

Looping Differences

Directions: Circle the two numbers next to each other that make the given difference. Find as many as you can in each row.

Difference of 1

(2 3) 0 (8 7) 2 (9 10) (6 5) 1 4 (4 3)

Difference of 1

8 (4 5) 3 7 (1 2) 4 (9 8) (0 1) (7 6)

Difference of 2

5 (4 2) (3 1) 0 (3 5) 8 9 3 (6 8) 5

Difference of 2

(7 5) (10 8) 1 (4 6) 3 2 6 (7 9) (2 0)

Difference of 3

1 (6 3) 2 8 (4 7) 6 10 (0 3) 9 (5 2)

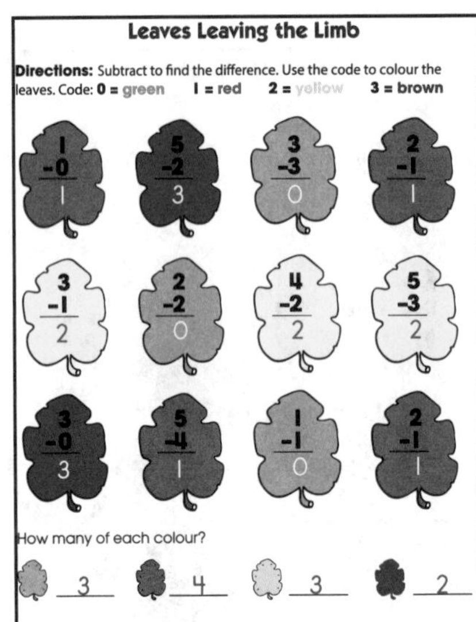

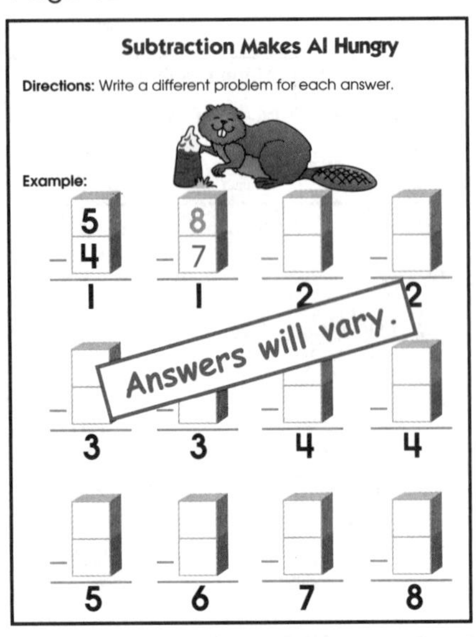

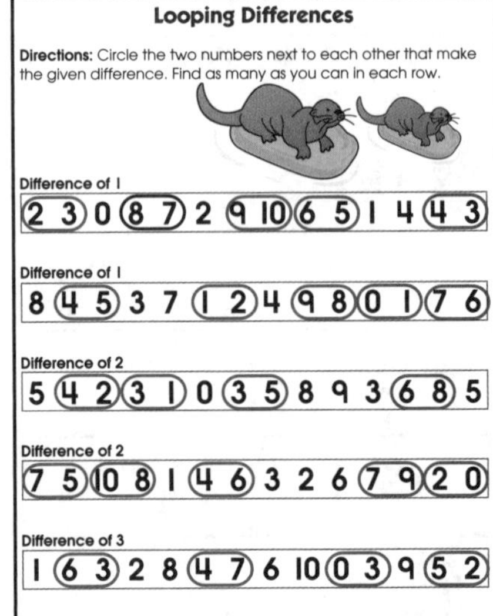

Page 85

Hidden Differences of 2

Directions: Circle the pairs that have a difference of **2**.

Page 86

Hidden Differences of 3

Directions: Circle the pairs that have a difference of **3**.

Page 87

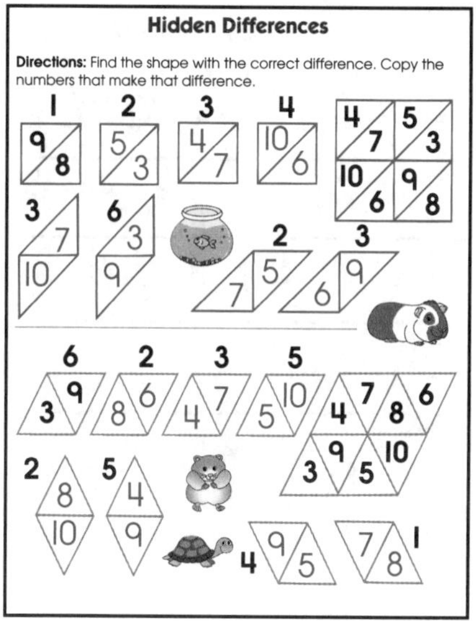

Hidden Differences

Directions: Find the shape with the correct difference. Copy the numbers that make that difference.

Page 88

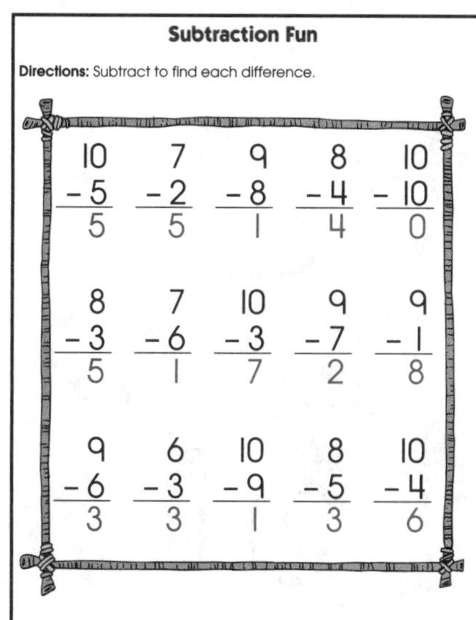

Subtraction Fun

Directions: Subtract to find each difference.

10 − 5 = 5	7 − 2 = 5	9 − 8 = 1	8 − 4 = 4	10 − 10 = 0
8 − 3 = 5	7 − 6 = 1	10 − 3 = 7	9 − 7 = 2	9 − 1 = 8
9 − 6 = 3	6 − 3 = 3	10 − 9 = 1	8 − 5 = 3	10 − 4 = 6

Page 89

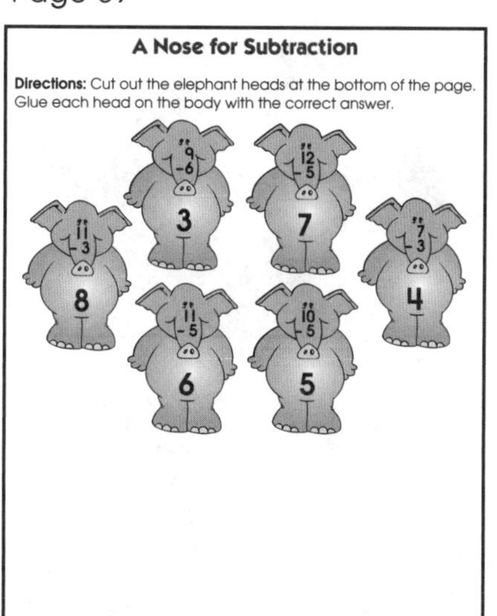

A Nose for Subtraction

Directions: Cut out the elephant heads at the bottom of the page. Glue each head on the body with the correct answer.

Page 91

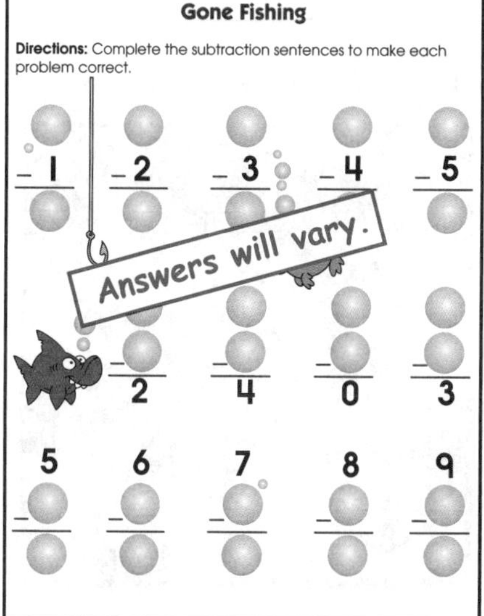

Gone Fishing

Directions: Complete the subtraction sentences to make each problem correct.

Page 92

Subtraction Facts Through 12

Directions: Subtract.

11 − 9 = 2	11 − 2 = 9	11 − 8 = 3	11 − 3 = 8
11 − 6 = 5	11 − 5 = 6	11 − 7 = 4	11 − 4 = 7
12 − 8 = 4	12 − 4 = 8	12 − 7 = 5	12 − 5 = 7
12 − 9 = 3	12 − 3 = 9	12 − 6 = 6	

Directions: Subtract.

11 − 3 = 8	11 − 6 = 5	12 − 3 = 9	11 − 8 = 3	12 − 7 = 5	12 − 9 = 3
11 − 7 = 4	12 − 4 = 8	12 − 5 = 7	12 − 6 = 6	11 − 2 = 9	12 − 8 = 4

Page 93

Subtraction Facts Through 4

Directions: Subtract.
Examples:

13 − 5 = 8	14 − 9 = 5
14 − 8 = 6	13 − 4 = 9
13 − 6 = 7	14 − 5 = 9

Directions: Subtract.

12 − 7 = 5	10 − 2 = 8	13 − 4 = 9	14 − 9 = 5	11 − 8 = 3	14 − 5 = 9
14 − 6 = 8	12 − 8 = 4	13 − 5 = 8	10 − 6 = 4	13 − 6 = 7	13 − 7 = 6
11 − 6 = 5	13 − 9 = 4	14 − 8 = 6	12 − 3 = 9	14 − 7 = 7	13 − 8 = 5

Page 94

Subtraction Facts Through 18

Directions: Subtract.
Example:

15 − 7 = 8	16 − 9 = 7
17 − 8 = 9	18 − 9 = 9

Directions: Subtract.

18 − 9 = 9	13 − 5 = 8	16 − 8 = 8	17 − 9 = 8	14 − 6 = 8	13 − 9 = 4
17 − 8 = 9	15 − 9 = 6	14 − 5 = 9	13 − 6 = 7	16 − 7 = 9	12 − 4 = 8
14 − 7 = 7	15 − 8 = 7	16 − 9 = 7	12 − 7 = 5	15 − 7 = 8	13 − 4 = 9
15 − 6 = 9	14 − 8 = 6	12 − 3 = 9	13 − 9 = 4	14 − 9 = 5	11 − 3 = 8

Page 95

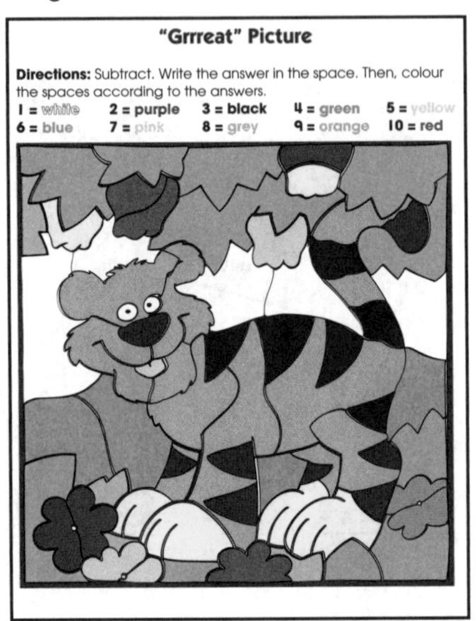

"Grrreat" Picture
Directions: Subtract. Write the answer in the space. Then, colour the spaces according to the answers.
1 = white 2 = purple 3 = black 4 = green 5 = yellow
6 = blue 7 = pink 8 = grey 9 = orange 10 = red

Page 96

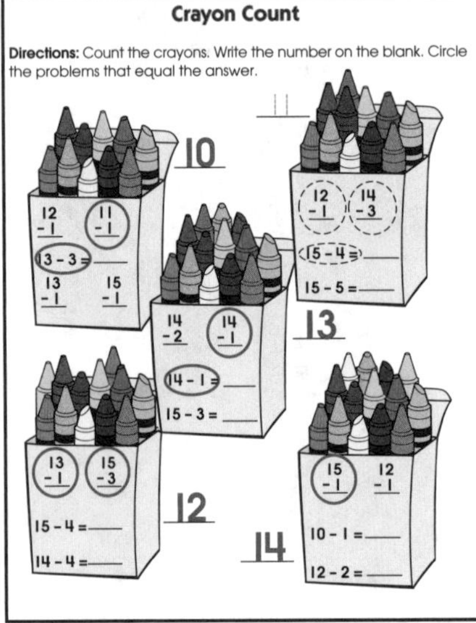

Crayon Count
Directions: Count the crayons. Write the number on the blank. Circle the problems that equal the answer.
10
11
13
12
14

Page 97

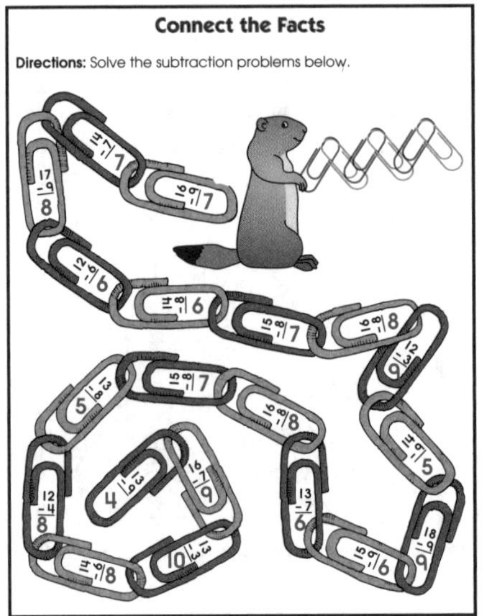

Connect the Facts
Directions: Solve the subtraction problems below.

Page 98

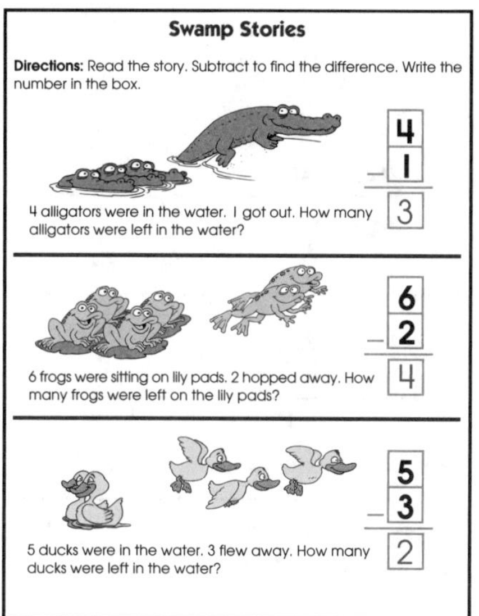

Swamp Stories

Directions: Read the story. Subtract to find the difference. Write the number in the box.

4 alligators were in the water. I got out. How many alligators were left in the water? $4 - 1 = 3$

6 frogs were sitting on lily pads. 2 hopped away. How many frogs were left on the lily pads? $6 - 2 = 4$

5 ducks were in the water. 3 flew away. How many ducks were left in the water? $5 - 3 = 2$

Page 99

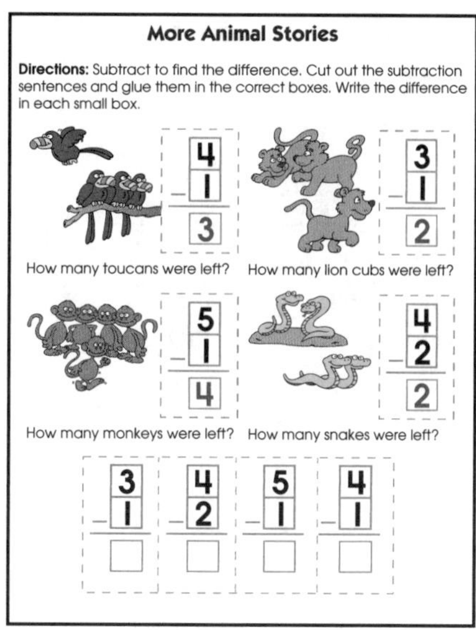

More Animal Stories

Directions: Subtract to find the difference. Cut out the subtraction sentences and glue them in the correct boxes. Write the difference in each small box.

How many toucans were left? $4 - 1 = 3$

How many lion cubs were left? $3 - 1 = 2$

How many monkeys were left? $5 - 1 = 4$

How many snakes were left? $4 - 2 = 2$

$3 - 1$ $4 - 2$ $5 - 1$ $4 - 1$

Page 101

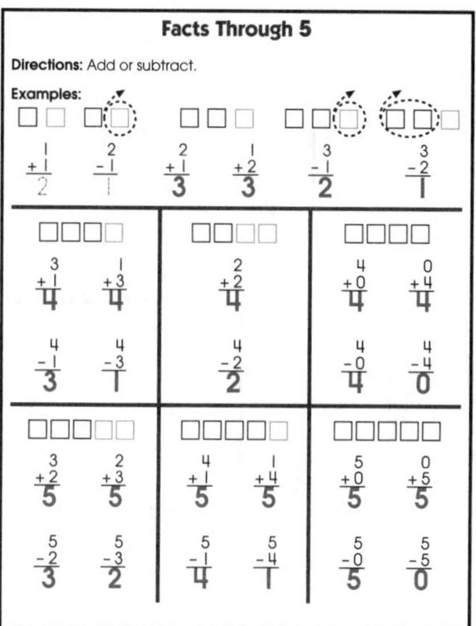

Facts Through 5

Directions: Add or subtract.

Examples:

$1 + 1 = 2$ $2 - 1 = 1$ $2 + 1 = 3$ $1 + 2 = 3$ $3 - 1 = 2$ $3 - 2 = 1$

$3 + 1 = 4$ $1 + 3 = 4$ $2 + 2 = 4$ $4 + 0 = 4$ $0 + 4 = 4$

$4 - 1 = 3$ $4 - 3 = 1$ $4 - 2 = 2$ $4 - 0 = 4$ $4 - 4 = 0$

$3 + 2 = 5$ $2 + 3 = 5$ $4 + 1 = 5$ $1 + 4 = 5$ $5 + 0 = 5$ $0 + 5 = 5$

$5 - 2 = 3$ $5 - 3 = 2$ $5 - 1 = 4$ $5 - 4 = 1$ $5 - 0 = 5$ $5 - 5 = 0$

Page 102

Facts for 6 and 7

Directions: Add or subtract.

Examples:

$5 + 1 = 6$ $1 + 5 = 6$ $6 - 1 = 5$ $6 - 5 = 1$

$3 + 3 = 6$ $6 - 3 = 3$ $4 + 2 = 6$ $2 + 4 = 6$ $6 - 2 = 4$ $6 - 4 = 2$

$4 + 3 = 7$ $3 + 4 = 7$ $5 + 2 = 7$ $2 + 5 = 7$ $6 + 1 = 7$ $1 + 6 = 7$

$7 - 3 = 4$ $7 - 4 = 3$ $7 - 2 = 5$ $7 - 5 = 2$ $7 - 1 = 6$ $7 - 6 = 1$

$3 + 3 = 6$ $5 + 2 = 7$ $6 + 0 = 6$ $7 - 7 = 0$ $7 - 4 = 3$ $6 - 2 = 4$

Page 103

Facts for 8

Directions: Add or subtract.

Examples:

$5 + 3 = 8$ $3 + 5 = 8$ $8 - 3 = 5$ $8 - 5 = 3$

$4 + 4 = 8$ $6 + 2 = 8$ $2 + 6 = 8$ $7 + 1 = 8$ $1 + 7 = 8$

$8 - 4 = 4$ $8 - 2 = 6$ $8 - 6 = 2$ $8 - 1 = 7$ $8 - 7 = 1$

$2 + 6 = 8$ $4 + 3 = 7$ $5 + 1 = 6$ $3 + 5 = 8$ $7 + 1 = 8$ $0 + 8 = 8$

$8 - 1 = 7$ $7 - 6 = 1$ $8 - 5 = 3$ $6 - 3 = 3$ $8 - 0 = 8$ $8 - 2 = 6$

Page 104

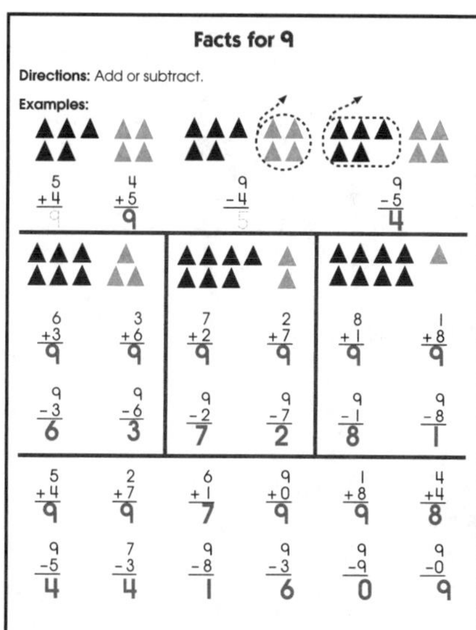

Facts for 9

Directions: Add or subtract.

Examples:

$5 + 4 = 9$ $4 + 5 = 9$ $9 - 4 = 5$ $9 - 5 = 4$

$6 + 3 = 9$ $3 + 6 = 9$ $7 + 2 = 9$ $2 + 7 = 9$ $8 + 1 = 9$ $1 + 8 = 9$

$9 - 3 = 6$ $9 - 6 = 3$ $9 - 2 = 7$ $9 - 7 = 2$ $9 - 1 = 8$ $9 - 8 = 1$

$5 + 4 = 9$ $2 + 7 = 9$ $6 + 1 = 7$ $9 + 0 = 9$ $1 + 8 = 9$ $4 + 4 = 8$

$9 - 5 = 4$ $7 - 3 = 4$ $9 - 8 = 1$ $9 - 3 = 6$ $9 - 9 = 0$ $9 - 0 = 9$

Page 105

Facts for 10

Directions: Add or subtract.

Examples:

5 + 5 = 10	6 + 4 = 10	4 + 6 = 10
10 − 5 = 5	10 − 4 = 6	10 − 6 = 4
7 + 3 = 10	3 + 7 = 10	
10 − 3 = 7	10 − 7 = 3	
8 + 2 = 10	2 + 8 = 10	
10 − 2 = 8	10 − 8 = 2	
9 + 1 = 10	1 + 9 = 10	
10 − 1 = 9	10 − 9 = 1	

4 + 6 = 10	5 + 5 = 10	9 + 1 = 10	10 − 8 = 2	10 − 3 = 7	10 − 0 = 10

Page 106

Facts Through 10

Directions: Add.

Example:

5 + 4 = 9	4 + 3 = 7	1 + 2 = 3	5 + 3 = 8	4 + 6 = 10	4 + 4 = 8
0 + 6 = 6	4 + 1 = 5	8 + 1 = 9	9 + 1 = 10	8 + 2 = 10	2 + 2 = 4
2 + 7 = 9	5 + 2 = 7	1 + 6 = 7	5 + 5 = 10	4 + 5 = 9	6 + 2 = 8

Directions: Subtract.

Example:

10 − 6 = 4	8 − 2 = 6	5 − 3 = 2	7 − 6 = 1	4 − 3 = 1	10 − 5 = 5
9 − 3 = 6	10 − 2 = 8	7 − 2 = 5	8 − 6 = 2	10 − 9 = 1	8 − 8 = 0
10 − 4 = 6	9 − 6 = 3	9 − 8 = 1	8 − 1 = 7	10 − 7 = 3	7 − 4 = 3

Page 107

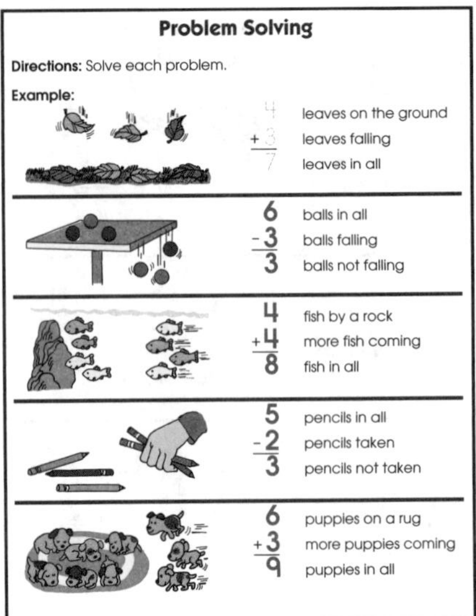

Problem Solving

Directions: Solve each problem.

Example:

4 leaves on the ground
+3 leaves falling
7 leaves in all

6 balls in all
−3 balls falling
3 balls not falling

4 fish by a rock
+4 more fish coming
8 fish in all

5 pencils in all
−2 pencils taken
3 pencils not taken

6 puppies on a rug
+3 more puppies coming
9 puppies in all

Page 108

Checkup

Directions: Add.

2 + 4 = 6	7 + 3 = 10	4 + 5 = 9	6 + 2 = 8	2 + 3 = 5	0 + 4 = 4
4 + 3 = 7	1 + 5 = 6	2 + 8 = 10	3 + 3 = 6	6 + 4 = 10	2 + 1 = 3
3 + 1 = 4	7 + 0 = 7	8 + 1 = 9	5 + 2 = 7	3 + 6 = 9	5 + 5 = 10

Directions: Subtract.

3 − 3 = 0	5 − 2 = 3	10 − 6 = 4	9 − 2 = 7	7 − 3 = 4	10 − 5 = 5
9 − 1 = 8	8 − 7 = 1	1 − 0 = 1	6 − 4 = 2	8 − 5 = 3	10 − 8 = 2
9 − 6 = 3	4 − 3 = 1	6 − 3 = 3	7 − 5 = 2	10 − 9 = 1	8 − 4 = 4

Page 109

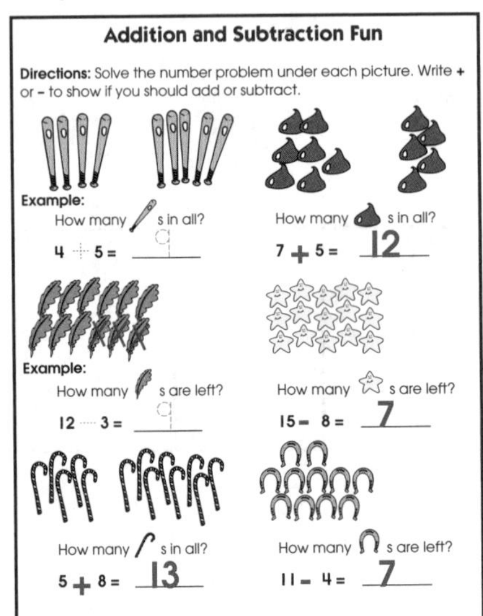

Addition and Subtraction Fun

Directions: Solve the number problem under each picture. Write + or − to show if you should add or subtract.

Example: How many s in all? 4 + 5 = 9

How many s in all? 7 + 5 = 12

Example: How many s are left? 12 − 3 = 9

How many s are left? 15 − 8 = 7

How many s in all? 5 + 8 = 13

How many s are left? 11 − 4 = 7

Page 110

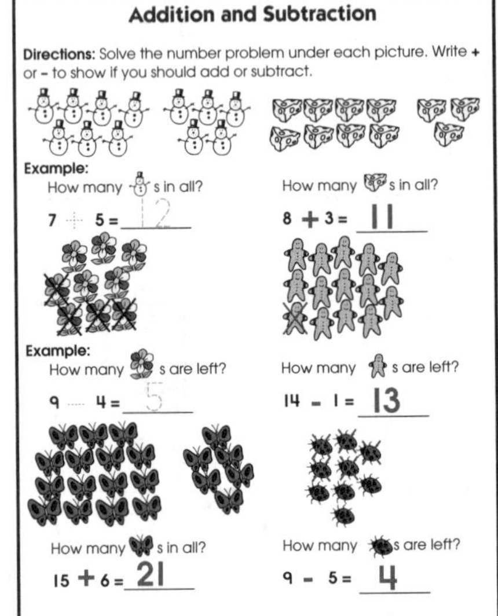

Addition and Subtraction

Directions: Solve the number problem under each picture. Write + or − to show if you should add or subtract.

Example: How many s in all? 7 + 5 = 12

How many s in all? 8 + 3 = 11

Example: How many s are left? 9 − 4 = 5

How many s are left? 14 − 1 = 13

How many s in all? 15 + 6 = 21

How many s are left? 9 − 5 = 4

Page 111

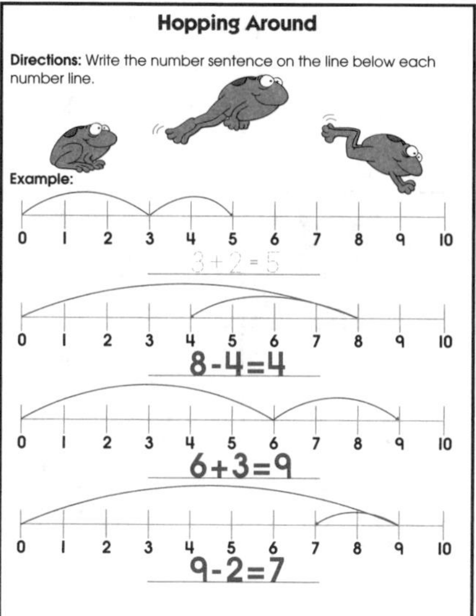
Hopping Around

Directions: Write the number sentence on the line below each number line.

Example:

0 1 2 3 4 5 6 7 8 9 10

3 + 2 = 5

8-4=4

6+3=9

9-2=7

Page 112

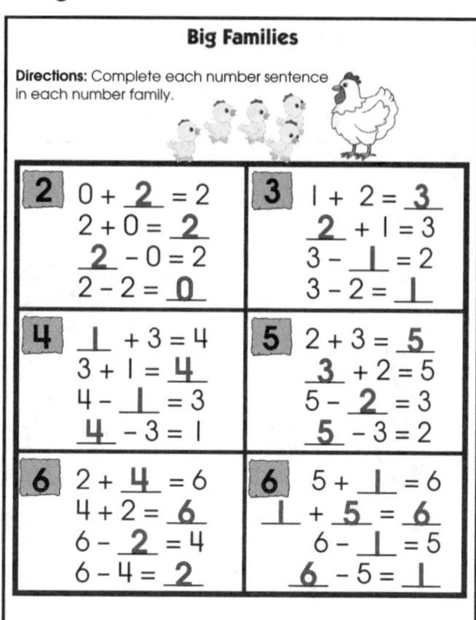
Big Families

Directions: Complete each number sentence in each number family.

2	3
0 + 2 = 2 2 + 0 = 2 2 - 0 = 2 2 - 2 = 0	1 + 2 = 3 2 + 1 = 3 3 - 1 = 2 3 - 2 = 1
4	**5**
1 + 3 = 4 3 + 1 = 4 4 - 1 = 3 4 - 3 = 1	2 + 3 = 5 3 + 2 = 5 5 - 2 = 3 5 - 3 = 2
6	**6**
2 + 4 = 6 4 + 2 = 6 6 - 2 = 4 6 - 4 = 2	5 + 1 = 6 1 + 5 = 6 6 - 1 = 5 6 - 5 = 1

Page 113

Sums and Differences

Directions: Colour two numbers in each box to show the given sum or difference.

Sum of 8

3 7 / 1 4   3 6 / 7 2   6 5 / 4 4   3 8 / 1 5

Difference of 1

6 3 / 1 5   5 9 / 10 7   8 5 / 3 2   5 2 / 4 0

Sum of 9

0 5 / 6 4   4 3 / 6 2   8 3 / 1 2   5 5 / 7 2

Difference of 2

6 9 / 1 4   4 10 / 7 5   5 8 / 1 10   0 2 / 7 3

Page 114

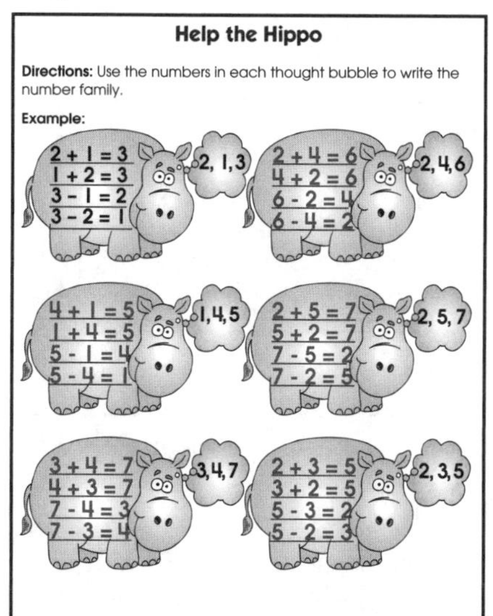
Help the Hippo

Directions: Use the numbers in each thought bubble to write the number family.

Example:

2, 1, 3: 2 + 1 = 3, 1 + 2 = 3, 3 - 1 = 2, 3 - 2 = 1

2, 4, 6: 2 + 4 = 6, 4 + 2 = 6, 6 - 2 = 4, 6 - 4 = 2

1, 4, 5: 4 + 1 = 5, 1 + 4 = 5, 5 - 1 = 4, 5 - 4 = 1

2, 5, 7: 2 + 5 = 7, 5 + 2 = 7, 7 - 5 = 2, 7 - 2 = 5

3, 4, 7: 3 + 4 = 7, 4 + 3 = 7, 7 - 4 = 3, 7 - 3 = 4

2, 3, 5: 2 + 3 = 5, 3 + 2 = 5, 5 - 3 = 2, 5 - 2 = 3

Page 115

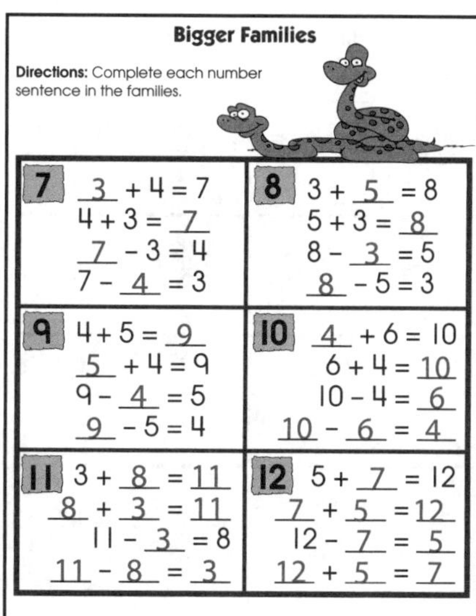
Bigger Families

Directions: Complete each number sentence in the families.

7	8
3 + 4 = 7 4 + 3 = 7 7 - 3 = 4 7 - 4 = 3	3 + 5 = 8 5 + 3 = 8 8 - 3 = 5 8 - 5 = 3
9	**10**
4 + 5 = 9 5 + 4 = 9 9 - 4 = 5 9 - 5 = 4	4 + 6 = 10 6 + 4 = 10 10 - 4 = 6 10 - 6 = 4
11	**12**
3 + 8 = 11 8 + 3 = 11 11 - 3 = 8 11 - 8 = 3	5 + 7 = 12 7 + 5 = 12 12 - 7 = 5 12 + 5 = 7

Page 116

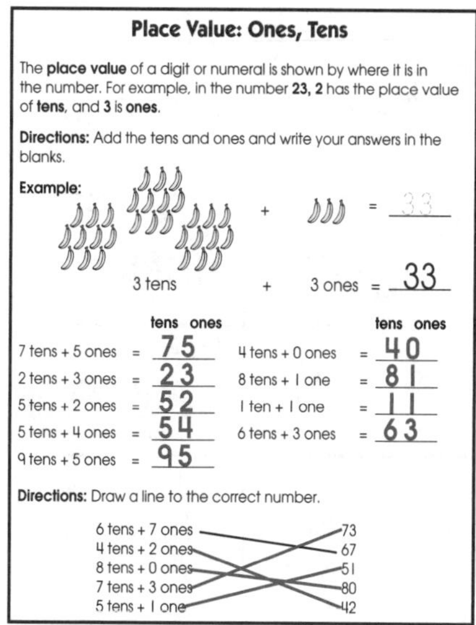
Place Value: Ones, Tens

The **place value** of a digit or numeral is shown by where it is in the number. For example, in the number **23, 2** has the place value of **tens**, and **3** is **ones**.

Directions: Add the tens and ones and write your answers in the blanks.

Example: + = 33

3 tens + 3 ones = 33

	tens ones		tens ones
7 tens + 5 ones =	75	4 tens + 0 ones =	40
2 tens + 3 ones =	23	8 tens + 1 one =	81
5 tens + 2 ones =	52	1 ten + 1 one =	11
5 tens + 4 ones =	54	6 tens + 3 ones =	63
9 tens + 5 ones =	95		

Directions: Draw a line to the correct number.

6 tens + 7 ones	73
4 tens + 2 ones	67
8 tens + 0 ones	51
7 tens + 3 ones	80
5 tens + 1 one	42

Page 117

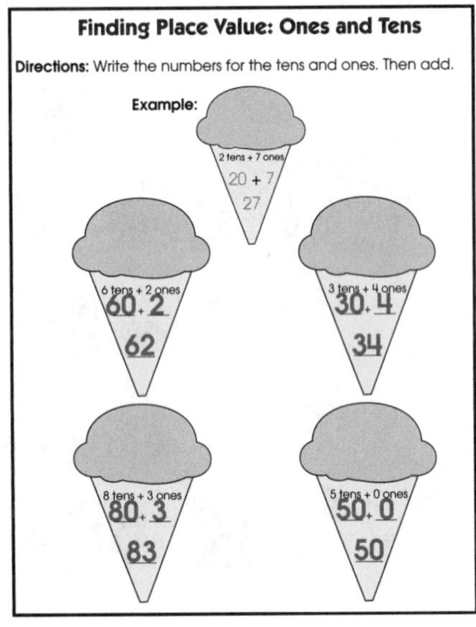

Finding Place Value: Ones and Tens

Directions: Write the numbers for the tens and ones. Then add.

Example: 2 tens + 7 ones: 20 + 7 = 27

6 tens + 2 ones: 60 + 2 = 62

3 tens + 4 ones: 30 + 4 = 34

8 tens + 3 ones: 80 + 3 = 83

5 tens + 0 ones: 50 + 0 = 50

Page 118

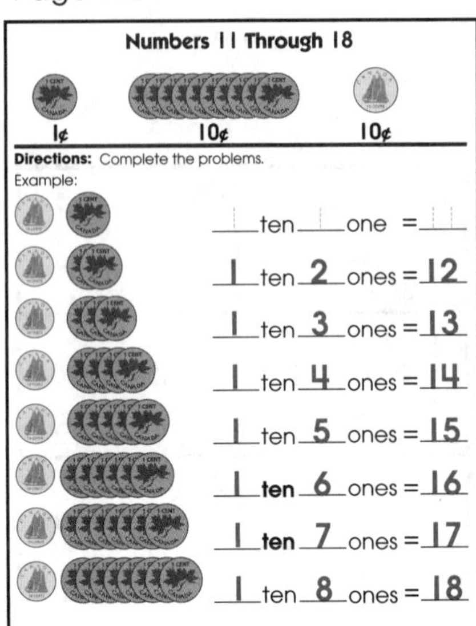

Numbers 11 Through 18

1¢ 10¢ 10¢

Directions: Complete the problems.

Example:

1 ten 1 one = 11
1 ten 2 ones = 12
1 ten 3 ones = 13
1 ten 4 ones = 14
1 ten 5 ones = 15
1 ten 6 ones = 16
1 ten 7 ones = 17
1 ten 8 ones = 18

Page 119

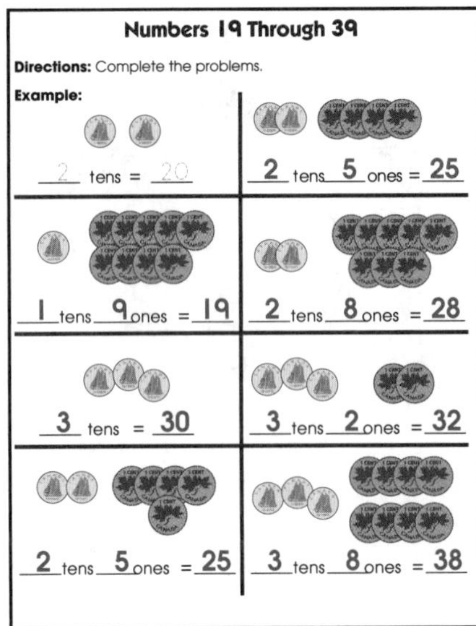

Numbers 19 Through 39

Directions: Complete the problems.

Example: 2 tens = 20

2 tens 5 ones = 25
1 tens 9 ones = 19
2 tens 8 ones = 28
3 tens = 30
3 tens 2 ones = 32
2 tens 5 ones = 25
3 tens 8 ones = 38

Page 120

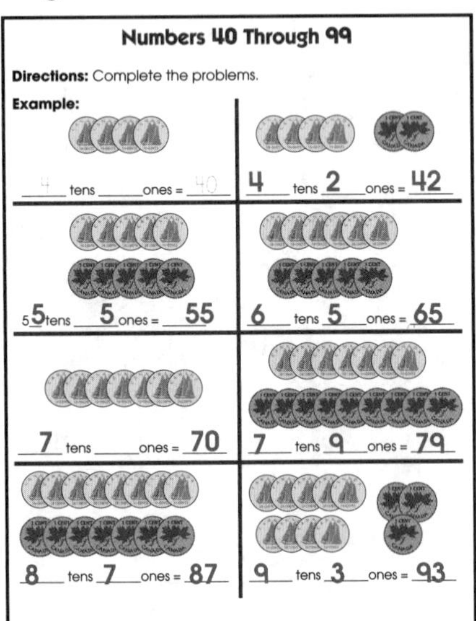

Numbers 40 Through 99

Directions: Complete the problems.

Example: 4 tens ones = 40

4 tens 2 ones = 42
5 tens 5 ones = 55
6 tens 5 ones = 65
7 tens ones = 70
7 tens 9 ones = 79
8 tens 7 ones = 87
9 tens 3 ones = 93

Page 121

Numbers 40 Through 99

Directions: Complete the problems.

Example: 4 tens 5 ones = 45

4 tens 3 ones = 43
5 tens = 50
5 tens 8 ones = 58
6 tens 6 ones = 66
7 tens 2 ones = 72
8 tens = 80
9 tens 9 ones = 99

Page 122

Numbers Through 99

Directions: Complete the problems.

Example:

4 tens 6 ones = 46
1 ten 2 ones = 12
3 tens 7 ones = 37
2 tens 4 ones = 24
9 tens = 90
6 tens = 60
5 tens 3 ones = 53
7 tens 8 ones = 78
1 ten 1 one = 11
8 tens 4 ones = 84
3 tens 5 ones = 35
4 tens 9 ones = 49
9 tens 6 ones = 96

2 tens 1 one = 21
5 tens 7 ones = 57
1 ten 9 ones = 19
8 tens 8 ones = 88
6 tens 7 ones = 67
7 tens 2 ones = 72
9 tens 5 ones = 95
4 tens 1 one = 41
3 tens 4 ones = 34
6 tens 6 ones = 66
8 tens 9 ones = 89
2 tens = 20
5 tens = 50

Page 123

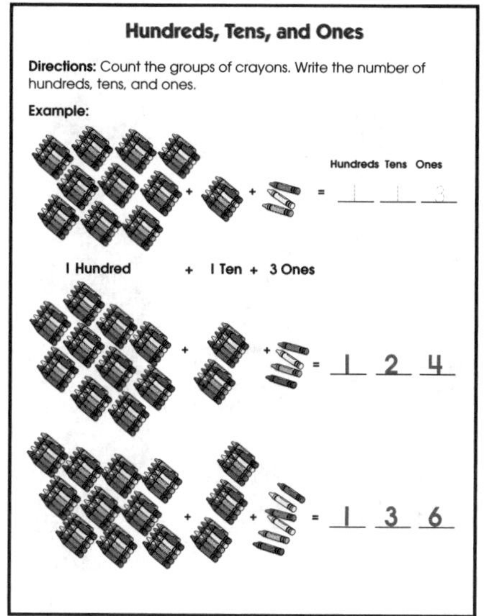
Hundreds, Tens, and Ones

Directions: Count the groups of crayons. Write the number of hundreds, tens, and ones.

Example:

Hundreds Tens Ones = 1 1 3

1 Hundred + 1 Ten + 3 Ones

= 1 2 4

= 1 3 6

Page 124

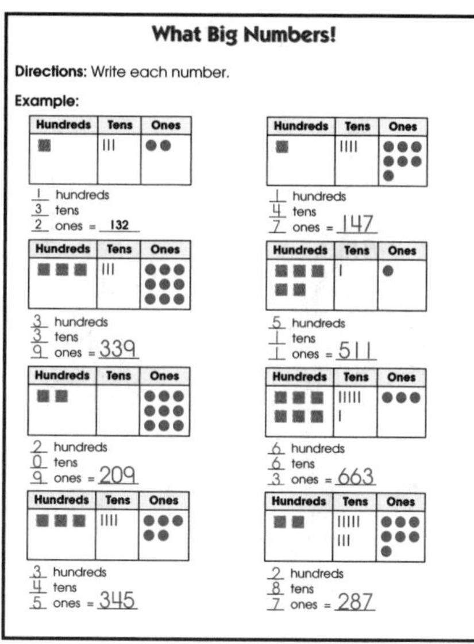
What Big Numbers!

Directions: Write each number.

Example:

1 hundreds, 3 tens, 2 ones = 132

1 hundreds, 4 tens, 7 ones = 147

3 hundreds, 3 tens, 9 ones = 339

5 hundreds, 1 tens, 1 ones = 511

2 hundreds, 0 tens, 9 ones = 209

6 hundreds, 6 tens, 3 ones = 663

3 hundreds, 4 tens, 5 ones = 345

2 hundreds, 8 tens, 7 ones = 287

Page 125

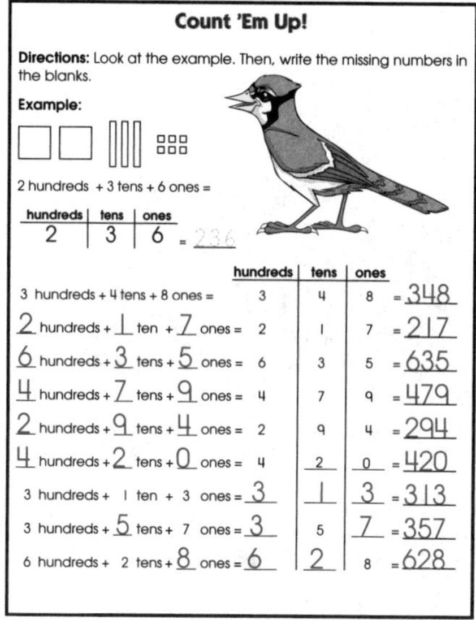
Count 'Em Up!

Directions: Look at the example. Then, write the missing numbers in the blanks.

Example:

2 hundreds + 3 tens + 6 ones =

hundreds	tens	ones	
2	3	6	= 236

	hundreds	tens	ones	
3 hundreds + 4 tens + 8 ones =	3	4	8	= 348
2 hundreds + 1 ten + 7 ones =	2	1	7	= 217
6 hundreds + 3 tens + 5 ones =	6	3	5	= 635
4 hundreds + 7 tens + 9 ones =	4	7	9	= 479
2 hundreds + 9 tens + 4 ones =	2	9	4	= 294
4 hundreds + 2 tens + 0 ones =	4	2	0	= 420
3 hundreds + 1 ten + 3 ones =	3	1	3	= 313
3 hundreds + 5 tens + 7 ones =	3	5	7	= 357
6 hundreds + 2 tens + 8 ones =	6	2	8	= 628

Page 126

Up, Up, and Away

Directions: Use the code to colour the balloons. If the answer has:

7 hundreds, colour it **red.**
6 hundreds, colour it **green.**
5 hundreds, colour it **orange.**
8 tens, colour it **yellow.**
3 ones, colour it **brown.**

Page 127

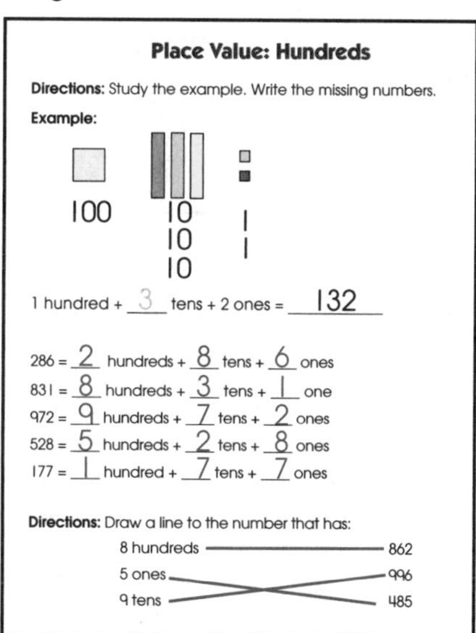
Place Value: Hundreds

Directions: Study the example. Write the missing numbers.

Example:

100 10 10 10 1 1

1 hundred + 3 tens + 2 ones = 132

286 = 2 hundreds + 8 tens + 6 ones
831 = 8 hundreds + 3 tens + 1 one
972 = 9 hundreds + 7 tens + 2 ones
528 = 5 hundreds + 2 tens + 8 ones
177 = 1 hundred + 7 tens + 7 ones

Directions: Draw a line to the number that has:

8 hundreds — 862
5 ones — 485
9 tens — 996

Page 128

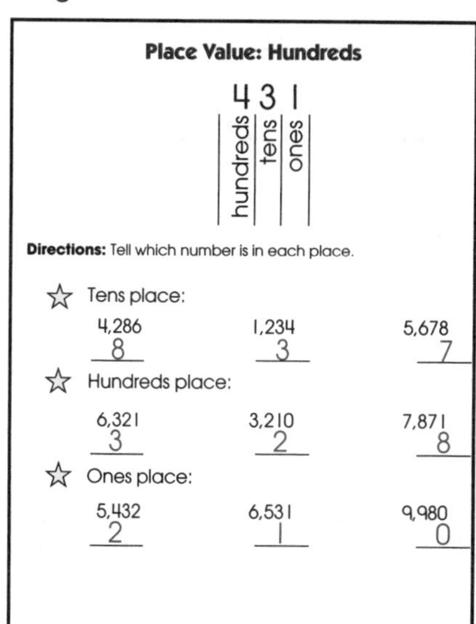
Place Value: Hundreds

4 3 1
hundreds tens ones

Directions: Tell which number is in each place.

☆ Tens place:

4,286 — 8
1,234 — 3
5,678 — 7

☆ Hundreds place:

6,321 — 3
3,210 — 2
7,871 — 8

☆ Ones place:

5,432 — 2
6,531 — 1
9,980 — 0

Page 129

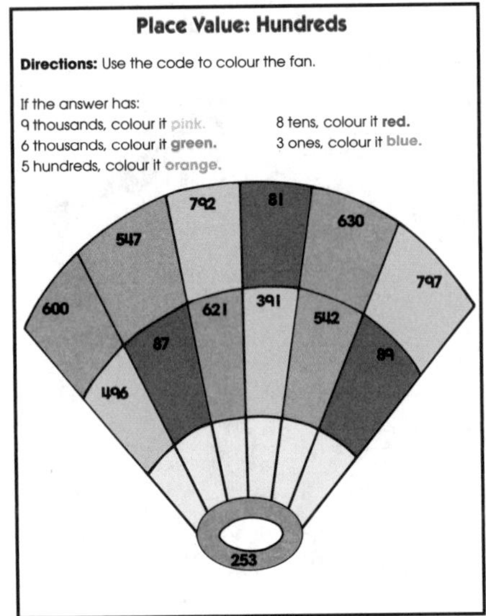

Place Value: Hundreds

Directions: Use the code to colour the fan.

If the answer has:
9 thousands, colour it pink.
6 thousands, colour it green.
5 hundreds, colour it orange.
8 tens, colour it red.
3 ones, colour it blue.

Page 130

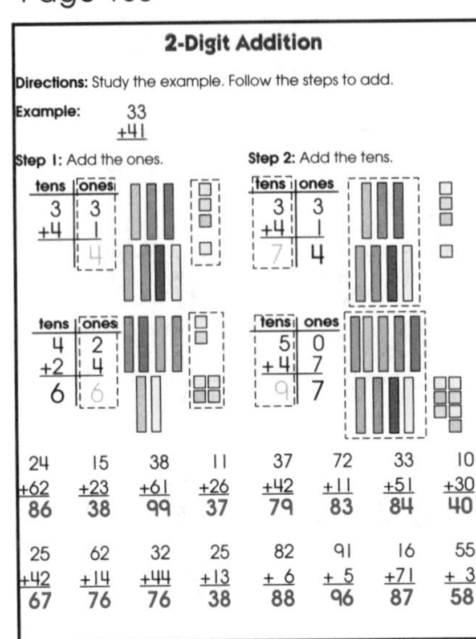

2-Digit Addition

Directions: Study the example. Follow the steps to add.

Example: 33 + 41

Step 1: Add the ones. **Step 2:** Add the tens.

tens	ones
3	3
+4	1
	4

tens	ones
3	3
+4	1
7	4

tens	ones
4	2
+2	4
6	6

tens	ones
5	0
+4	7
9	7

24 + 62 = 86; 15 + 23 = 38; 38 + 61 = 99; 11 + 26 = 37; 37 + 42 = 79; 72 + 11 = 83; 33 + 51 = 84; 10 + 30 = 40

25 + 42 = 67; 62 + 14 = 76; 32 + 44 = 76; 25 + 13 = 38; 82 + 6 = 88; 91 + 5 = 96; 16 + 71 = 87; 55 + 3 = 58

Page 131

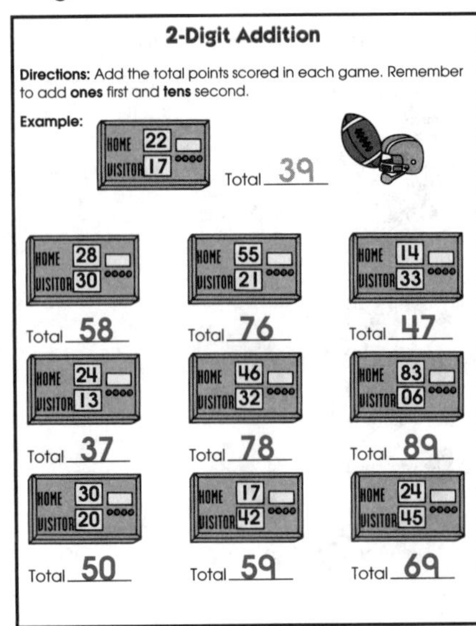

2-Digit Addition

Directions: Add the total points scored in each game. Remember to add **ones** first and **tens** second.

Example: HOME 22, VISITOR 17 — Total 39

HOME 28, VISITOR 30 — Total 58
HOME 55, VISITOR 21 — Total 76
HOME 14, VISITOR 33 — Total 47
HOME 24, VISITOR 13 — Total 37
HOME 46, VISITOR 32 — Total 78
HOME 83, VISITOR 06 — Total 89
HOME 30, VISITOR 20 — Total 50
HOME 17, VISITOR 42 — Total 59
HOME 24, VISITOR 45 — Total 69

Page 132

Adding Tens

3 tens + 4 tens = 7 tens	30 + 40 = 70	6 tens + 2 tens = 8 tens	60 + 20 = 80

Directions: Add.

2 tens + 4 tens = 6 tens	20 + 40 = 60	6 tens + 2 tens = 8 tens	60 + 20 = 80

20 + 20 = 40	10 + 50 = 60	40 + 20 = 60	30 + 40 = 70	50 + 30 = 80
30 + 20 = 50	60 + 10 = 70	20 + 50 = 70	70 + 10 = 80	10 + 10 = 20
10 + 20 = 30	40 + 40 = 80	80 + 10 = 90	60 + 30 = 90	20 + 60 = 80
70 + 20 = 90	40 + 10 = 50	30 + 10 = 40	50 + 40 = 90	30 + 30 = 60

Page 133

Problem Solving

Directions: Solve each problem.

Example:

There are 20 men in the plane.
30 women get in the plane.
How many men and women are in the plane? 20 + 30 = 50

Jill buys 10 apples.
Carol buys 20 apples.
How many apples in all? 10 + 20 = 30

There are 30 ears of corn in one pile.
There are 50 ears of corn in another pile.
How many ears of corn in all? 30 + 50 = 80

Henry cut 40 pieces of wood.
Art cut 20 pieces of wood.
How many pieces of wood were cut? 40 + 20 = 60

Adolpho had 60 baseball cards.
Maria had 30 baseball cards.
How many baseball cards in all? 60 + 30 = 90

Page 134

Picture This

Directions: Add the ones, then the tens in each problem. Then, write the sum in the blank.

Example:
2 tens and 6 ones + 1 ten and 3 ones = 3 tens and 9 ones = 39

1 ten and 4 ones + 3 tens and 3 ones = 3 tens and 7 ones = 47
2 tens and 5 ones + 2 tens and 3 ones = 4 tens and 8 ones = 48
1 ten and 6 ones + 5 tens and 1 one = 6 tens and 7 ones = 67
1 ten and 3 ones + 1 ten and 1 one = 2 tens and 4 ones = 24
2 tens and 5 ones + 2 tens and 0 ones = 4 tens and 5 ones = 45
1 ten and 5 ones + 2 tens and 4 ones = 3 tens and 9 ones = 39
7 tens and 6 ones + 2 tens and 2 ones = 9 tens and 8 ones = 98

Page 135

Digital Addition

Add the ones.

tens	ones
2	4
+3	2
	6

Then, add the tens.

tens	ones
2	4
+3	2
5	6

Directions: Solve the addition problems below.

17 + 21 = 38; 34 + 52 = 86; 5 + 62 = 67; 6 + 52 = 58

20 + 40 = 60; 51 + 8 = 59; 72 + 17 = 89; 47 + 21 = 68

25 + 62 = 87; 42 + 24 = 66; 83 + 14 = 97; 32 + 25 = 57

Page 136

Circus Fun

Directions: Add to solve the problems. Add the ones first. Then, add the tens.

25 + 14 = 39; 53 + 32 = 85; 71 + 28 = 99

44 + 32 = 76; 51 + 37 = 88; 26 + 52 = 78

26 + 42 = 68; 37 + 51 = 88; 19 + 30 = 49

Page 137

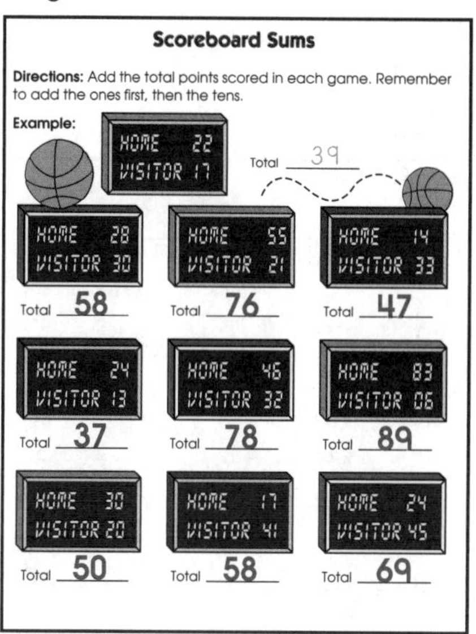

Scoreboard Sums

Directions: Add the total points scored in each game. Remember to add the ones first, then the tens.

Example: HOME 22 VISITOR 17 Total 39

HOME 28 VISITOR 30 Total 58; HOME 55 VISITOR 21 Total 76; HOME 14 VISITOR 33 Total 47

HOME 24 VISITOR 13 Total 37; HOME 46 VISITOR 32 Total 78; HOME 83 VISITOR 06 Total 89

HOME 30 VISITOR 20 Total 50; HOME 17 VISITOR 41 Total 58; HOME 24 VISITOR 45 Total 69

Page 138

Raccoon Roundup

Directions: Solve the addition problems. Write your answers inside the ropes.

26 + 43 = 69; 43 + 31 = 74

34 + 10 = 44; 48 + 20 = 68

57 + 20 = 77; 52 + 34 = 86

43 + 55 = 98; 67 + 22 = 89

Page 139

Anchors Away

Directions: Solve the addition problems. Use the code to find the answer to this riddle:

What did the pirate have to do before every trip out to sea?

48	36	58	96	69	75	89	29
O	H	G	B	T	E	N	A

Example:

42 + 16 = 58 G; 34 + 41 = 75 E; 60 + 9 = 69 T

17 + 31 = 48 O; 55 + 34 = 89 N

26 + 43 = 69 T; 14 + 22 = 36 H; 52 + 23 = 75 E

83 + 13 = 96 B; 24 + 24 = 48 O; 5 + 24 = 29 A; 52 + 17 = 69 T!

Page 140

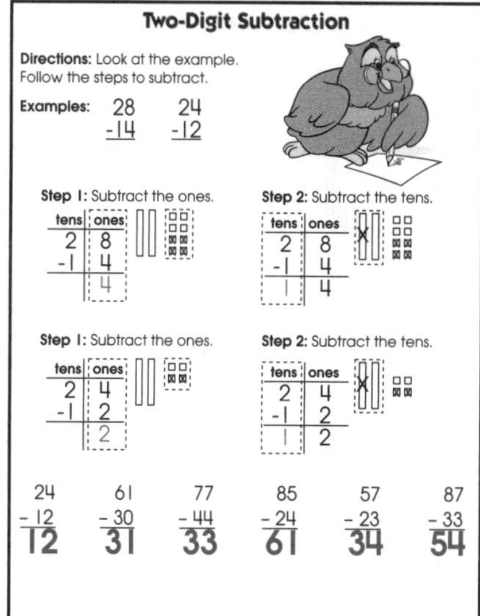

Two-Digit Subtraction

Directions: Look at the example. Follow the steps to subtract.

Examples: 28 − 14; 24 − 12

Step 1: Subtract the ones. 28 − 14: ones 4

Step 2: Subtract the tens. 28 − 14 = 14

Step 1: Subtract the ones. 24 − 12: ones 2

Step 2: Subtract the tens. 24 − 12 = 12

24 − 12 = 12; 61 − 30 = 31; 77 − 44 = 33; 85 − 24 = 61; 57 − 23 = 34; 87 − 33 = 54

Page 141

Subtracting Tens

Examples:

6 tens	60	8 tens	80
- 3 tens	- 30	- 2 tens	- 20
3 tens	30	6 tens	60

Directions: Subtract.

7 tens - 5 tens = 2 tens	70 - 50 = 20		4 tens - 2 tens = 2 tens	40 - 20 = 20
50 - 30 = 20	60 - 20 = 40	20 - 10 = 10	80 - 40 = 40	40 - 40 = 0
90 - 50 = 40	80 - 20 = 60	70 - 30 = 40	30 - 20 = 10	50 - 40 = 10
60 - 30 = 30	40 - 10 = 30	80 - 30 = 50	90 - 20 = 70	70 - 50 = 20
80 - 70 = 10	90 - 80 = 10	70 - 40 = 30	60 - 40 = 20	50 - 20 = 30

Page 142

Problem Solving

Directions: Solve each problem.

Example:

Mr. Cobb counts 70 pencils. He sells 30 pencils. How many pencils are left? 70 - 30 = 40

Keith has 20 hammers. Leon has 10 hammers. How many more hammers does Keith have than Leon? 20 - 10 = 10

Tina plants 60 flowers. Melody plants 30 flowers. How many more flowers did Tina plant than Melody? 60 - 30 = 30

Link has 80 balls. Jessica has 50 balls. How many more balls does Link have than Jessica? 80 - 50 = 30

Maranda hits 40 baseballs. Harold hits 30 baseballs. How many more baseballs does Maranda hit than Harold? 40 - 30 = 10

Page 143

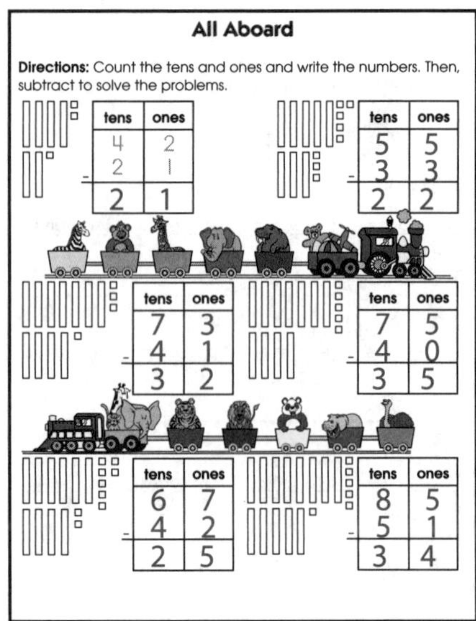

All Aboard

Directions: Count the tens and ones and write the numbers. Then, subtract to solve the problems.

tens	ones
4	2
- 2	1
2	1

tens	ones
5	5
- 3	3
2	2

tens	ones
7	3
- 4	1
3	2

tens	ones
7	5
- 4	0
3	5

tens	ones
6	7
- 4	2
2	5

tens	ones
8	5
- 5	1
3	4

Page 144

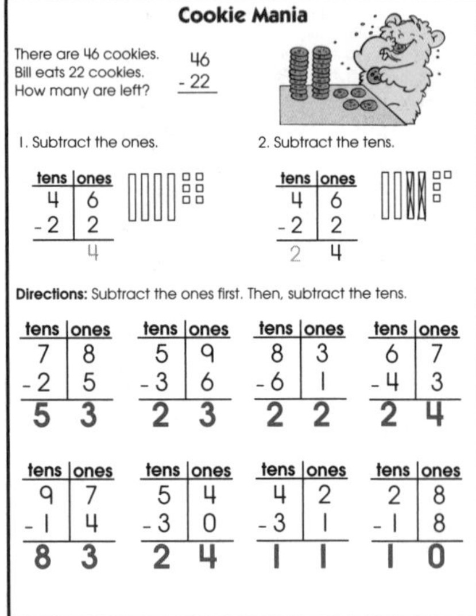

Cookie Mania

There are 46 cookies. Bill eats 22 cookies. How many are left? 46 - 22

1. Subtract the ones.

tens	ones
4	6
- 2	2
	4

2. Subtract the tens.

tens	ones
4	6
- 2	2
2	4

Directions: Subtract the ones first. Then, subtract the tens.

tens	ones	tens	ones	tens	ones	tens	ones
7	8	5	9	8	3	6	7
- 2	5	- 3	6	- 6	1	- 4	3
5	3	2	3	2	2	2	4

tens	ones	tens	ones	tens	ones	tens	ones
9	7	5	4	4	2	2	8
- 1	4	- 3	0	- 3	1	- 1	8
8	3	2	4	1	1	1	0

Page 145

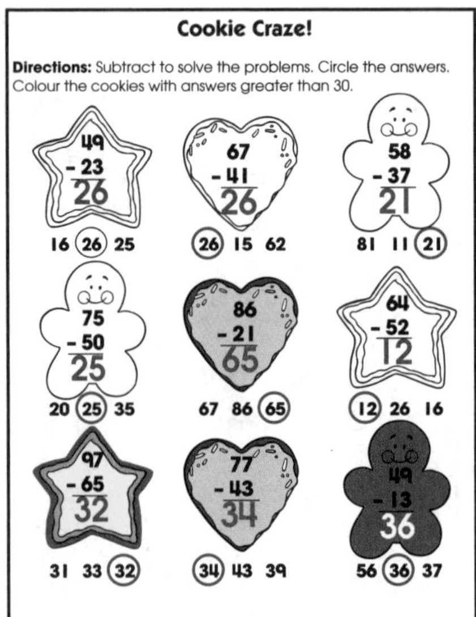

Cookie Craze!

Directions: Subtract to solve the problems. Circle the answers. Colour the cookies with answers greater than 30.

49 - 23 = 26 (16 (26) 25)

67 - 41 = 26 ((26) 15 62)

58 - 37 = 21 (81 11 (21))

75 - 50 = 25 (20 (25) 35)

86 - 21 = 65 (67 86 (65))

64 - 52 = 12 ((12) 26 16)

97 - 65 = 32 (31 33 (32))

77 - 43 = 34 ((34) 43 39)

49 - 13 = 36 (56 (36) 37)

Page 146

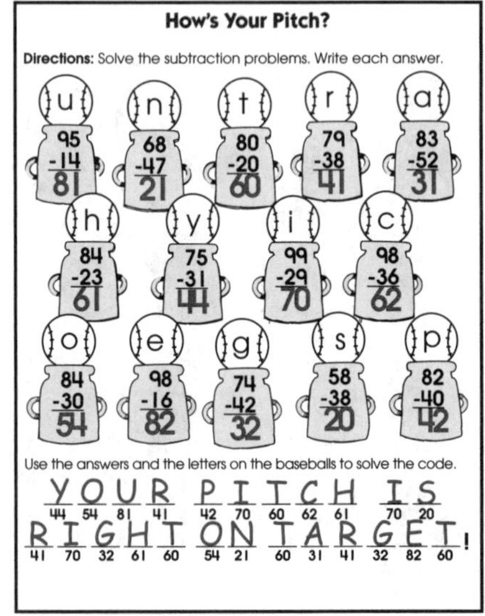

How's Your Pitch?

Directions: Solve the subtraction problems. Write each answer.

u: 95 - 14 = 81

n: 68 - 47 = 21

t: 80 - 20 = 60

r: 79 - 38 = 41

a: 83 - 52 = 31

h: 84 - 23 = 61

y: 75 - 31 = 44

i: 99 - 29 = 70

c: 98 - 36 = 62

o: 84 - 30 = 54

e: 98 - 16 = 82

g: 74 - 42 = 32

s: 58 - 38 = 20

p: 82 - 40 = 42

Use the answers and the letters on the baseballs to solve the code.

YOUR PITCH IS RIGHT ON TARGET!

44 54 81 41 42 70 60 62 61 70 20 41 70 32 61 60 54 21 60 31 41 32 82 60

Page 147

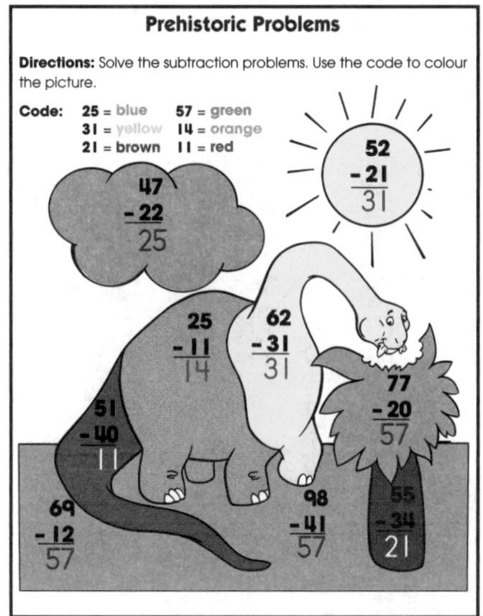

Prehistoric Problems

Directions: Solve the subtraction problems. Use the code to colour the picture.

Code: **25** = blue **31** = yellow **21** = brown **57** = green **14** = orange **11** = red

Page 148

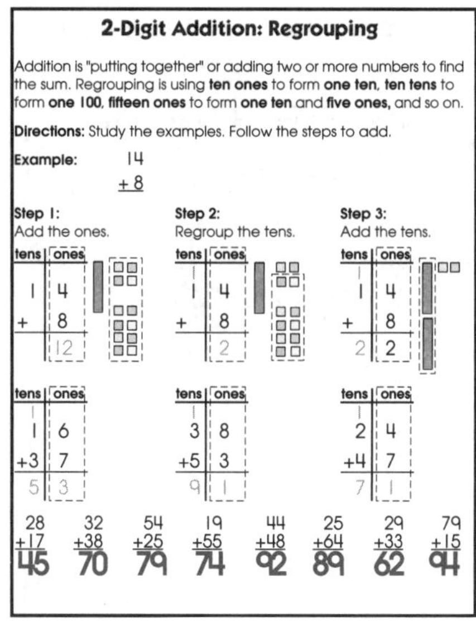

2-Digit Addition: Regrouping

Addition is "putting together" or adding two or more numbers to find the sum. Regrouping is using **ten ones** to form **one ten**, **ten tens** to form **one 100**, **fifteen ones** to form **one ten** and **five ones**, and so on.

Directions: Study the examples. Follow the steps to add.

Example: 14 + 8

Step 1: Add the ones. **Step 2:** Regroup the tens. **Step 3:** Add the tens.

28 + 17 = 45 32 + 38 = 70 54 + 25 = 79 19 + 55 = 74 44 + 48 = 92 25 + 64 = 89 29 + 33 = 62 79 + 15 = 94

Page 149

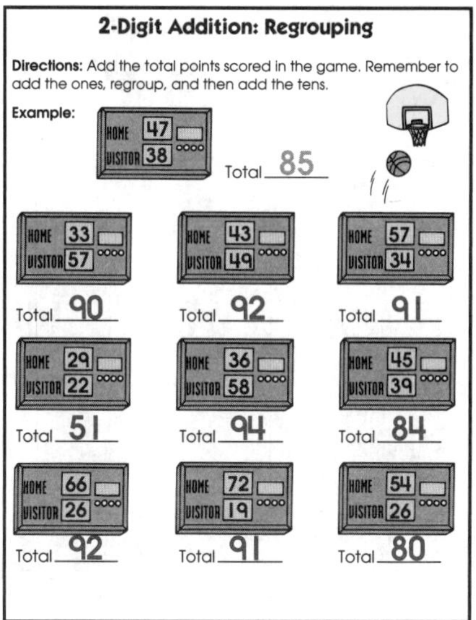

2-Digit Addition: Regrouping

Directions: Add the total points scored in the game. Remember to add the ones, regroup, and then add the tens.

Example: HOME 47 VISITOR 38 Total 85

Page 150

2-Digit Addition

Directions: Add the ones. Rename 15 as 10 + 5. Add the tens.

56 + 29: 6 + 9 = 15 or 10 + 5 → 56 + 29 = 85

Directions: Add the ones. Rename 12 as 10 + 2. Add the tens.

47 + 35: 7 + 5 = 12 or 10 + 2 → 47 + 35 = 82

Directions: Add.

Examples:

45 + 28 = 73	13 + 19 = 32	48 + 35 = 83	69 + 18 = 87	54 + 39 = 93
44 + 17 = 61	37 + 18 = 55	28 + 36 = 64	73 + 18 = 91	66 + 29 = 95
52 + 39 = 91	38 + 47 = 85	64 + 18 = 82	29 + 45 = 74	75 + 17 = 92

Page 151

2-Digit Addition

Directions: Add the ones. Rename 11 as 10 + 1. Add the tens.

38 + 43: 8 + 3 = 11 or 10 + 1 → 38 + 43 = 81

Directions: Add.

Example:

17 + 34 = 51	26 + 47 = 73	47 + 35 = 82	68 + 24 = 92	37 + 28 = 65
29 + 48 = 77	58 + 27 = 85	69 + 17 = 86	78 + 13 = 91	19 + 44 = 63
55 + 28 = 83	27 + 35 = 62	39 + 52 = 91	57 + 27 = 84	38 + 36 = 74
49 + 43 = 92	65 + 18 = 83	23 + 18 = 41	64 + 18 = 82	46 + 39 = 85
54 + 27 = 81	38 + 44 = 82	66 + 26 = 92	28 + 34 = 62	19 + 56 = 75

Page 152

Problem Solving

Directions: Solve each problem.

Example:

16 boys ride their bikes to school.
18 girls ride their bikes to school.
How many bikes are ridden to school? 16 + 18 = 34

Dad reads 26 pages.
Mike reads 37 pages.
How many pages did Dad and Mike read? 26 + 37 = 63

Tiffany counts 46 stars.
Mike counts 39 stars.
How many stars did they count? 46 + 39 = 85

Mom has 29 golf balls.
Dad has 43 golf balls.
How many golf balls do they have? 29 + 43 = 72

Vicki ran in 26 races.
Kay ran in 14 races.
How many races did they run? 26 + 14 = 40

Page 153

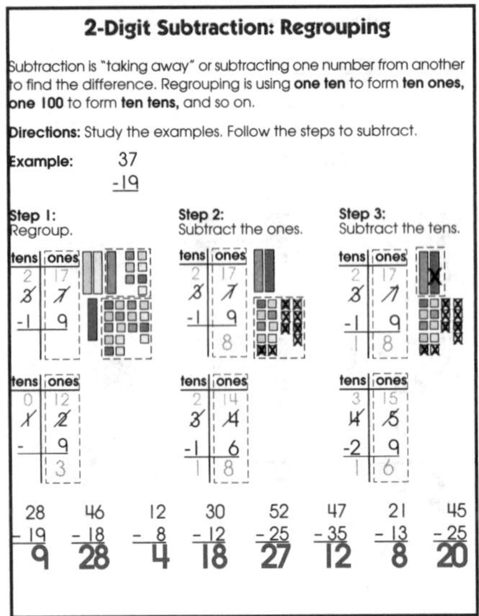

2-Digit Subtraction: Regrouping

Subtraction is "taking away" or subtracting one number from another to find the difference. Regrouping is using **one ten** to form **ten ones, one 100** to form **ten tens,** and so on.

Directions: Study the examples. Follow the steps to subtract.

Example: 37 − 19

Step 1: Regroup.
Step 2: Subtract the ones.
Step 3: Subtract the tens.

28 − 19	46 − 18	12 − 8	30 − 12	52 − 25	47 − 35	21 − 13	45 − 25
9	28	4	18	27	12	8	20

Page 154

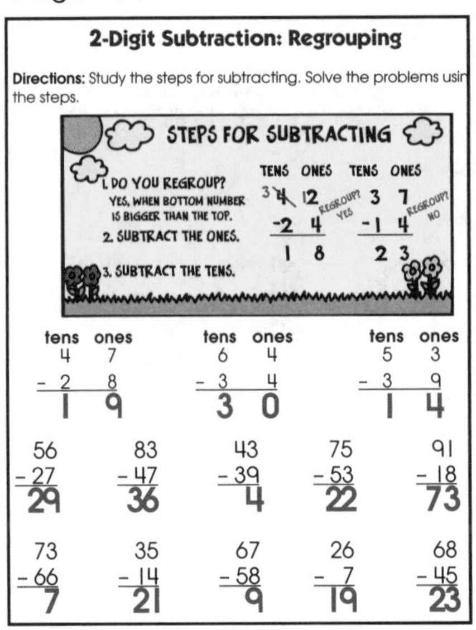

2-Digit Subtraction: Regrouping

Directions: Study the steps for subtracting. Solve the problems using the steps.

47 − 28	64 − 34	53 − 39		
19	30	14		
56 − 27	83 − 47	43 − 39	75 − 53	91 − 18
29	36	4	22	73
73 − 66	35 − 14	67 − 58	26 − 7	68 − 45
7	21	9	19	23

Page 156

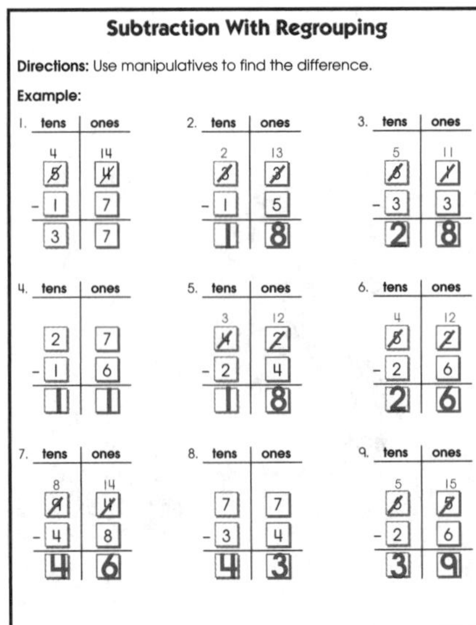

Subtraction With Regrouping

Directions: Use manipulatives to find the difference.

Example:

1. 54 − 17	2. 33 − 15	3. 61 − 33
37	18	28
4. 27 − 16	5. 42 − 24	6. 52 − 26
11	18	26
7. 94 − 48	8. 77 − 34	9. 65 − 26
46	43	39

Page 157

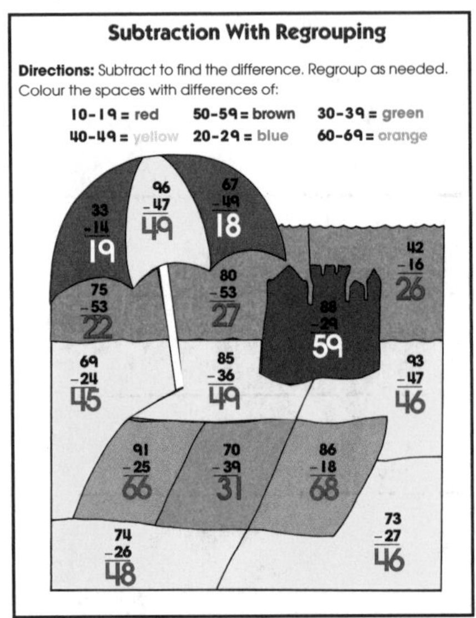

Subtraction With Regrouping

Directions: Subtract to find the difference. Regroup as needed. Colour the spaces with differences of:

10-19 = red **50-59** = brown **30-39** = green
40-49 = yellow **20-29** = blue **60-69** = orange

Page 158

2-Digit Subtraction

Directions: Rename 53 as 4 tens and 13 ones. → Subtract the ones. → Subtract the tens.

53 − 26 → 4 tens 13 ones − 26 → 7 → 27

Rename 45 as 3 tens and 15 ones.

45 − 18 → 3 tens 15 ones − 18 → 7 → 27

Directions: Subtract.

Examples:

63 − 28	74 − 39	47 − 28	52 − 26	64 − 36
35	35	19	26	28
84 − 47	93 − 56	71 − 23	26 − 18	67 − 48
37	37	48	8	19
44 − 28	53 − 37	82 − 46	94 − 66	55 − 39
16	16	36	28	16
86 − 58	34 − 18	54 − 29	73 − 59	86 − 69
28	16	25	14	17

Page 159

2-Digit Subtraction

Directions: Rename 73 as 6 tens and 13 ones. → Subtract the ones. → Subtract the tens.

73 − 48 → 6 tens 13 ones − 48 → 5 → 25

Directions: Subtract.

Example:

63 − 48	83 − 45	74 − 29	94 − 48	62 − 25
15	38	45	46	37
45 − 27	33 − 24	24 − 8	86 − 37	72 − 48
18	9	16	49	24
36 − 17	26 − 18	43 − 19	63 − 48	93 − 18
19	8	24	15	75
82 − 26	73 − 28	95 − 69	57 − 38	41 − 25
56	45	26	19	16
54 − 18	61 − 34	91 − 37	81 − 44	32 − 15
36	27	54	37	17

Page 160

Problem Solving

Directions: Solve each problem.

Example:

Dad cooks 23 potatoes.
He uses 19 potatoes in the potato salad.
How many potatoes are left?

23 − 19 = 4

Susan draws 32 butterflies.
She coloured 15 of them brown.
How many butterflies does she have left to colour?

32 − 15 = 17

A book has 66 pages.
Pedro reads 39 pages.
How many pages are left to read?

66 − 39 = 27

Jerry picks up 34 sea shells.
He puts 15 of them in a box.
How many does he have left?

34 − 15 = 19

Beth buys 72 sheets of paper.
She uses 44 sheets for her school work.
How many sheets of paper are left?

72 − 44 = 28

Page 161

Addition and Subtraction Review

Directions: Add.

4 + 9 = 13 | 8 + 6 = 14 | 9 + 8 = 17 | 7 + 6 = 13 | 5 + 7 = 12 | 6 + 5 = 11

9 + 6 = 15 | 5 + 8 = 13 | 7 + 4 = 11 | 9 + 9 = 18 | 8 + 7 = 15 | 7 + 9 = 16

30 + 40 = 70 | 20 + 30 = 50 | 45 + 23 = 68 | 52 + 23 = 75 | 60 + 25 = 85 | 83 + 15 = 98

Directions: Subtract.

16 − 7 = 9 | 15 − 9 = 6 | 13 − 4 = 9 | 12 − 7 = 5 | 11 − 9 = 2 | 17 − 8 = 9

18 − 9 = 9 | 17 − 9 = 8 | 16 − 8 = 8 | 15 − 8 = 7 | 14 − 7 = 7 | 16 − 9 = 7

40 − 30 = 10 | 60 − 10 = 50 | 85 − 23 = 62 | 73 − 41 = 32 | 96 − 43 = 53 | 54 − 44 = 10

Page 162

Addition and Subtraction Review

Directions: Add.

4 + 8 = 12 | 9 + 2 = 11 | 5 + 9 = 14 | 6 + 6 = 12 | 7 + 5 = 12 | 9 + 4 = 13

8 + 8 = 16 | 7 + 6 = 13 | 3 + 9 = 12 | 7 + 7 = 14 | 6 + 9 = 15 | 6 + 5 = 11

40 + 20 = 60 | 50 + 30 = 80 | 75 + 20 = 95 | 66 + 31 = 97 | 47 + 51 = 98 | 34 + 23 = 57

Directions: Subtract.

17 − 9 = 8 | 15 − 6 = 9 | 12 − 3 = 9 | 13 − 7 = 6 | 14 − 6 = 8 | 16 − 8 = 8

15 − 7 = 8 | 14 − 9 = 5 | 13 − 6 = 7 | 15 − 7 = 8 | 12 − 9 = 3 | 11 − 8 = 3

30 − 10 = 20 | 50 − 30 = 20 | 65 − 30 = 35 | 87 − 34 = 53 | 75 − 23 = 52 | 66 − 43 = 23

Page 163

Review: 2-Digit Addition

Directions: Add the ones. Rename 12 as 10 + 2. Add the tens.

64 + 28 → 4 + 8 = 12 or 10 + 2 → 64 + 28 = …2 → 64 + 28 = 92

Directions: Add.

Example:

28 + 19 = 47 | 34 + 49 = 83 | 25 + 16 = 41 | 46 + 29 = 75 | 54 + 39 = 93

16 + 39 = 55 | 64 + 28 = 92 | 58 + 24 = 82 | 39 + 17 = 56 | 34 + 19 = 53

57 + 39 = 96 | 14 + 48 = 62 | 37 + 39 = 76 | 61 + 19 = 80 | 29 + 44 = 73

17 + 35 = 52 | 39 + 14 = 53 | 44 + 37 = 81 | 25 + 49 = 74 | 18 + 18 = 36

26 + 48 = 74 | 39 + 27 = 66 | 14 + 27 = 41 | 65 + 25 = 90 | 59 + 18 = 77

Page 164

Review: 2-Digit Addition

Directions: Add.

36 + 55 = 91 | 14 + 28 = 42 | 57 + 38 = 95 | 44 + 48 = 92 | 33 + 29 = 62

23 + 18 = 41 | 27 + 27 = 54 | 68 + 25 = 93 | 23 + 19 = 42 | 42 + 19 = 61

56 + 28 = 84 | 49 + 27 = 76 | 38 + 49 = 87 | 36 + 18 = 54 | 49 + 24 = 73

18 + 54 = 72 | 51 + 39 = 90 | 74 + 17 = 91 | 35 + 28 = 63 | 52 + 19 = 71

48 + 26 = 74 | 25 + 28 = 53 | 39 + 33 = 72 | 29 + 44 = 73 | 54 + 27 = 81

Page 165

Problem Solving

Directions: Solve each problem.

Example:

Simon sees 36 birds flying.
Julie sees 28 birds flying.
How many birds do they see flying?

36 + 28 = 64

Brandon ran the race in 35 seconds.
Ryan ran the race in 28 seconds.
How many seconds did they run?

35 + 28 = 63

Tom has 63 nickels.
Connie has 29 nickels.
How many nickels do they have?

63 + 29 = 92

Pam sees 48 monkeys at the zoo.
Brenda sees 35 different monkeys.
How many monkeys did they see?

48 + 35 = 83

There are 29 cows in one pen.
There are 47 cows in the other pen.
How many cows in all?

29 + 47 = 76

Page 166

Keep on Truckin'
Directions: Write each sum. Connect the sums of 83 to make a road for the truck.
17 +66 83
48 +26 74
42 +19 61
28 +38 66
64 +19 83
26 +57 83
58 +25 83
17 +75 92
65 +29 94
37 +39 76
48 +35 83
58 +37 95
65 +16 81
38 +25 63
39 +59 98
59 +27 86
55 +28 83
39 +44 83

Page 167

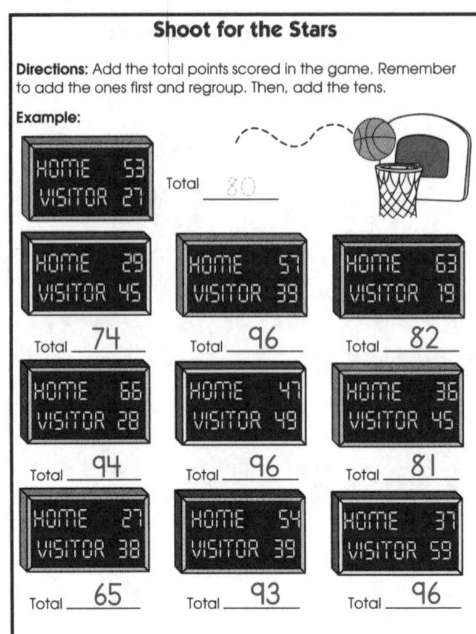

Shoot for the Stars
Directions: Add the total points scored in the game. Remember to add the ones first and regroup. Then, add the tens.
Example:
HOME 53 VISITOR 27 Total 80
HOME 29 VISITOR 45 Total 74
HOME 57 VISITOR 39 Total 96
HOME 63 VISITOR 19 Total 82
HOME 66 VISITOR 28 Total 94
HOME 47 VISITOR 49 Total 96
HOME 36 VISITOR 45 Total 81
HOME 27 VISITOR 38 Total 65
HOME 54 VISITOR 39 Total 93
HOME 37 VISITOR 59 Total 96

Page 168

Review: 2-Digit Subtraction

Directions: Rename 61 as 5 tens and 11 ones.

61 − 43 → $\overset{5\,11}{\cancel{6}\cancel{1}}$ − 43 → Subtract the ones. (8) → Subtract the tens. (18)

Directions: Subtract.

Example: $\overset{3\,17}{\cancel{4}\cancel{7}}$ − 28 = 19

Example: 47 − 28 = 19	73 − 48 = 25	84 − 66 = 18	95 − 18 = 77	64 − 29 = 35
56 − 38 = 18	31 − 15 = 16	25 − 17 = 8	33 − 19 = 14	46 − 29 = 17
93 − 64 = 29	82 − 55 = 27	72 − 14 = 58	45 − 28 = 17	61 − 23 = 38
51 − 44 = 7	62 − 48 = 14	37 − 19 = 18	50 − 32 = 18	83 − 47 = 36
92 − 73 = 19	82 − 75 = 7	76 − 38 = 38	47 − 29 = 18	74 − 39 = 35

Page 169

Review: 2-Digit Subtraction

Directions: Add.

85 − 16 = 69	93 − 48 = 45	72 − 35 = 37	63 − 27 = 36	43 − 38 = 5
56 − 29 = 27	75 − 49 = 26	84 − 38 = 46	91 − 65 = 26	37 − 18 = 19
21 − 14 = 7	35 − 18 = 17	42 − 29 = 13	72 − 47 = 25	81 − 54 = 27
64 − 38 = 26	53 − 28 = 25	94 − 57 = 37	48 − 39 = 9	23 − 18 = 5
74 − 58 = 16	83 − 36 = 47	62 − 26 = 36	54 − 28 = 26	32 − 17 = 15

Page 170

Go "Fore" It!
Directions: Add or subtract using regrouping.
tens ones
2 15
3 5
-2 7
8
56 -27 29
40 -16 24
35 +27 62
93 -39 54
44 +28 72
42 -14 28
97 -48 49
33 +18 51
73 -24 49
56 -17 39
68 -49 19
49 +32 81
77 -68 9
27 +19 46

Page 171

Monster Math
Directions: Add or subtract using regrouping.
84 -56 28
41 -17 24
52 -28 24
84 -27 57
57 -39 18
72 -19 53
33 -15 18
64 +17 81
36 -19 17
65 -28 37
48 -30 18
33 +18 51
25 +35 60

Page 172

Adding Hundreds

Examples:

5 hundreds + 3 hundreds = 8 hundreds | 500 + 300 = 800

4 hundreds + 5 hundreds = 9 hundreds | 400 + 500 = 900

Directions: Add.

3 hundreds + 1 hundreds = 4 hundreds | 300 + 100 = 400

6 hundreds + 2 hundreds = 8 hundreds | 600 + 200 = 800

200 + 200 = 400 | 100 + 700 = 800 | 600 + 300 = 900 | 400 + 500 = 900

300 + 400 = 700 | 800 + 100 = 900 | 400 + 400 = 800 | 700 + 200 = 900

500 + 100 = 600 | 100 + 600 = 700 | 500 + 200 = 700 | 300 + 200 = 500

300 + 300 = 600 | 400 + 200 = 600 | 300 + 500 = 800 | 200 + 100 = 300

Page 173

Problem Solving

Directions: Solve each problem.

Example:

Ria packed 300 boxes.
Melvin packed 200 boxes.
How many boxes did Ria and Melvin pack?
300 + 200 = 500

Santo typed 500 letters.
Hale typed 400 letters.
How many letters did they type?
500 + 400 = 900

Paula used 100 paper clips.
Milton used 600 paper clips.
How many paper clips did they use?
100 + 600 = 700

The grocery store sold 400 red apples.
The grocery store also sold 100 yellow apples.
How many apples did the grocery store sell in all?
400 + 100 = 500

Miles worked 200 days.
Julia worked 500 days.
How many days did they work?
200 + 500 = 700

Page 174

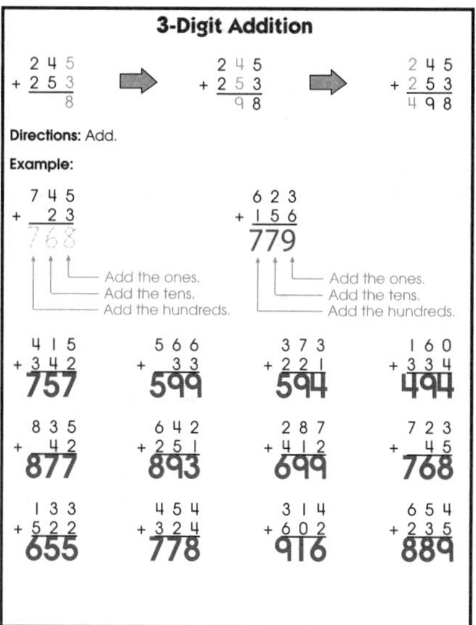

3-Digit Addition

245 + 253 = 8 → 245 + 253 = 98 → 245 + 253 = 498

Directions: Add.

Example:

745 + 23 = 768

623 + 156 = 779

Add the ones.
Add the tens.
Add the hundreds.

415 + 342 = 757 | 566 + 33 = 599 | 373 + 221 = 594 | 160 + 334 = 494

835 + 42 = 877 | 642 + 251 = 893 | 287 + 412 = 699 | 723 + 45 = 768

133 + 522 = 655 | 454 + 324 = 778 | 314 + 602 = 916 | 654 + 235 = 889

Page 175

Problem Solving

Directions: Solve each problem.

Example:

Gene collected 342 rocks.
Lester collected 201 rocks.
How many rocks did they collect?
342 + 201 = 543

Tina jumped the rope 403 times.
Henry jumped the rope 426 times.
How many times did they jump?
403 + 426 = 829

There are 210 people wearing blue hats.
There are 432 people wearing red hats.
How many hats in all?
210 + 432 = 642

Asta used 135 paper plates.
Clyde used 143 paper plates.
How many paper plates did they use in all?
135 + 143 = 278

Aunt Mary had 536 dollars.
Uncle Lewis had 423 dollars.
How many dollars did they have in all?
536 + 423 = 959

Page 176

Problem Solving

Directions: Solve each problem.

There are 236 boys in school.
There are 250 girls in school.
How many boys and girls are in school?
236 + 250 = 486

Mary saw 131 cars.
Marvin saw 268 trucks.
How many cars and trucks did they see in all?
131 + 268 = 399

Jack has 427 pennies.
Jill has 370 pennies.
How many pennies do they have in all?
427 + 370 = 797

There are 582 red apples.
There are 206 yellow apples.
How many apples are there in all?
582 + 206 = 788

Ann found 122 shells.
Pedro found 76 shells.
How many shells did they find?
122 + 76 = 198

Page 177

Subtracting Hundreds

8 hundreds - 3 hundreds = 5 hundreds | 800 - 300 = 500

6 hundreds - 2 hundreds = 4 hundreds | 600 - 200 = 400

Directions: Subtract.

Example:

9 hundreds - 7 hundreds = 2 hundreds | 900 - 700 = 200

3 hundreds - 1 hundreds = 2 hundreds | 300 - 100 = 200

700 - 300 = 400 | 500 - 400 = 100 | 900 - 400 = 500 | 800 - 500 = 300

600 - 500 = 100 | 300 - 200 = 100 | 500 - 100 = 400 | 400 - 200 = 200

900 - 100 = 800 | 800 - 400 = 400 | 600 - 200 = 400 | 500 - 300 = 200

400 - 100 = 300 | 700 - 600 = 100 | 800 - 200 = 600 | 900 - 600 = 300

Page 178

Problem Solving

Directions: Solve each problem.

Example:

There were 400 apples in a box.
Jesse took 100 apples from the box.
How many apples are still in the box?

400 - 100 = 300

Tommy bought 300 golf balls.
He gave Irene 200 golf balls.
How many golf balls does he have left?

300 - 200 = 100

The black horse ran 900 feet.
The brown horse ran 700 feet.
How many more feet did the black horse run?

900 - 700 = 200

The paint store has 800 gallons of paint.
It sells 300 gallons of paint.
How many gallons of paint are left?

800 - 300 = 500

There are 700 children.
There are 200 boys.
How many girls are there?

700 - 200 = 500

Page 179

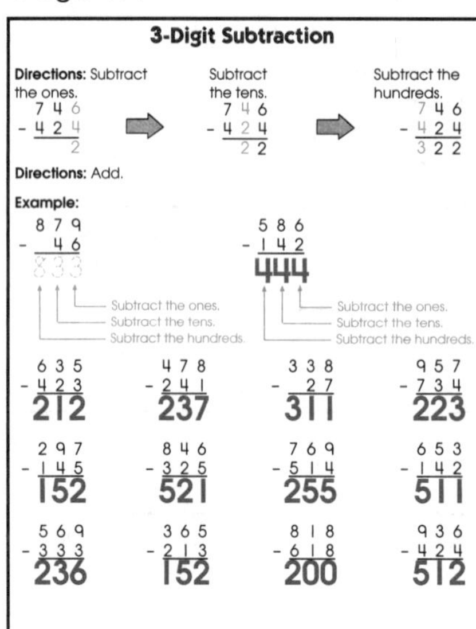

3-Digit Subtraction

Directions: Subtract the ones. 746 - 424 = 2 → Subtract the tens. 746 - 424 = 22 → Subtract the hundreds. 746 - 424 = 322

Directions: Add.

Example:

879 - 46 = 833

586 - 142 = 444

Subtract the ones.
Subtract the tens.
Subtract the hundreds.

635 - 423 = 212 | 478 - 241 = 237 | 338 - 27 = 311 | 957 - 734 = 223

297 - 145 = 152 | 846 - 325 = 521 | 769 - 514 = 255 | 653 - 142 = 511

569 - 333 = 236 | 365 - 213 = 152 | 818 - 618 = 200 | 936 - 424 = 512

Page 180

Problem Solving

Directions: Solve each problem.

Example:

The grocery store buys 568 cans of beans.
It sells 345 cans of beans.
How many cans of beans are left?

568 - 345 = 223

The cooler holds 732 gallons of milk.
It has 412 gallons of milk in it.
How many more gallons of milk will it take to fill the cooler?

732 - 412 = 320

Ann does 635 push-ups.
Carl does 421 push-ups.
How many more push-ups does Ann do?

635 - 421 = 214

Kurt has 386 pennies.
Neal has 32 pennies.
How many more pennies does Kurt have?

386 - 32 = 354

It takes 874 nails to build a tree house.
Jillian has 532 nails.
How many more nails does she need?

874 - 532 = 342

Page 181

Problem Solving

Directions: Solve each problem.

Example:

There were 787 bales of hay.
Glenda fed the cows 535 bales.
How many bales of hay are left?

787 - 535 = 252

There are 673 bolts in a box.
Maria took 341 bolts out of the box.
How many bolts are left in the box?

673 - 341 = 332

The secretary types 459 letters.
138 of the letters were mailed.
How many letters are left?

459 - 138 = 321

Mr. Jones had 569 dollars.
He spent 203 dollars.
How many dollars does he have left?

569 - 203 = 366

There are 342 riding horses in the rodeo.
There are 132 bucking horses in the rodeo.
How many more riding horses are there?

342 - 132 = 210

Page 182

Review: Addition and Subtraction

Directions: Add.

124 + 323 = 447 | 520 + 407 = 927 | 739 + 150 = 889 | 861 + 6 = 867

Directions: Subtract.

900 - 600 = 300 | 800 - 200 = 600 | 974 - 564 = 410 | 508 - 7 = 501

728 - 326 = 402 | 657 - 45 = 612 | 894 - 464 = 430 | 596 - 352 = 244

Directions: Solve each problem.

There are 275 nails in a box.
123 nails are taken out of the box.
How many nails are still in the box?

275 - 123 = 152

Gerald peeled 212 apples.
Anna peeled 84 apples.
How many apples did they peel in all?

212 + 84 = 296

Page 183

Review: 3-Digit Addition

Directions: Add.

Examples:

340 + 225 = 565 | 754 + 32 = 786 | 826 + 3 = 829 | 632 + 322 = 954

198 + 200 = 398 | 456 + 31 = 487 | 541 + 333 = 874 | 273 + 415 = 688

900 + 34 = 934 | 847 + 131 = 978 | 721 + 176 = 897 | 402 + 383 = 785

156 + 423 = 579 | 644 + 251 = 895 | 215 + 542 = 757 | 372 + 417 = 789

518 + 351 = 869 | 783 + 5 = 788 | 684 + 14 = 698 | 710 + 260 = 970

Page 184

Review: 3-Digit Subtraction

Directions: Subtract.

Example:

856 − 352 = 504	432 − 21 = 411	598 − 416 = 182	769 − 345 = 424
319 − 6 = 313	954 − 731 = 223	275 − 3 = 272	643 − 313 = 330
775 − 261 = 514	834 − 12 = 822	942 − 111 = 831	478 − 324 = 154
562 − 431 = 131	444 − 212 = 232	385 − 152 = 233	754 − 3 = 751
868 − 234 = 634	943 − 843 = 100	689 − 417 = 272	577 − 37 = 540

Page 185

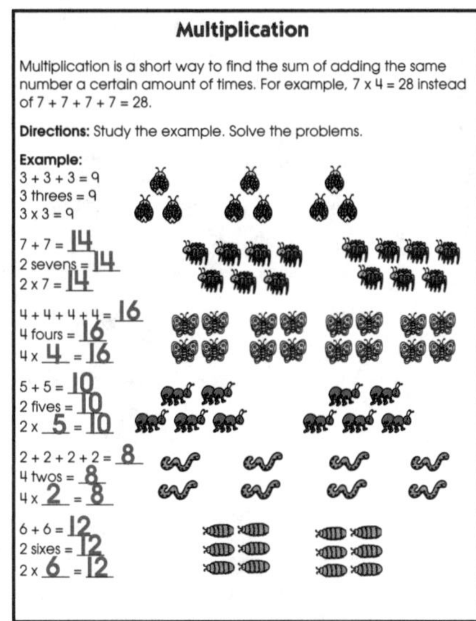

Multiplication

Multiplication is a short way to find the sum of adding the same number a certain amount of times. For example, 7 x 4 = 28 instead of 7 + 7 + 7 + 7 = 28.

Directions: Study the example. Solve the problems.

Example:
3 + 3 + 3 = 9
3 threes = 9
3 x 3 = 9

7 + 7 = 14
2 sevens = 14
2 x 7 = 14

4 + 4 + 4 + 4 = 16
4 fours = 16
4 x 4 = 16

5 + 5 = 10
2 fives = 10
2 x 5 = 10

2 + 2 + 2 + 2 = 8
4 twos = 8
4 x 2 = 8

6 + 6 = 12
2 sixes = 12
2 x 6 = 12

Page 186

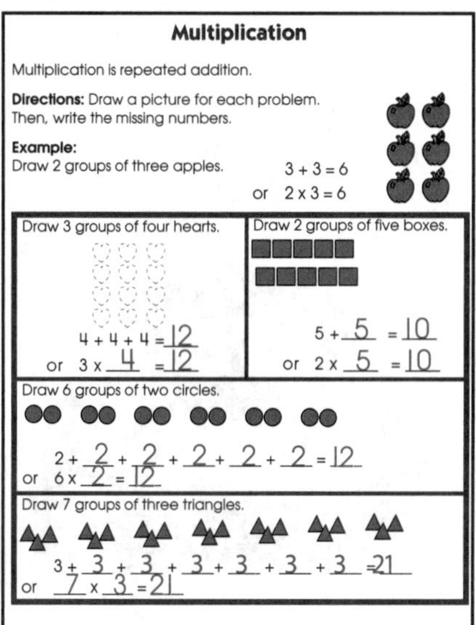

Multiplication

Multiplication is repeated addition.

Directions: Draw a picture for each problem. Then, write the missing numbers.

Example:
Draw 2 groups of three apples.
3 + 3 = 6
or 2 x 3 = 6

Draw 3 groups of four hearts.
4 + 4 + 4 = 12
or 3 x 4 = 12

Draw 2 groups of five boxes.
5 + 5 = 10
or 2 x 5 = 10

Draw 6 groups of two circles.
2 + 2 + 2 + 2 + 2 + 2 = 12
or 6 x 2 = 12

Draw 7 groups of three triangles.
3 + 3 + 3 + 3 + 3 + 3 + 3 = 21
or 7 x 3 = 21

Page 187

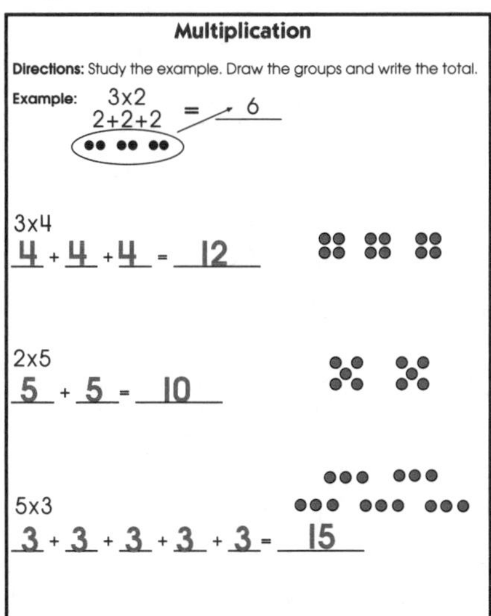

Multiplication

Directions: Study the example. Draw the groups and write the total.

Example: 3x2
2+2+2 = 6

3x4
4 + 4 + 4 = 12

2x5
5 + 5 = 10

5x3
3 + 3 + 3 + 3 + 3 = 15

Page 188

Multiplication

Directions: Solve the problems.

Multiplication saves time. It's faster than addition!

9 + 9 = 18
2 nines = 18
2 x 9 = 18

7 + 7 = 14
2 sevens = 14
2 x 7 = 14

4 + 4 + 4 + 4 = 16
4 fours = 16
4 x 4 = 16

8 + 8 + 8 + 8 + 8 = 40
5 eights = 40
5 x 8 = 40

5 + 5 + 5 = 15
3 fives = 15
3 x 5 = 15

9 + 9 = 18
2 nines = 18
2 x 9 = 18

6 + 6 + 6 = 18
3 sixes = 18
3 x 6 = 18

3 + 3 = 6
2 threes = 6
2 x 3 = 6

7 + 7 + 7 + 7 = 28
4 sevens = 28
4 x 7 = 28

2 + 2 = 4
2 twos = 4
2 x 2 = 4

Page 189

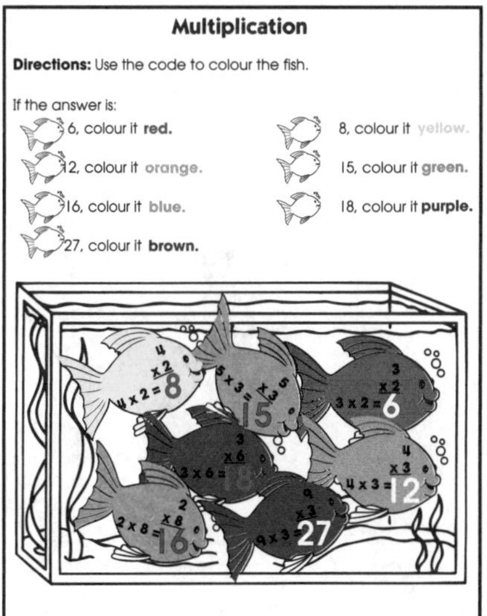

Multiplication

Directions: Use the code to colour the fish.

If the answer is:
6, colour it **red**.
12, colour it **orange**.
16, colour it **blue**.
27, colour it **brown**.
8, colour it **yellow**.
15, colour it **green**.
18, colour it **purple**.

Page 190

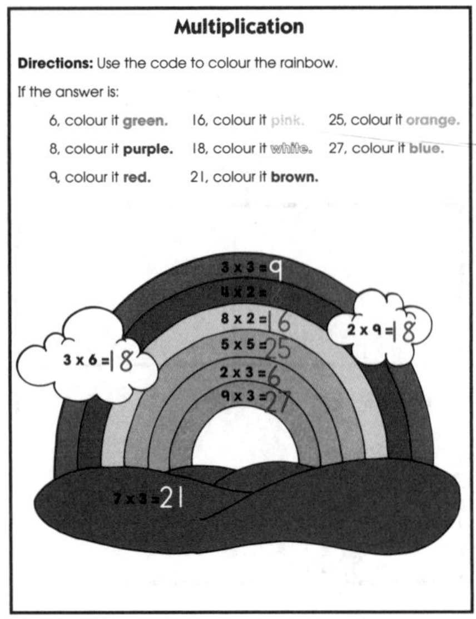

Page 191

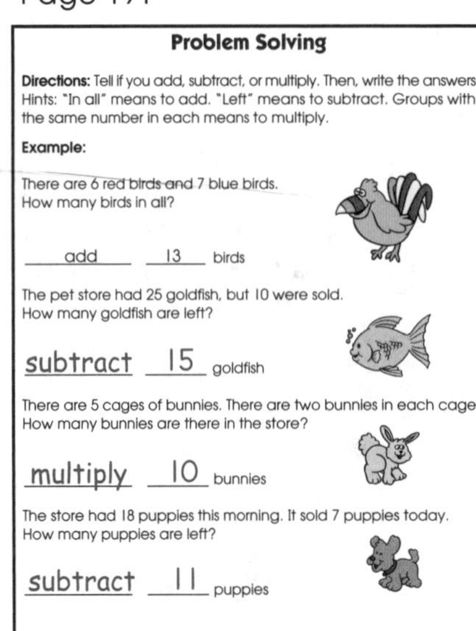

Page 192

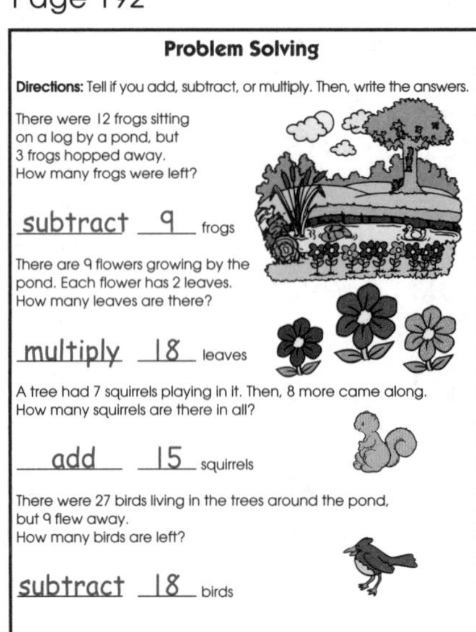

Page 193

Circle
A circle is a shape that is round. This is a circle:
Directions: Find the circles and draw squares around them.
Directions: Trace the word. Then, write the word.
circle circle

Page 194

Page 195

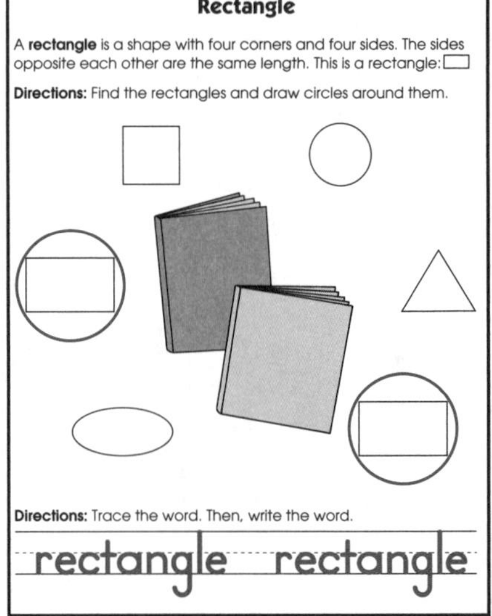

Page 196

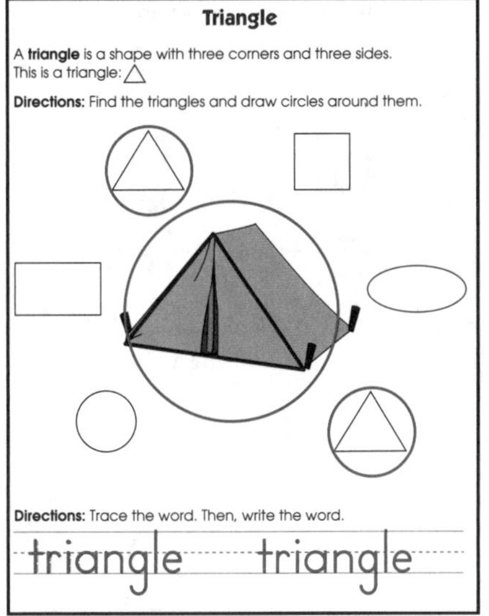

Triangle

A **triangle** is a shape with three corners and three sides.
This is a triangle: △

Directions: Find the triangles and draw circles around them.

Directions: Trace the word. Then, write the word.

triangle triangle

Page 197

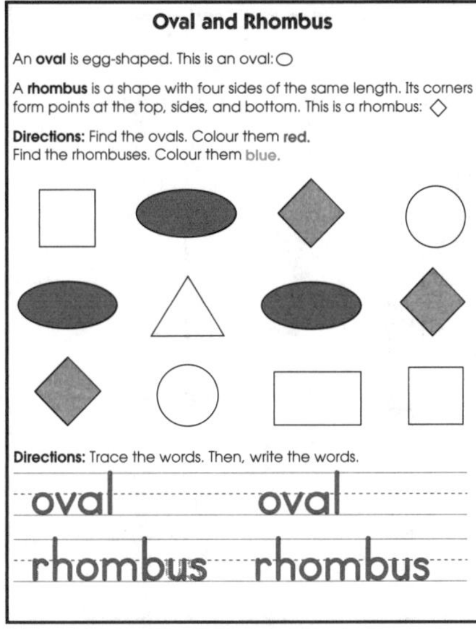

Oval and Rhombus

An **oval** is egg-shaped. This is an oval: ○

A **rhombus** is a shape with four sides of the same length. Its corners form points at the top, sides, and bottom. This is a rhombus: ◇

Directions: Find the ovals. Colour them **red**.
Find the rhombuses. Colour them blue.

Directions: Trace the words. Then, write the words.

oval oval

rhombus rhombus

Page 198

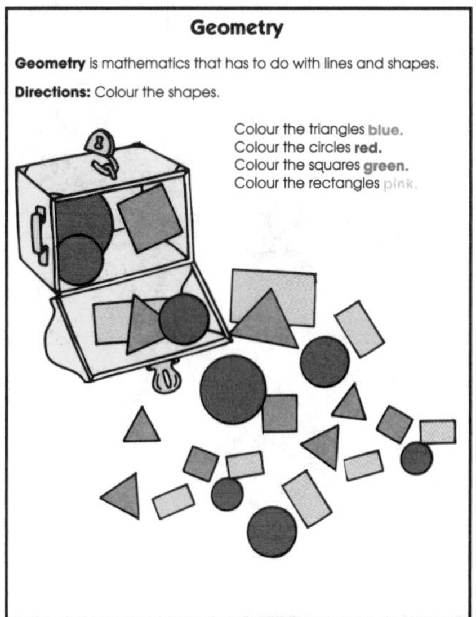

Geometry

Geometry is mathematics that has to do with lines and shapes.

Directions: Colour the shapes.

Colour the triangles **blue.**
Colour the circles **red.**
Colour the squares **green.**
Colour the rectangles pink.

Page 199

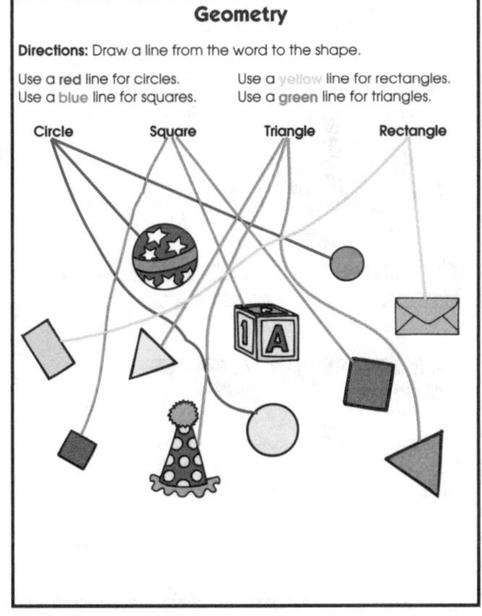

Geometry

Directions: Draw a line from the word to the shape.

Use a **red** line for circles. Use a yellow line for rectangles.
Use a **blue** line for squares. Use a **green** line for triangles.

Circle Square Triangle Rectangle

Page 200

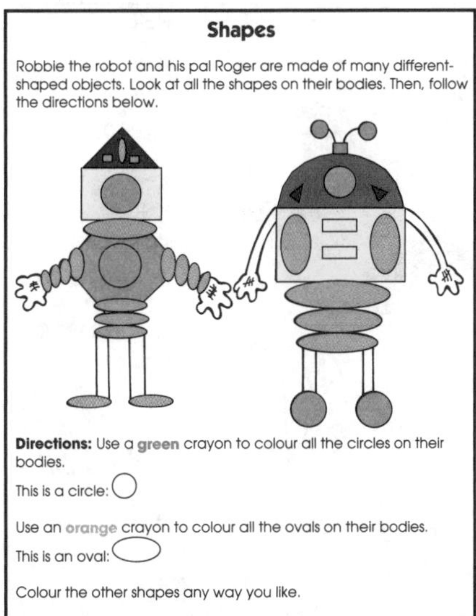

Shapes

Robbie the robot and his pal Roger are made of many different-shaped objects. Look at all the shapes on their bodies. Then, follow the directions below.

Directions: Use a **green** crayon to colour all the circles on their bodies.

This is a circle: ○

Use an **orange** crayon to colour all the ovals on their bodies.

This is an oval: ⬭

Colour the other shapes any way you like.

Page 201

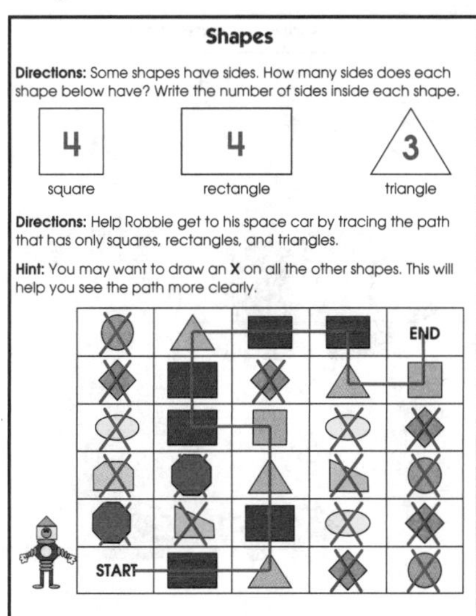

Shapes

Directions: Some shapes have sides. How many sides does each shape below have? Write the number of sides inside each shape.

4 square 4 rectangle 3 triangle

Directions: Help Robbie get to his space car by tracing the path that has only squares, rectangles, and triangles.

Hint: You may want to draw an **X** on all the other shapes. This will help you see the path more clearly.

END

START

Page 202

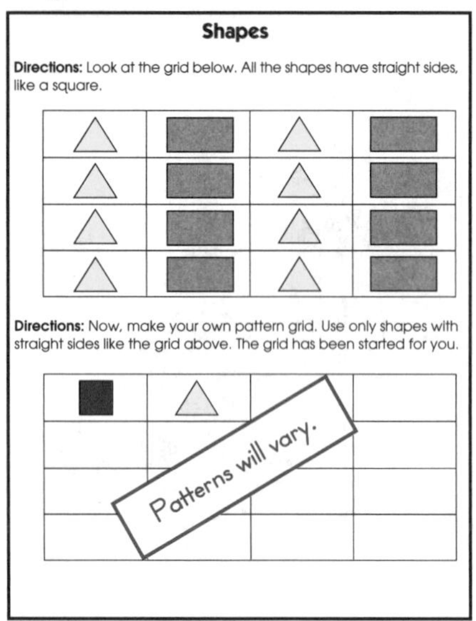

Shapes

Directions: Look at the grid below. All the shapes have straight sides, like a square.

Directions: Now, make your own pattern grid. Use only shapes with straight sides like the grid above. The grid has been started for you.

Patterns will vary.

Page 203

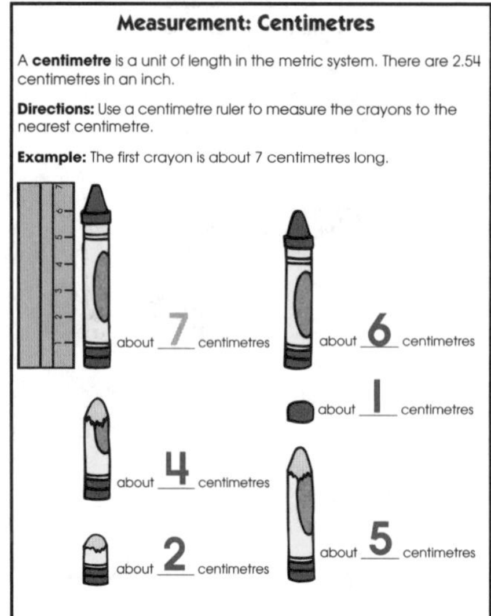

Measurement: Centimetres

A **centimetre** is a unit of length in the metric system. There are 2.54 centimetres in an inch.

Directions: Use a centimetre ruler to measure the crayons to the nearest centimetre.

Example: The first crayon is about 7 centimetres long.

about **7** centimetres

about **6** centimetres

about **1** centimetres

about **4** centimetres

about **5** centimetres

about **2** centimetres

Page 204

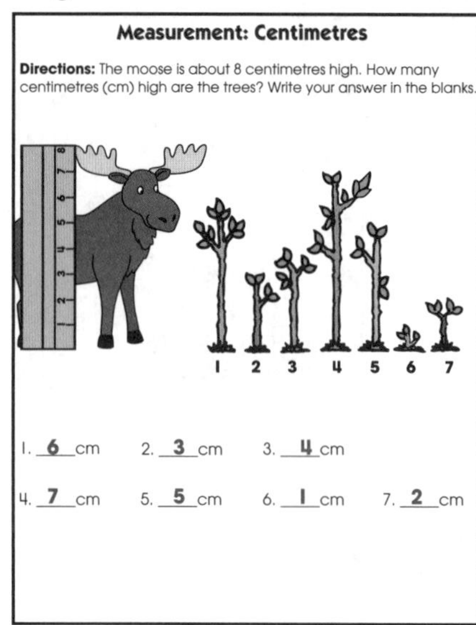

Measurement: Centimetres

Directions: The moose is about 8 centimetres high. How many centimetres (cm) high are the trees? Write your answer in the blanks.

1. **6** cm
2. **3** cm
3. **4** cm
4. **7** cm
5. **5** cm
6. **1** cm
7. **2** cm

Page 205

Measuring in Centimetres

Directions: Use a centimetre ruler to find the height or the length of the objects below. Write the answer in each blank.

Example: **10** cm

centimetres

about **14** cm

about **9** cm

about **3** cm

about **6** cm

Page 206

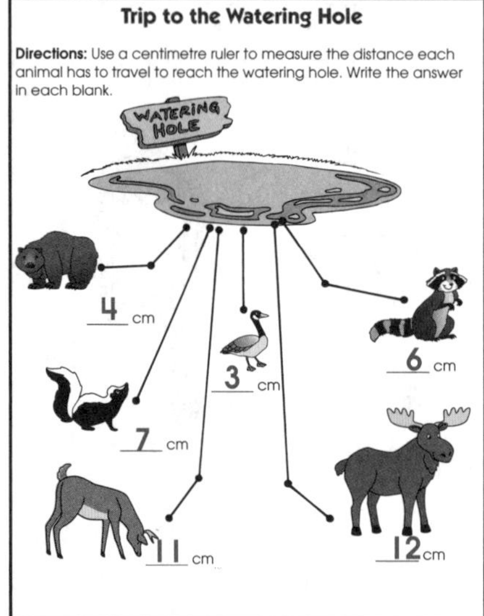

Trip to the Watering Hole

Directions: Use a centimetre ruler to measure the distance each animal has to travel to reach the watering hole. Write the answer in each blank.

4 cm

3 cm

6 cm

7 cm

11 cm

12 cm

Page 207

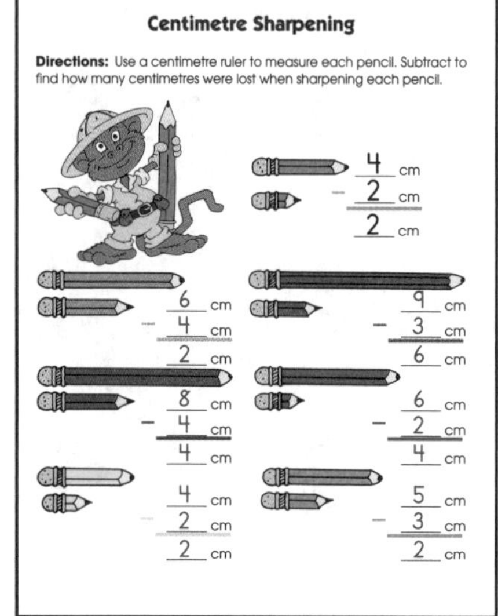

Centimetre Sharpening

Directions: Use a centimetre ruler to measure each pencil. Subtract to find how many centimetres were lost when sharpening each pencil.

4 cm − **2** cm = **2** cm

6 cm − **4** cm = **2** cm

9 cm − **3** cm = **6** cm

8 cm − **4** cm = **4** cm

6 cm − **2** cm = **4** cm

4 cm − **2** cm = **2** cm

5 cm − **3** cm = **2** cm

Page 208

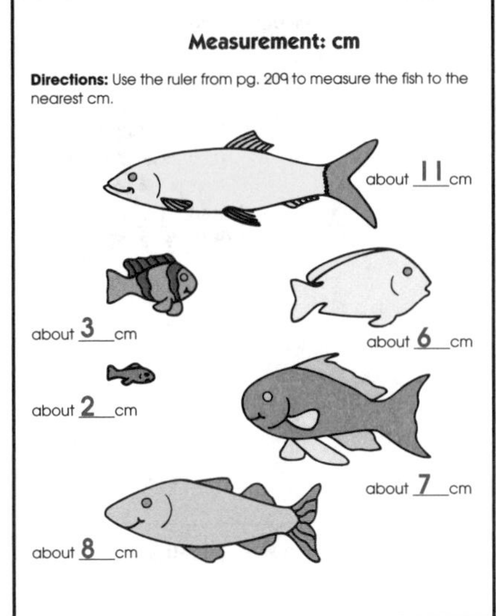

Page 209

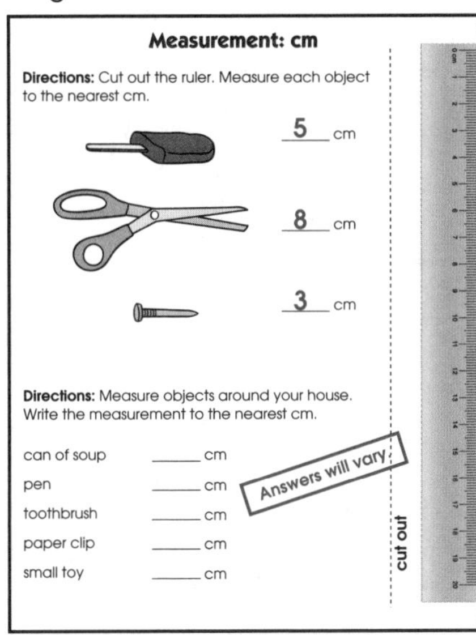

Page 211

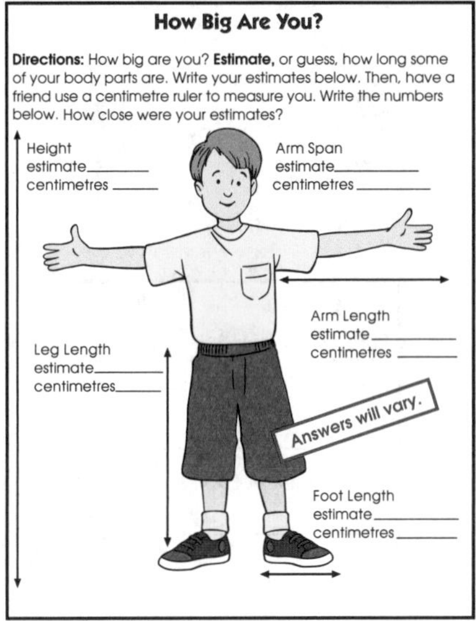

Page 212

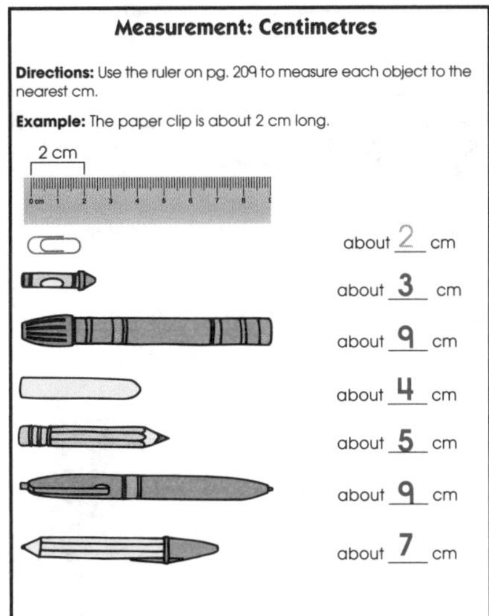

Measurement: Centimetres
Directions: Use the ruler on pg. 209 to measure each object to the nearest cm.
Example: The paper clip is about 2 cm long.
2 cm
about 2 cm
about 3 cm
about 9 cm
about 4 cm
about 5 cm
about 9 cm
about 7 cm

Page 213

Page 214

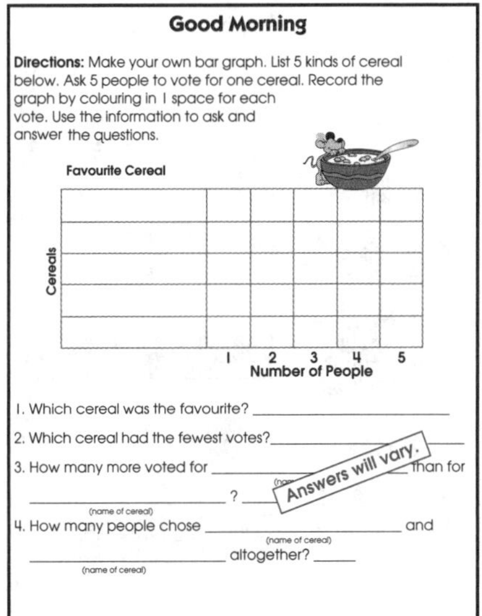

Page 215

Jungle Weather

Directions: The pictures show the weather for one month. Count the number of sunny, cloudy, and rainy days.

𝍸𝍸𝍸   𝍸𝍸   𝍸

Directions: Complete the pictograph using the tallies above.

Weather for 1 Month

Number of Days

Page 216

What a Meal!

Directions: Use the pictograph to complete each sentence below.

= 2 worms

Grace Goldfish	4 worm pictures
Willie Walleye	5 worm pictures
Calvin Catfish	4 worm pictures
Benny Bluegill	2 worm pictures
Beth Bass	6 worm pictures
Patty Perch	3 worm pictures

1. Benny got the fewest worms.
2. Beth got the most worms.
3. Grace and Calvin got the same number of worms.
4. Benny and Patty together caught the same number of worms as Willie.
5. Write the number of worms that each fish ate.

8	10	8	4	12	6
Grace	Willie	Calvin	Benny	Beth	Patty

Page 217

"Hockey Season"

Directions: Eight hockey teams have just completed their season Each team played eight games. Use this pictograph to a questions below.

= 1 goal

Wiggle Worms	7 pucks
Jaguars	8 pucks
Pandas	6 pucks
Toucans	3 pucks
Centipedes	4 pucks
Lightning Bugs	1 puck
Hornets	2 pucks
Monkeys	1 puck

1. How many games did the Monkeys lose? 7
2. Which teams tied for last place?
   Lightning Bugs and Monkeys
3. Which team won the most games? Jaguars
4. How many more games did the Wiggle Worms win than the Toucans? 4
5. Which four teams' total number of games won equal the Jaguars' number of games won? Centipedes and Lightning Bugs and Hornets and Monkeys

Page 218

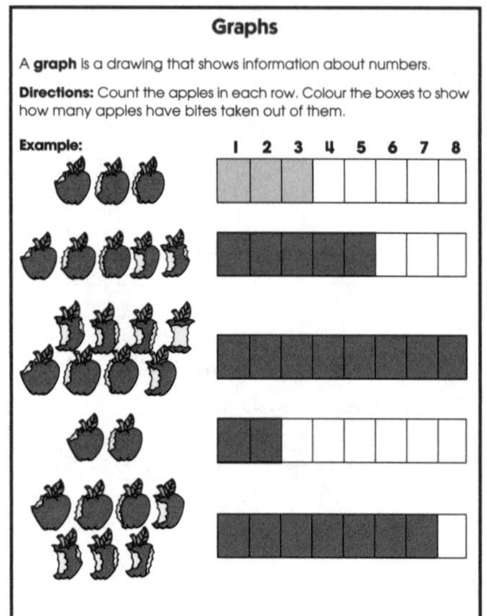

Graphs

A **graph** is a drawing that shows information about numbers.

Directions: Count the apples in each row. Colour the boxes to show how many apples have bites taken out of them.

Example:

1 2 3 4 5 6 7 8

Page 219

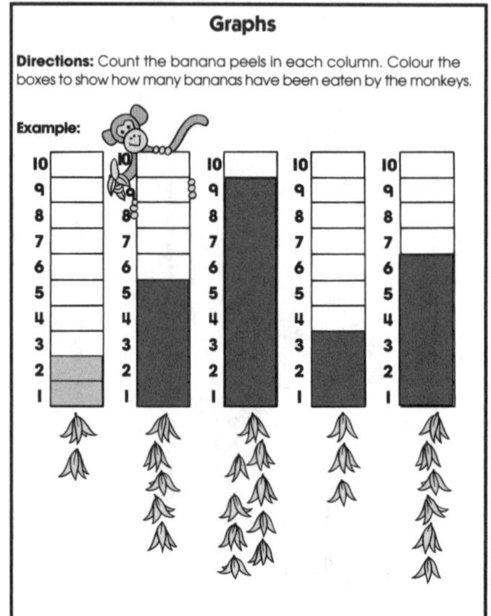

Graphs

Directions: Count the banana peels in each column. Colour the boxes to show how many bananas have been eaten by the monkeys.

Example:

Page 220

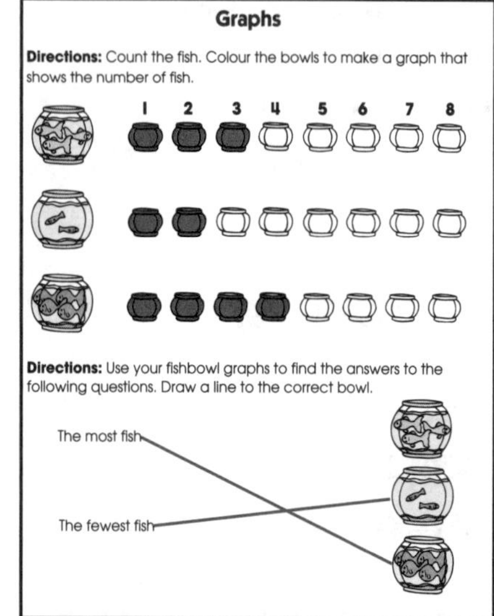

Graphs

Directions: Count the fish. Colour the bowls to make a graph that shows the number of fish.

1 2 3 4 5 6 7 8

Directions: Use your fishbowl graphs to find the answers to the following questions. Draw a line to the correct bowl.

The most fish

The fewest fish

Page 221

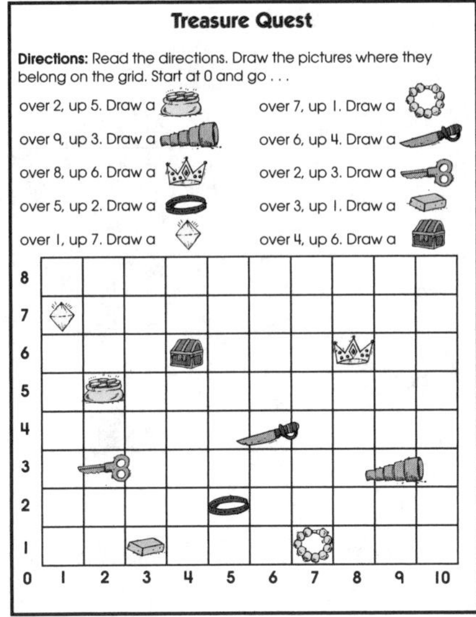

Treasure Quest

Directions: Read the directions. Draw the pictures where they belong on the grid. Start at 0 and go . . .

over 2, up 5. Draw a

over 7, up 1. Draw a

over 9, up 3. Draw a

over 6, up 4. Draw a

over 8, up 6. Draw a

over 2, up 3. Draw a

over 5, up 2. Draw a

over 3, up 1. Draw a

over 1, up 7. Draw a

over 4, up 6. Draw a

Page 222

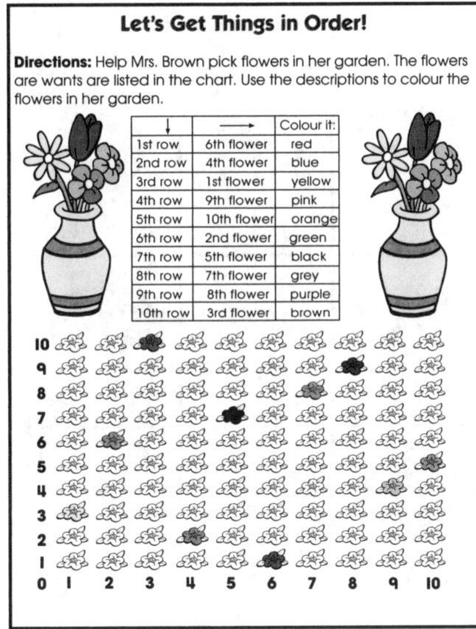

Let's Get Things in Order!

Directions: Help Mrs. Brown pick flowers in her garden. The flowers are wants are listed in the chart. Use the descriptions to colour the flowers in her garden.

↓	⟶	Colour it:
1st row	6th flower	red
2nd row	4th flower	blue
3rd row	1st flower	yellow
4th row	9th flower	pink
5th row	10th flower	orange
6th row	2nd flower	green
7th row	5th flower	black
8th row	7th flower	grey
9th row	8th flower	purple
10th row	3rd flower	brown

Page 223

Whole and Half

A **fraction** is a number that names part of a whole, such $\frac{1}{2}$.

Directions: Colour half of each thing.

Example: whole apple half an apple

Page 224

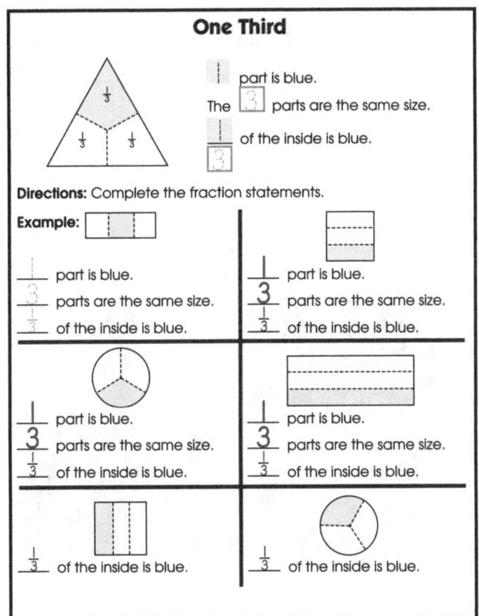

One Third

1 part is blue.

The 3 parts are the same size.

$\frac{1}{3}$ of the inside is blue.

Directions: Complete the fraction statements.

Example:

1 part is blue.
3 parts are the same size.
$\frac{1}{3}$ of the inside is blue.

Page 225

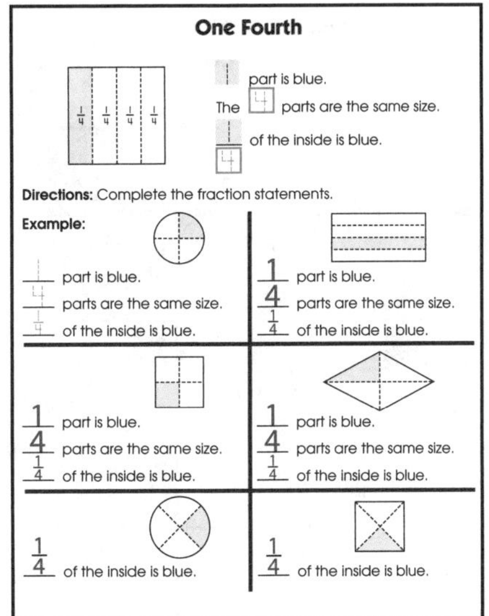

One Fourth

1 part is blue.

The 4 parts are the same size.

$\frac{1}{4}$ of the inside is blue.

Directions: Complete the fraction statements.

Example:

1 part is blue.
4 parts are the same size.
$\frac{1}{4}$ of the inside is blue.

Page 226

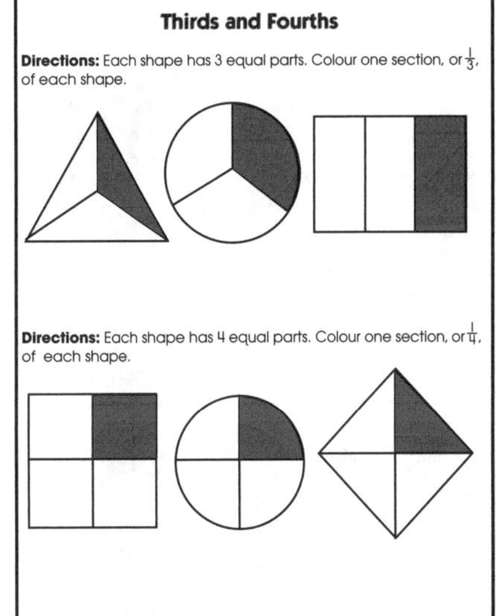

Thirds and Fourths

Directions: Each shape has 3 equal parts. Colour one section, or $\frac{1}{3}$, of each shape.

Directions: Each shape has 4 equal parts. Colour one section, or $\frac{1}{4}$, of each shape.

Page 227

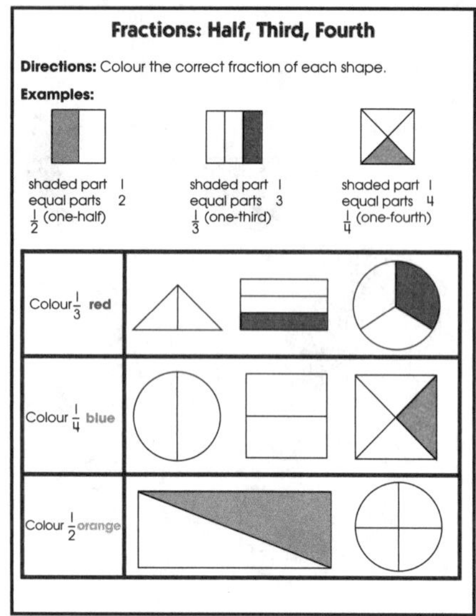

Fractions: Half, Third, Fourth

Directions: Colour the correct fraction of each shape.

Examples:

shaded part 1
equal parts 2
$\frac{1}{2}$ (one-half)

shaded part 1
equal parts 3
$\frac{1}{3}$ (one-third)

shaded part 1
equal parts 4
$\frac{1}{4}$ (one-fourth)

Colour $\frac{1}{3}$ red

Colour $\frac{1}{4}$ blue

Colour $\frac{1}{2}$ orange

Page 228

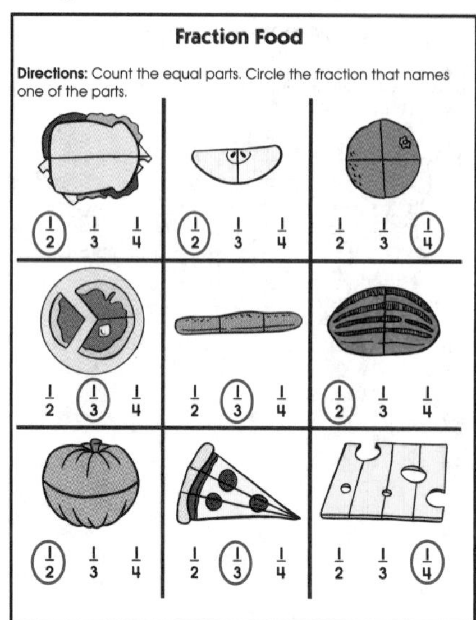

Fraction Food

Directions: Count the equal parts. Circle the fraction that names one of the parts.

$\frac{1}{2}$ $\frac{1}{3}$ $\frac{1}{4}$ (×9)

Page 229

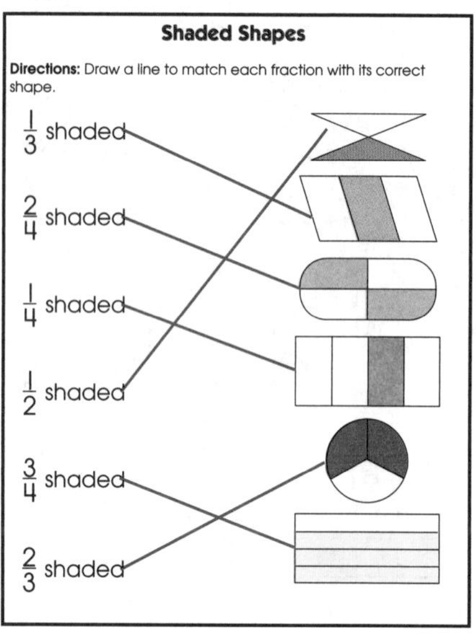

Shaded Shapes

Directions: Draw a line to match each fraction with its correct shape.

$\frac{1}{3}$ shaded

$\frac{2}{4}$ shaded

$\frac{1}{4}$ shaded

$\frac{1}{2}$ shaded

$\frac{3}{4}$ shaded

$\frac{2}{3}$ shaded

Page 230

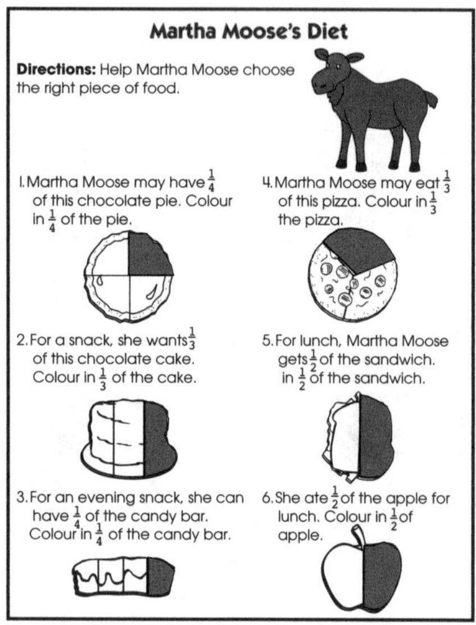

Martha Moose's Diet

Directions: Help Martha Moose choose the right piece of food.

1. Martha Moose may have $\frac{1}{4}$ of this chocolate pie. Colour in $\frac{1}{4}$ of the pie.
2. For a snack, she wants $\frac{1}{3}$ of this chocolate cake. Colour in $\frac{1}{3}$ of the cake.
3. For an evening snack, she can have $\frac{1}{4}$ of the candy bar. Colour in $\frac{1}{4}$ of the candy bar.
4. Martha Moose may eat $\frac{1}{3}$ of this pizza. Colour in $\frac{1}{3}$ the pizza.
5. For lunch, Martha Moose gets $\frac{1}{2}$ of the sandwich. Colour in $\frac{1}{2}$ of the sandwich.
6. She ate $\frac{1}{2}$ of the apple for lunch. Colour in $\frac{1}{2}$ of apple.

Page 231

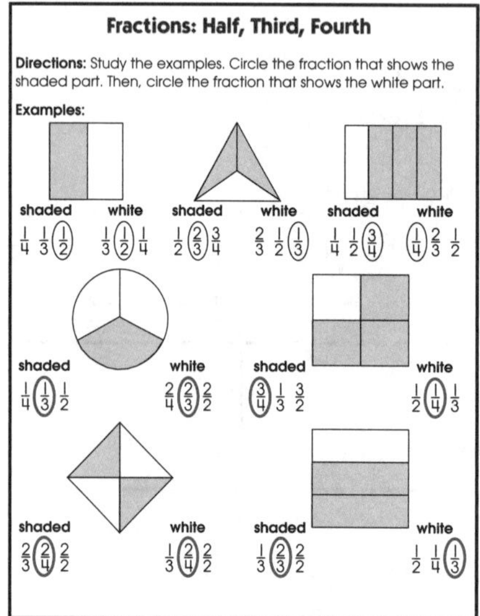

Fractions: Half, Third, Fourth

Directions: Study the examples. Circle the fraction that shows the shaded part. Then, circle the fraction that shows the white part.

Examples:

shaded white shaded white shaded white

Page 232

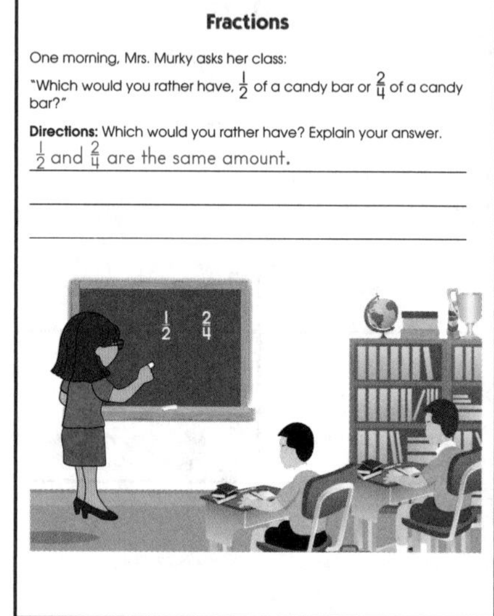

Fractions

One morning, Mrs. Murky asks her class:

"Which would you rather have, $\frac{1}{2}$ of a candy bar or $\frac{2}{4}$ of a candy bar?"

Directions: Which would you rather have? Explain your answer.

$\frac{1}{2}$ and $\frac{2}{4}$ are the same amount.

Page 233

Fractions

Directions: Rodney, Jed, and Ursula had a pizza party. They ordered I large fish-eye pizza and I large toadstool pizza. Draw lines through the pizzas to divide them equally into slices. Colour the pizza slices in 3 colours, I for each monster, to show how many slices each monster gets.

Answers will vary.

How many slices will each monster get? ______

Page 235

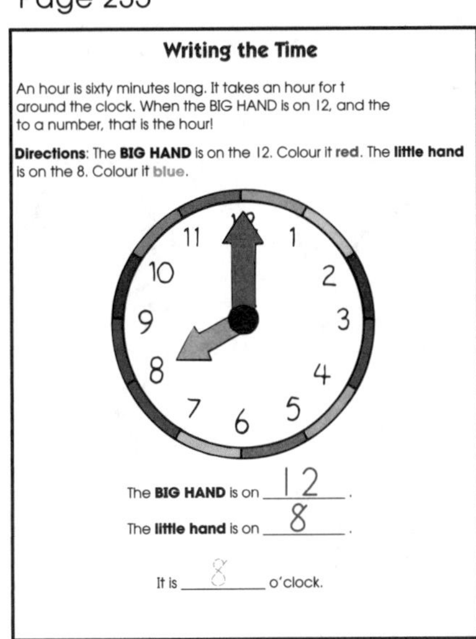

Writing the Time

An hour is sixty minutes long. It takes an hour for t around the clock. When the BIG HAND is on 12, and the to a number, that is the hour!

Directions: The **BIG HAND** is on the 12. Colour it **red**. The **little hand** is on the 8. Colour it **blue**.

The **BIG HAND** is on 12.

The **little hand** is on 8.

It is 8 o'clock.

Page 236

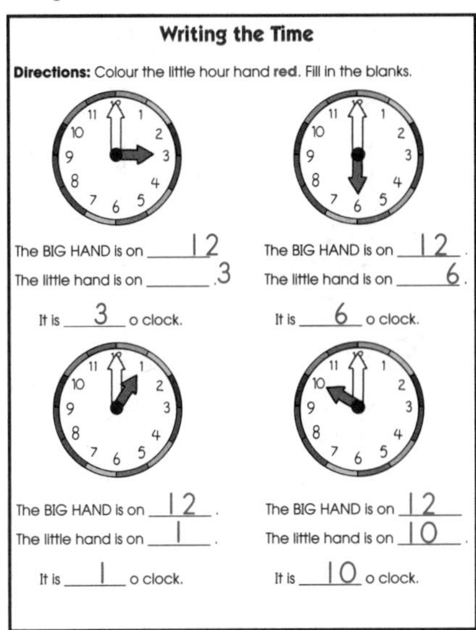

Writing the Time

Directions: Colour the little hour hand **red**. Fill in the blanks.

The BIG HAND is on 12. The little hand is on 3. It is 3 o clock.

The BIG HAND is on 12. The little hand is on 6. It is 6 o clock.

The BIG HAND is on 12. The little hand is on 1. It is 1 o clock.

The BIG HAND is on 12. The little hand is on 10. It is 10 o clock.

Page 237

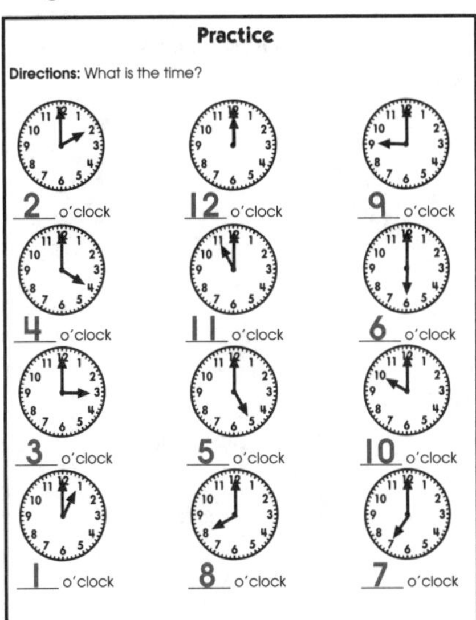

Practice

Directions: What is the time?

2 o'clock — 12 o'clock — 9 o'clock

4 o'clock — 11 o'clock — 6 o'clock

3 o'clock — 5 o'clock — 10 o'clock

1 o'clock — 8 o'clock — 7 o'clock

Page 238

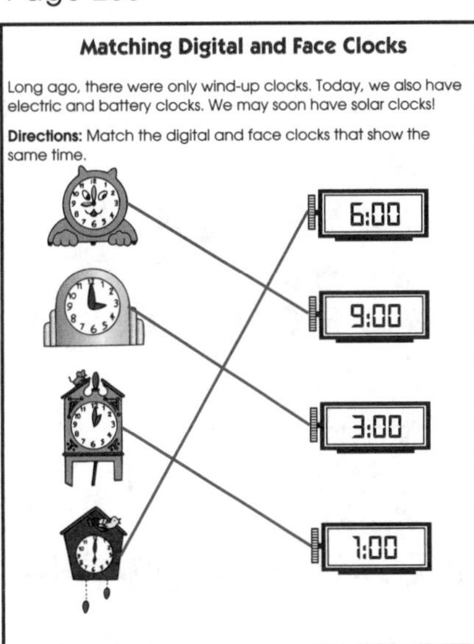

Matching Digital and Face Clocks

Long ago, there were only wind-up clocks. Today, we also have electric and battery clocks. We may soon have solar clocks!

Directions: Match the digital and face clocks that show the same time.

6:00

9:00

3:00

1:00

Page 239

Writing Time on the Half-Hour

Directions: Write the times.

11:00 — Half-hour later — 11:30

30 minutes past 11 o'clock

1:00 — Half-hour later — 1:30

30 minutes past 1 o'clock

What is your dinner time?

Directions: Circle the time you eat.

4:30 — 6:30 — 7:30

Answers will vary.

Page 240

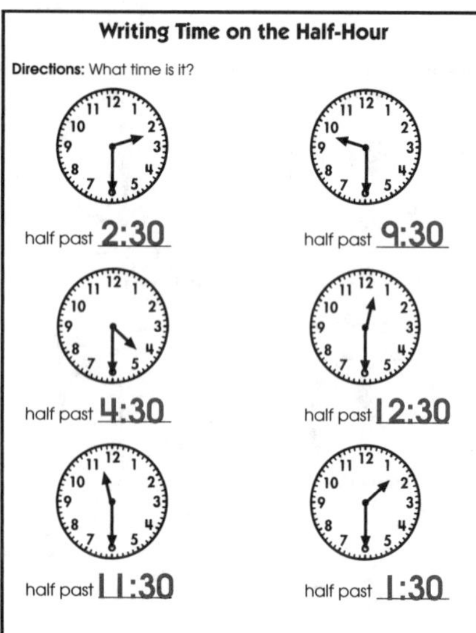

Writing Time on the Half-Hour

Directions: What time is it?

half past 2:30

half past 9:30

half past 4:30

half past 12:30

half past 11:30

half past 1:30

Page 242

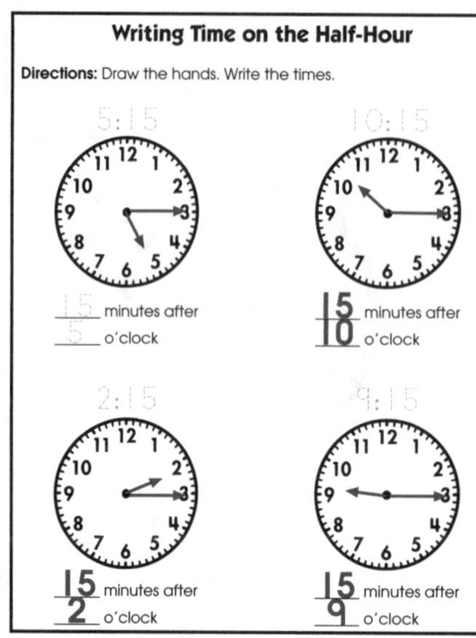

Writing Time on the Half-Hour

Directions: Draw the hands. Write the times.

5:15

15 minutes after
5 o'clock

10:15

15 minutes after
10 o'clock

2:15

15 minutes after
2 o'clock

9:15

15 minutes after
9 o'clock

Page 243

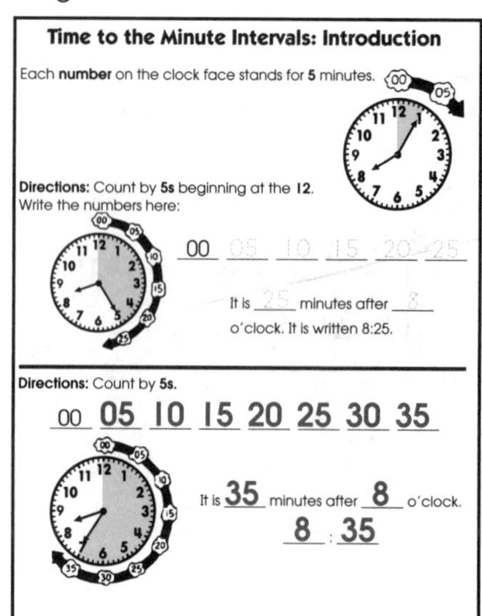

Time to the Minute Intervals: Introduction

Each **number** on the clock face stands for **5** minutes.

Directions: Count by **5s** beginning at the **12**.
Write the numbers here:

00 05 10 15 20 25

It is 25 minutes after 8 o'clock. It is written 8:25.

Directions: Count by **5s**.

00 05 10 15 20 25 30 35

It is 35 minutes after 8 o'clock.

8 : 35

Page 244

Drawing the Minute Hand

Directions: Draw the hands on these fish clocks.

7:45 8:05 11:15

3:20 5:55 1:50

12:10 10:25 4:40

Page 245

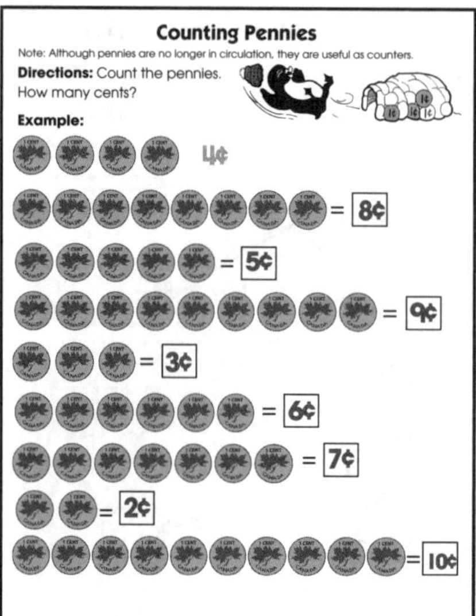

Counting Pennies

Note: Although pennies are no longer in circulation, they are useful as counters.

Directions: Count the pennies.
How many cents?

Example: 4¢

= 8¢

= 5¢

= 9¢

= 3¢

= 6¢

= 7¢

= 2¢

= 10¢

Page 246

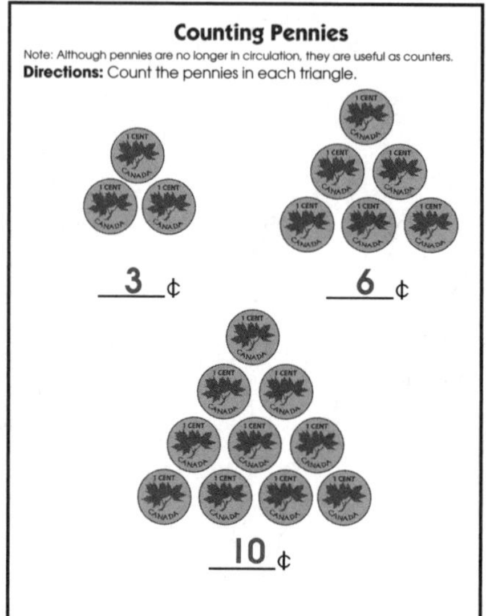

Counting Pennies

Note: Although pennies are no longer in circulation, they are useful as counters.

Directions: Count the pennies in each triangle.

3 ¢

6 ¢

10 ¢

Page 247

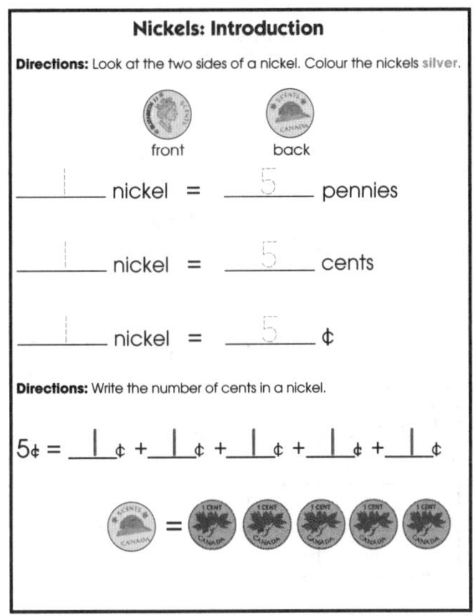

Nickels: Introduction

Directions: Look at the two sides of a nickel. Colour the nickels silver.

front back

1 nickel = 5 pennies

1 nickel = 5 cents

1 nickel = 5 ¢

Directions: Write the number of cents in a nickel.

5¢ = 1 ¢ + 1 ¢ + 1 ¢ + 1 ¢ + 1 ¢

Page 248

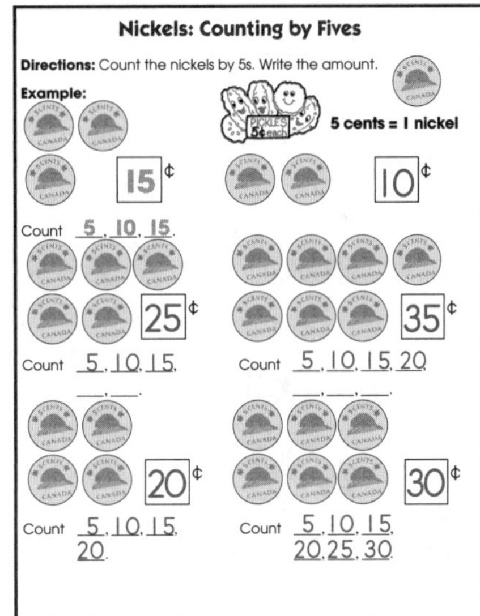

Nickels: Counting by Fives

Directions: Count the nickels by 5s. Write the amount.

Example:

PICKLES 5¢ each

5 cents = 1 nickel

15 ¢ 10 ¢

Count 5, 10, 15.

25 ¢ 35 ¢

Count 5, 10, 15, ___, ___. Count 5, 10, 15, 20, ___, ___, ___.

20 ¢ 30 ¢

Count 5, 10, 15, 20. Count 5, 10, 15, 20, 25, 30

Page 249

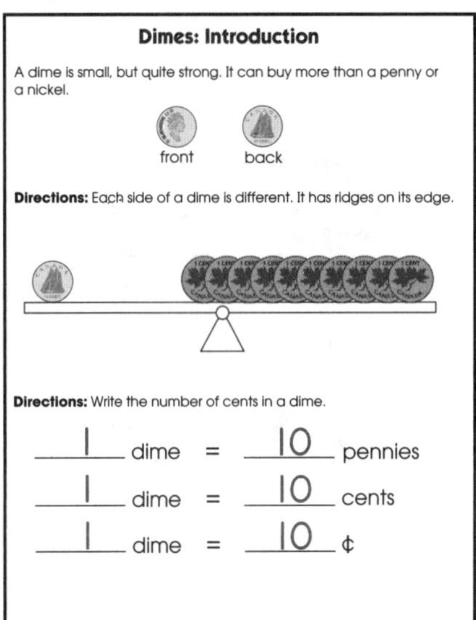

Dimes: Introduction

A dime is small, but quite strong. It can buy more than a penny or a nickel.

front back

Directions: Each side of a dime is different. It has ridges on its edge.

Directions: Write the number of cents in a dime.

1 dime = 10 pennies

1 dime = 10 cents

1 dime = 10 ¢

Page 250

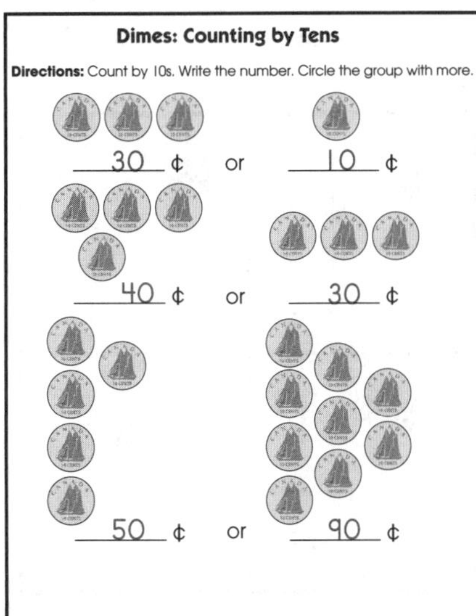

Dimes: Counting by Tens

Directions: Count by 10s. Write the number. Circle the group with more.

30 ¢ or 10 ¢

40 ¢ or 30 ¢

50 ¢ or 90 ¢

Page 251

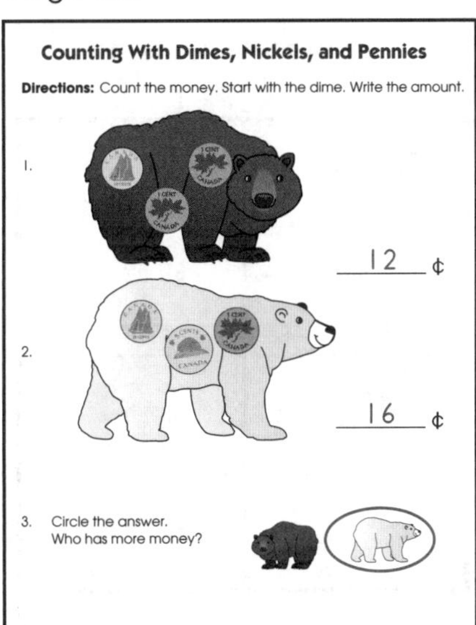

Counting With Dimes, Nickels, and Pennies

Directions: Count the money. Start with the dime. Write the amount.

1. 12 ¢

2. 16 ¢

3. Circle the answer. Who has more money?

Page 252

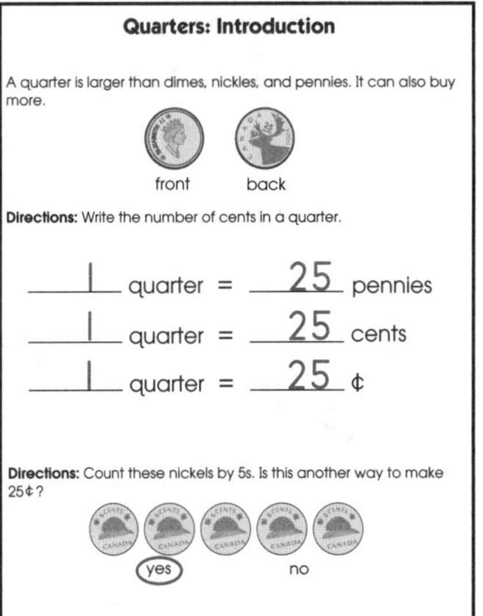

Quarters: Introduction

A quarter is larger than dimes, nickles, and pennies. It can also buy more.

front back

Directions: Write the number of cents in a quarter.

1 quarter = 25 pennies

1 quarter = 25 cents

1 quarter = 25 ¢

Directions: Count these nickels by 5s. Is this another way to make 25¢?

yes no

Page 253

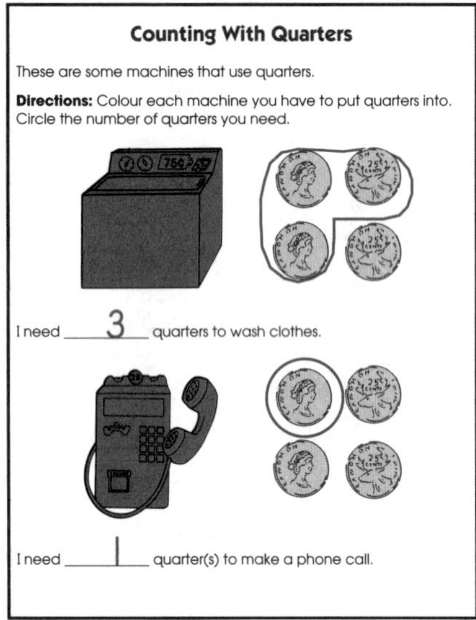

Counting With Quarters

These are some machines that use quarters.

Directions: Colour each machine you have to put quarters into. Circle the number of quarters you need.

I need 3 quarters to wash clothes.

I need 1 quarter(s) to make a phone call.

Page 254

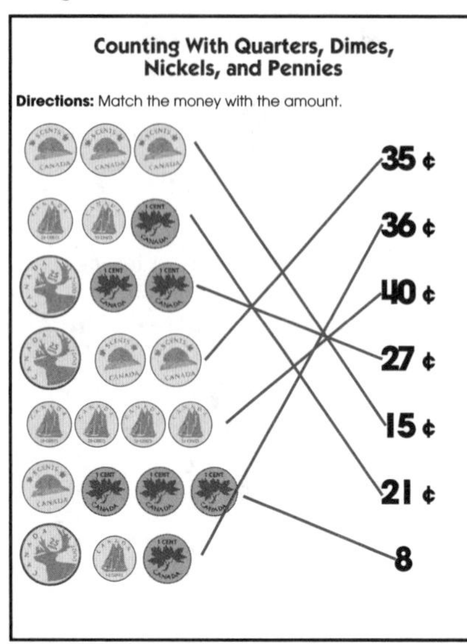

Counting With Quarters, Dimes, Nickels, and Pennies

Directions: Match the money with the amount.

35 ¢

36 ¢

40 ¢

27 ¢

15 ¢

21 ¢

8

Page 255

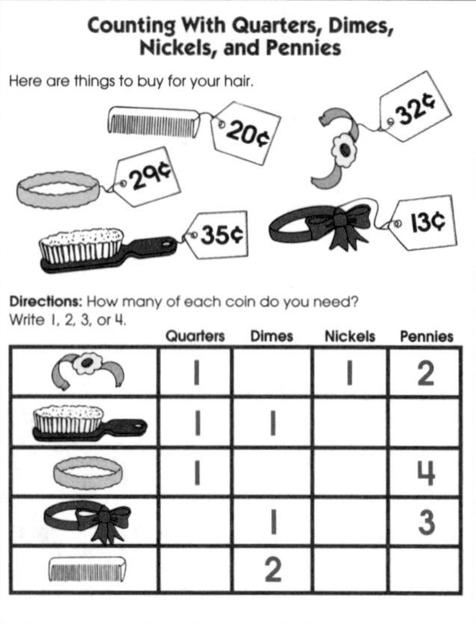

Counting With Quarters, Dimes, Nickels, and Pennies

Here are things to buy for your hair.

Directions: How many of each coin do you need? Write 1, 2, 3, or 4.

	Quarters	Dimes	Nickels	Pennies
	1		1	2
	1	1		
	1			4
		1		3
		2		

Page 256

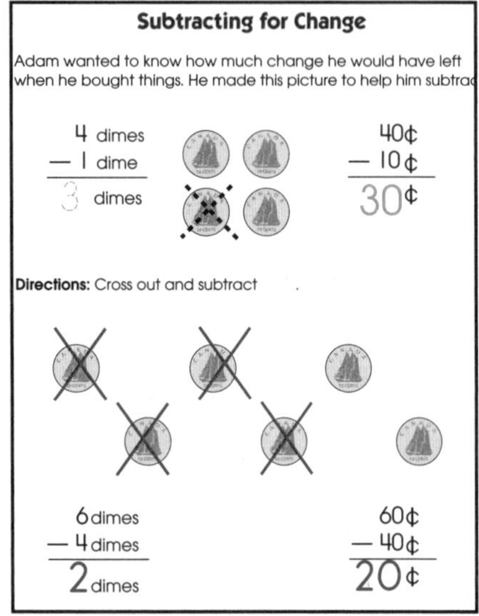

Subtracting for Change

Adam wanted to know how much change he would have left when he bought things. He made this picture to help him subtrac

4 dimes
− 1 dime
3 dimes

40¢
− 10¢
30¢

Directions: Cross out and subtract

6 dimes
− 4 dimes
2 dimes

60¢
− 40¢
20¢

Page 257

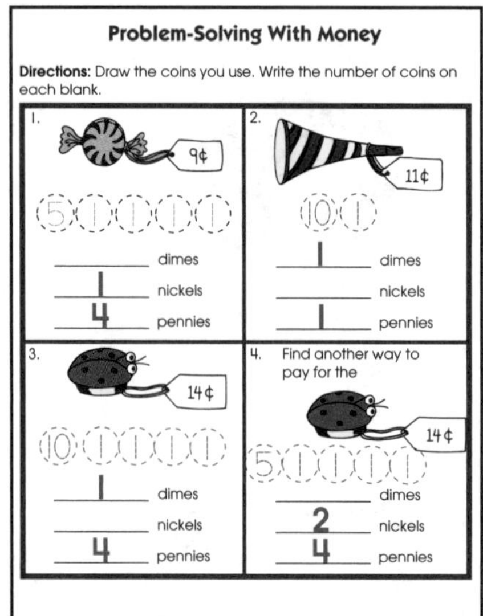

Problem-Solving With Money

Directions: Draw the coins you use. Write the number of coins on each blank.

1. 9¢ — 5, 1, 1, 1, 1 — ___ dimes, 1 nickels, 4 pennies

2. 11¢ — 10, 1 — 1 dimes, ___ nickels, 1 pennies

3. 14¢ — 10, 1, 1, 1, 1 — 1 dimes, ___ nickels, 4 pennies

4. Find another way to pay for the 14¢ — 5, 1, 1, 1, 1 — ___ dimes, 2 nickels, 4 pennies

Page 258

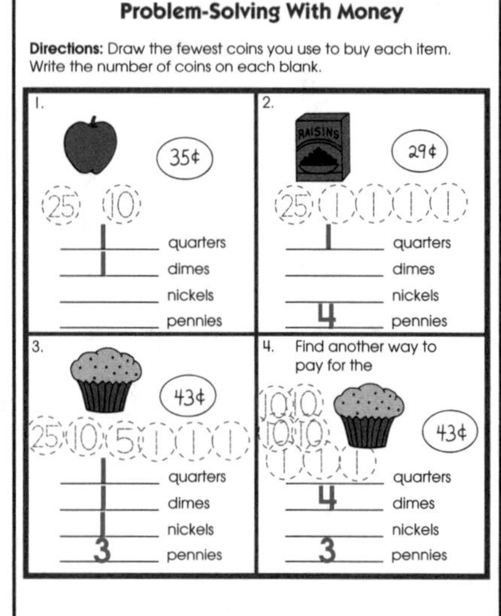

Problem-Solving With Money

Directions: Draw the fewest coins you use to buy each item. Write the number of coins on each blank.

1. 35¢ — 25, 10 — 1 quarters, 1 dimes, ___ nickels, ___ pennies

2. 29¢ — 25, 1, 1, 1, 1 — 1 quarters, ___ dimes, ___ nickels, 4 pennies

3. 43¢ — 25, 10, 5, 1, 1, 1 — 1 quarters, 1 dimes, 1 nickels, 3 pennies

4. Find another way to pay for the 43¢ — 10, 10, 10, 10, 1, 1, 1 — ___ quarters, 4 dimes, ___ nickels, 3 pennies

Page 259

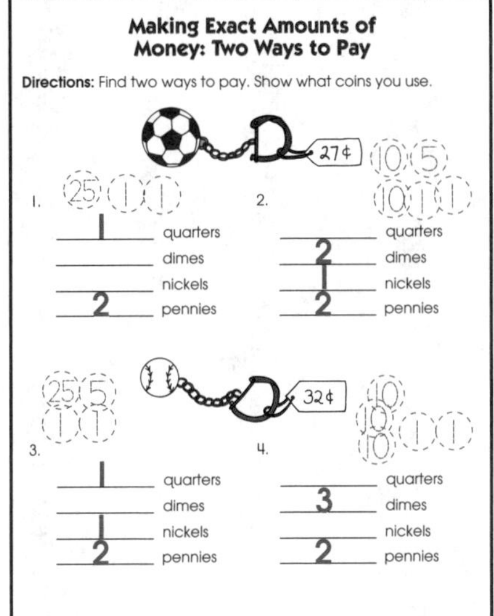

Making Exact Amounts of Money: Two Ways to Pay

Directions: Find two ways to pay. Show what coins you use.

27¢

1. 25 1 1
1 quarters
dimes
nickels
2 pennies

2. 10 5 10 1 1
quarters
2 dimes
1 nickels
2 pennies

32¢

3. 25 5 1 1
1 quarters
dimes
1 nickels
2 pennies

4. 10 10 10 1 1
quarters
3 dimes
nickels
2 pennies

Page 260

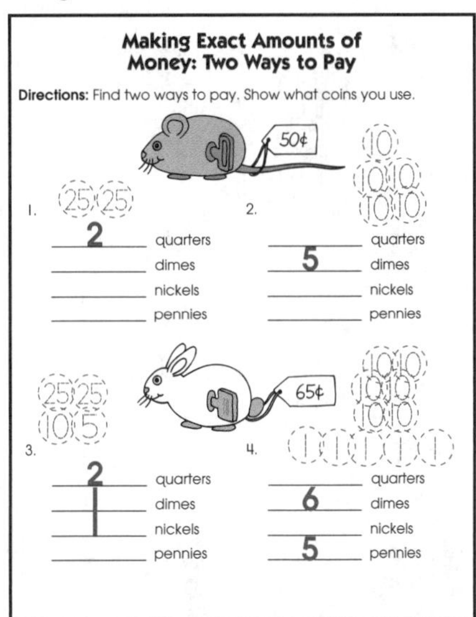

Making Exact Amounts of Money: Two Ways to Pay

Directions: Find two ways to pay. Show what coins you use.

50¢

1. 25 25
2 quarters
dimes
nickels
pennies

2. 10 10 10 10 10
quarters
5 dimes
nickels
pennies

65¢

3. 25 25 10 5
2 quarters
1 dimes
1 nickels
pennies

4. 10 10 10 10 10 10 1 1 1 1 1
quarters
6 dimes
nickels
5 pennies

Page 261

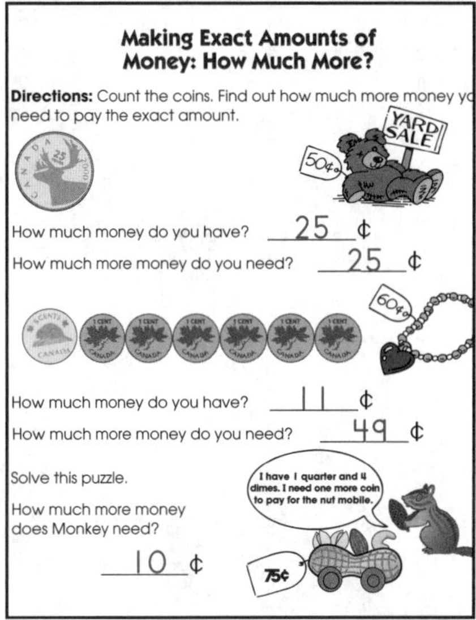

Making Exact Amounts of Money: How Much More?

Directions: Count the coins. Find out how much more money you need to pay the exact amount.

How much money do you have? 25 ¢

How much more money do you need? 25 ¢

How much money do you have? 11 ¢

How much more money do you need? 49 ¢

Solve this puzzle.

How much more money does Monkey need?

10 ¢

I have 1 quarter and 4 dimes. I need one more coin to pay for the nut mobile.
75¢

Page 262

A flip is a transformation where an image is turned over a line. The flipped image has the same angle, length, and size as the original image, but it is flipped in another direction. Example:

Draw the flip to show the other position.

Draw the flip to show the other position.

Page 263

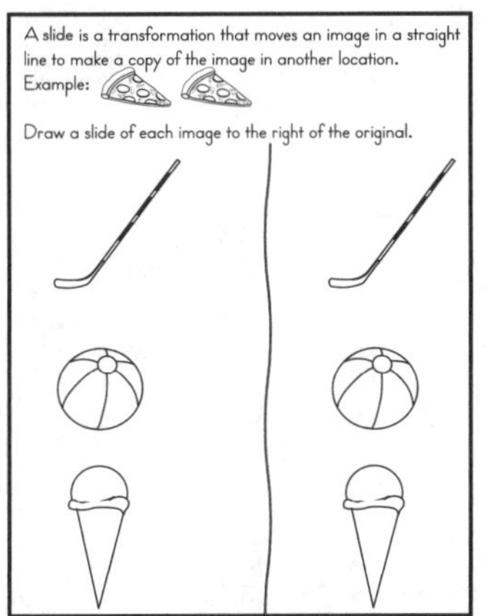

A slide is a transformation that moves an image in a straight line to make a copy of the image in another location.
Example:

Draw a slide of each image to the right of the original.

Page 264

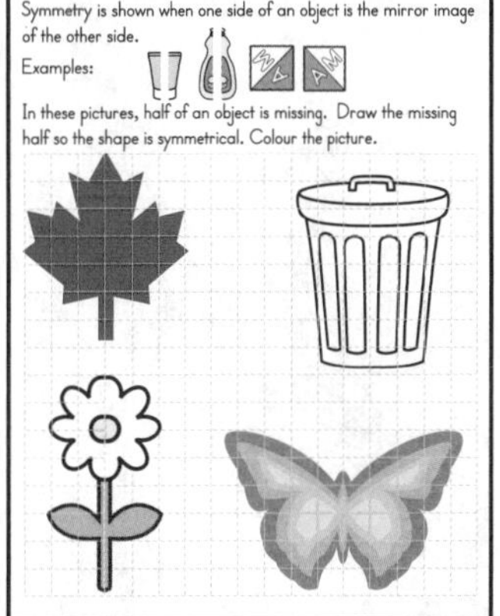

Symmetry is shown when one side of an object is the mirror image of the other side.
Examples:

In these pictures, half of an object is missing. Draw the missing half so the shape is symmetrical. Colour the picture.

Page 265

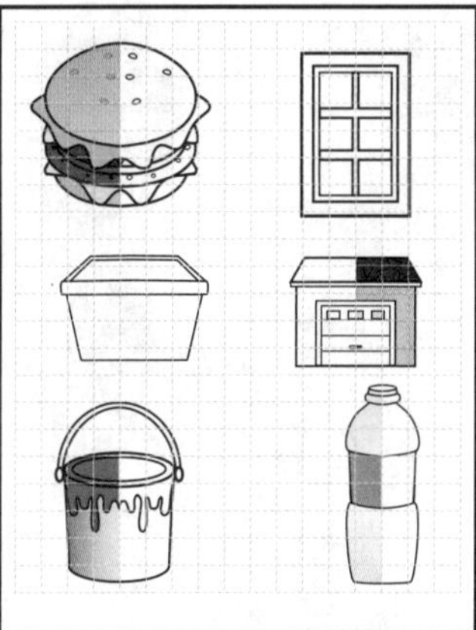

This page was left intentionally blank for cutting activity on previous page.

Suggestions for Parents

Suggestions for Parents

Number Recognition

Have your child read the numbers on the licence plates of other vehicles as you drive around town. This will not only reinforce number recognition, but letter recognition as well!

123 ABC

Safety Tip: Make sure your child knows his/her address. Have your child write his/her address (with your assistance) and keep it with him/her:

My Child
12345 Oak Street
Any City, Any Province AIA AIA

Help your child memorize his/her phone number as well. Practise writing it and dialing it on the phone.

Sequencing Numbers

Talk to your child about order and sequencing in everyday life. Make lists together.

Example: 1. Go to the bank.
2. Go to the grocery store.

Have your child make a list of the things he/she will do today.

Put a puzzle together with your child. Talk about order and the way the pieces fit together to make the picture.

Suggestions for Parents

Counting

Have your child write his/her name. Count the number of letters in his/her name and the number of time each letter appears. Have your child do the same with your name and other family members' names.

Buy or make a calendar for your child to keep in his/her room. Have your child number the calendar. Put stickers on or draw pictures to mark special days. Have your child X each day.

Play the card game "War" with your child. Each player needs an equal number of cards. Each player places a card face down and turns them over at the same time. The player with the higher number gets to keep both cards.

Shapes

Encourage your child to look at the different shapes of traffic signs and road signs. What shapes does your child see?

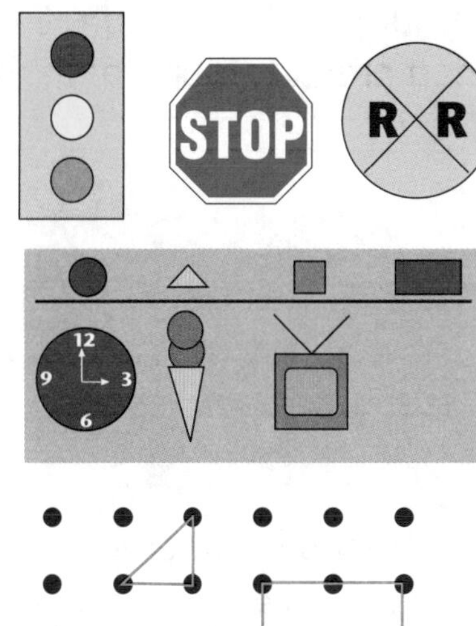

Shapes are part of our everyday lives. What shapes does your child see in his/her home, yard, etc.? List the shapes and objects. Add more as you find them.

Play the "Dot" game with your child. Create your own "dot boards" and review other geometric shapes with your child.

Purchase or make a geoboard. To make a geoboard, pound 16 two-inch nails an equal distance apart in a one-inch thick piece of wood. Pull rubber bands over the nails to create various geometric shapes. Talk with your child about the shapes he/she has created.

Colours

Fill six clear plastic glasses half full with water. Have your child experiment with mixing drops of food colouring into each cup. Talk about the colours created, and how they were created. Help your child record his/her findings: red + yellow = orange. Have your child write the number problem on paper and read it to you.

Suggestions for Parents

Fractions

Let your child help you cut pie or pizza into equal slices.

Peel an orange. Separate the sections and talk about "fractions" as parts of a whole.

Pick clovers. Talk about equal parts as you pull off the petals.

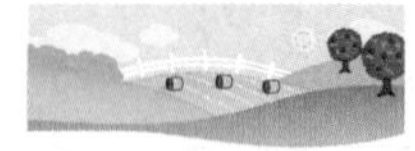

Fold a piece of paper into four equal sections. Have your child shade three sections blue and one brown. Explain that $\frac{3}{4}$ of the Earth is water and $\frac{1}{4}$ is land.

Addition

Make your own "plus" sign. Glue two toothpicks or popsicle sticks together. Then, your child can create groups of manipulatives on either side of the "plus" sign to add.

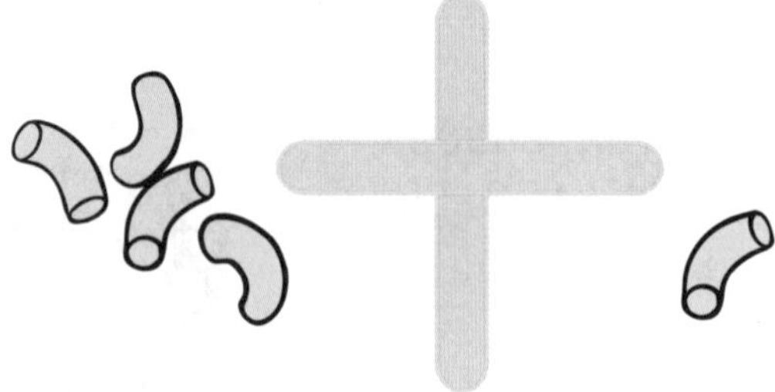

4 + 1 = 5

Use dry beans or other small manipulatives to practice counting. Have your child divide ten beans into two separate groups and combine them by adding.
For example:
Have your child write the number problem on paper and read it to you.

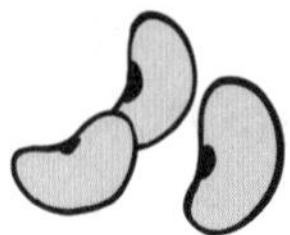

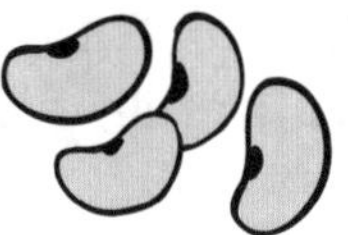

3 + 4 = 7

Look through magazines with your child. Encourage him/her to create addition problems from the pictures. For example: "One mommy plus two children equals three!"

Suggestions for Parents

Tens and Ones

Let your child practice "trading" with pennies, dimes and a dollar to reinforce the concept of ones, tens and hundreds. Roll a die and let your child take as many pennies from the "pot" as the die indicates. When he/she has ten pennies, he/she can trade them in for a dime. Continue playing and trading pennies for dimes. When your child gets ten dimes, he/she can trade them in for a dollar!

Rubber band or glue ten toothpicks together to represent "tens" and let your child practice counting by tens.

Money

Practice counting by fives with nickels and by tens with dimes.

Let your child label canned goods in your home with "prices." Your child will gain valuable practice counting and exchanging money by playing "store."

Give your child small amounts of money to purchase items when you go shopping. Encourage him/her to count his/her change after the transaction.

Encourage your child to create other combinations of money for the same amount. For example, ten cents can be made with one dime, with two nickels, with ten pennies and with one nickel and five pennies.

Measurement

Purchase a plastic or wooden ruler for your child, and let him/her measure various objects around the house. Record his/her findings and talk about length.

Skills Checklists

Do you need more practise in math? Find out. Use the checklists below. Read each sentence. Is it true for you? Put a check next to it. Then look at the unchecked sentences. These are the skills you need to review.

Keep in mind that if you are using these checklists in the middle of the school year, you may not have learned some skills yet. Talk to your teacher or a parent if you need help with a new skill.

Numeration

- ❑ I can read and print in words whole numbers to 20.
- ❑ I can count objects to 100.
- ❑ I can compare numbers.
- ❑ I can count on by 2s, 5s, 10s, and 25s to 200.
- ❑ I understand place value to the hundreds place.
- ❑ I can put numbers in order.
- ❑ I can complete number patterns.

Addition, Subtraction, and Multiplication

- ❑ I know addition and subtraction facts to 18.
- ❑ I can add and subtract two-digit numbers with regrouping.
- ❑ I can multiply one-digit numbers by 2, 3, 4, 5, and 10.
- ❑ I can write and solve number sentences.

Problem Solving

- ❑ When I do number problems, I read the directions carefully.
- ❑ When I do word problems, I read the problem carefully.
- ❑ I look for words that tell whether I must add or subtract to solve the problem.

Time, Measurement, Money, and Geometry

- ❑ I can use charts and graphs.
- ❑ I can understand a calendar.
- ❑ I can tell time on both kinds of clocks.
- ❑ I can use basic measuring tools.
- ❑ I can compare and measure lengths.
- ❑ I understand how much coins are worth.
- ❑ I know the basic shapes.
- ❑ I can match and complete shape patterns.
- ❑ I can find lines of symmetry.
- ❑ I understand basic fractions.

Getting Ready All Year

You can do better in school and on tests if you know how to study and make good use of your time. Here are some tips.

Make it easy to get your homework done. Set up a place in which to do it each day. Choose a place that is quiet. Get the things you need, such as pencils, paper, and markers. Put them in your homework place.

Homework Log and Weekly Calendar Make your own homework log. Or copy the one on pages 320–321 of this section. Write down your homework each day. Also list other things you have to do, such as sports practise or music lessons. Then you won't forget easily.

Do your homework right away. Do it soon after you get home from school. Give yourself a lot of time. Then you won't be too tired to do it later on.

Get help if you need it. If you need help, just ask. Call a friend. Or ask a family member. If they cannot help you, ask your teacher the next day.

Figure out how you learn best. Some people learn best by listening, others by looking. Some learn best by doing something with their hands or moving around. Some children like to work in groups. And some are very happy working alone.

Think about your favorite parts of school. Are you good in art, mathematics, or maybe gym? Your favorite class may be a clue to how you learn best. Try to figure it out. Then use it to study and learn better.

Practise, practise, practise! The best way to get better is by practising a lot. You may have trouble in a school subject. Do some extra work in that subject. It can give you just the boost you need.

Name ____________________

Homework Log and Weekly Schedule

	MONDAY	TUESDAY	WEDNESDAY
MATHEMATICS			
READING			
LANGUAGE ARTS			
OTHER			

Name ________________________

for the week of __________

THURSDAY	FRIDAY	SATURDAY/SUNDAY	
$\begin{array}{r}2\\+3\\\hline 5\end{array}$		MATH	MATHEMATICS
			READING
			LANGUAGE ARTS
			OTHER

Everyone in school has to take tests. This book will help you get ready for them. Ask a family member to help you.

The best way to get ready for tests is to do your best in school. You can also learn about the kinds of questions that will be on them. That is what this book is about. It will help you know what to do on the day of the test.

You will learn about the questions that will be on the test. You will get questions on which to practise. You will get hints for how to answer the questions.

In this section, there is a Practice Test and Final Test for Grade 2. These tests look like the ones you take in school. There is also a list of answers to help you check your answers.

If you practise, you will be all ready on test day.

Math Questions

On some tests, you will have to answer math questions. Some of these questions will tell a story or show pictures.

EXAMPLE

Look at the picture. Which number sentence shows how many treats there are in all?

○ 1 + 2 + 1

○ 4 + 6

○ 3 + 2 + 1

When you answer math questions on a test:

- Look at the picture. Read all the choices. Then mark your answer.
- Look for important words and numbers.
- Draw pictures or write numbers on scratch paper.
- Look for clue words like *in all, more, less, left,* and *equal.*

Testing It Out

Look at the sample question more closely.

Think: I see 3 groups of treats. The number sentence should have 3 numbers. The first sentence has 3 numbers. But it does not match the pictures. The next sentence only has 2 numbers. They are also too big. The last sentence matches the picture. There are 3 cookies, 2 lollipops, and 1 candy bar.

Name ____________________

Math Questions Practice

Directions: Fill in the circle next to the answer that matches the picture.

1

○ 39 cents

○ 40 cents

○ 50 cents

2

○ 13 books

○ 11 books

○ 14 books

Directions: Use scratch paper to work out your answer.
Then fill in the circle next to the right number.

3

$$\begin{array}{r} 26 \\ +\ 7 \\ \hline \end{array}$$

○ 33

○ 36

○ 39

4

$$\begin{array}{r} 11 \\ 21 \\ +\ 32 \\ \hline \end{array}$$

○ 34

○ 54

○ 64

Name ______________________

Using a Graph

You will have to read a graph to answer some questions.

EXAMPLE

Who read the same amount of books?

○ Barbara and Tom

○ Sue and Barbara

○ Sammy and Sue

When answering graph questions:

- Read the question carefully.
- Look for clue words such as *most, least, same, more*, and *less*.
- You don't always need to count. Try to see how much of each column or row is filled in.

Testing It Out

Now look at the sample question more closely.

Think: Barbara read 2 books and Tom only read 1. Sue read 2 books and Barbara read 2 books. That is the same number. Sammy read 3 books and Sue read 2. The answer is Sue and Barbara.

Name ________________________

Using a Graph Practice

Directions: The graph shows how many children get to school by bus, car, train, bike, and walking. Look at the graph. Then fill in the circle next to your answer.

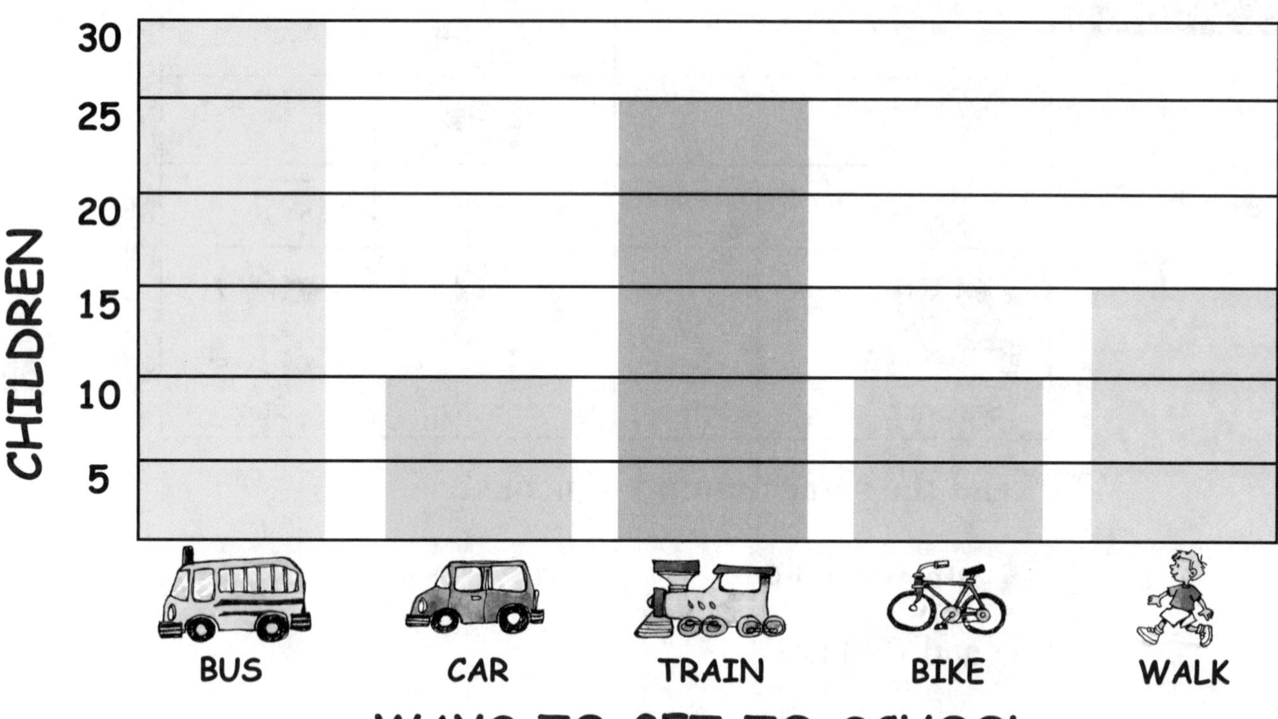

1 **How do most children get to school?**

○ Bus

○ Car

○ Train

○ Bike

○ Walk

2 **How many children walk to school?**

○ 10

○ 15

○ 20

3 **Do more children ride in cars or on the train?**

○ Car

○ Train

Name ____________________

Grade 2 Introduction to Practice Test and Final Test

The rest of this book is made up of two tests. On page 328, you will find Grade 2 Math Practice Test. On page 336, you will find Grade 2 Math Final Test. These tests will give you a chance to put the tips you have learned to work.

Here are some things to remember as you take these tests:

- Read and listen carefully to all the directions.
- Be sure you understand all the directions before you begin.
- Ask an adult questions about the directions if you do not understand them.
- Work as quickly as you can during each test.
- Using a pencil, make sure to fill in only one little answer circle for each question. Don't mark outside the circle. If you change an answer, be sure to erase your first mark completely.
- If you're not sure about an answer, you can guess.
- Use the tips you have learned whenever you can.
- It is OK to be a little nervous. You may even do better.
- When you complete all the lessons in this book, you will be on your way to test success!

Name ______________________

Mathematics Practice Test

Lesson 1 Mathematics Skills

SAMPLE A **Directions:** Choose the longest bug.

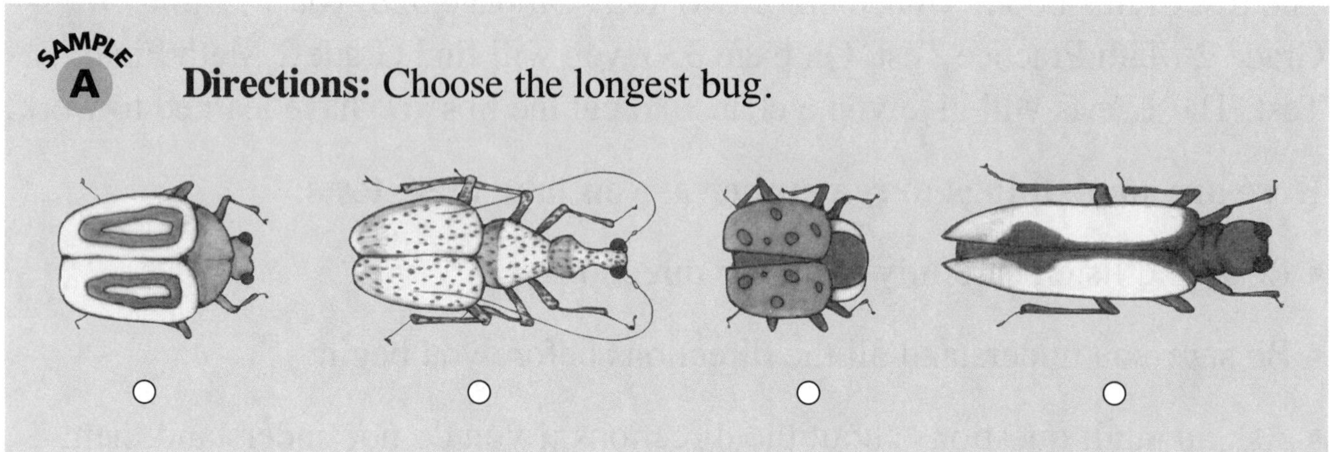

Listen carefully while you look at the problem and all the answer choices.

Listen for key words and numbers.

Mark the right answer as soon as you know which one it is. Then get ready for the next item.

GO 

Name ____________________

1 **What number is shown on the place value chart?**

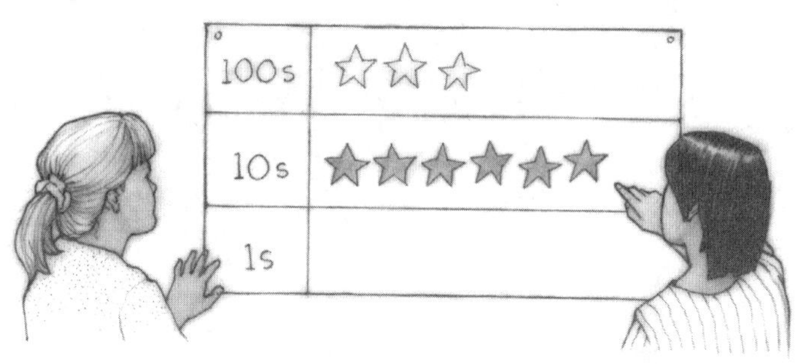

36	360	306	63
○	○	○	○

---

2 **Find the shape that is one-third shaded.**

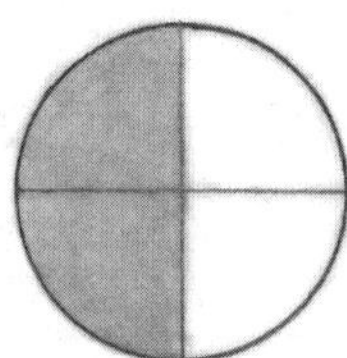
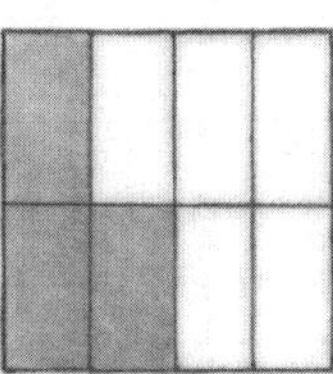
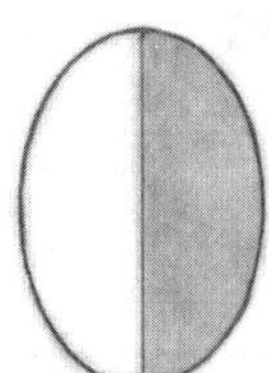
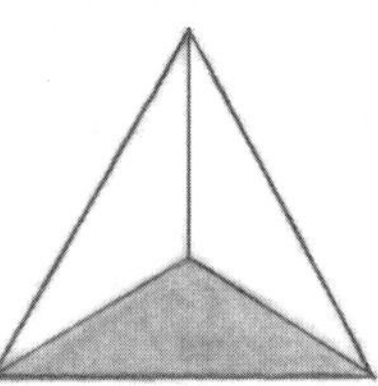

Shape 1	Shape 2	Shape 3	Shape 4
○	○	○	○

---

3 **Which number sentence can be used to show the total number of books?**

○ 4 + 2 = □

○ 4 + 4 + 4 + 4 = □

○ 2 + 2 + 2 + 2 = □

○ 4 + 4 = □

Name ____________________

4 **Which tool would students use to measure a litre of water from the stream?**

hanging scale	tape measure	measuring cup	thermometer
○	○	○	○

---

5 **Pablo has two quarters, two dimes, and three nickels. How much money does he have in all?**

85¢	65¢	60¢	70¢
○	○	○	○

GO

Name ____________________

6 **Which child is third from the lifeguard?**

Ann	Tom	Reg	Beth
○	○	○	○

7 **Which squares contain numbers that are all less than 19?**

○ 7 15 10 18 ○ 18 6 23 65

○ 91 20 32 57 ○ 12 81 17 44

8 **Which answer choice names a shape not in the circle?**

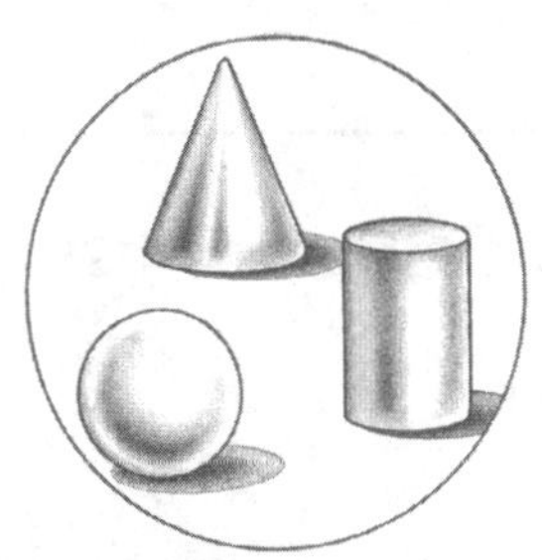

○ cone ○ box

○ can ○ ball

9 **Which number is missing from the pattern?**

6	8	9	10
○	○	○	○

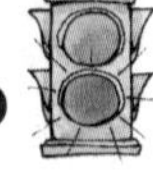
GO

Name ______________________

Directions: The students in Mr. Naldo's class are having a Math Fair. One of the games is a number wheel. The chart shows how many times the spinner landed on each number after 20 spins. Use the chart to do numbers 10 and 11.

10 **How many times did the spinner land on the number 3?**

3 ○ 5 ○ 7 ○ 12 ○

11 **Which spinner looks most like the one the students are using?**

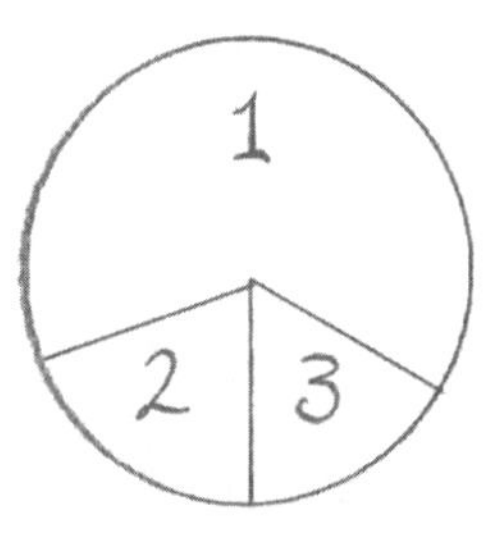

spinner 1 ○

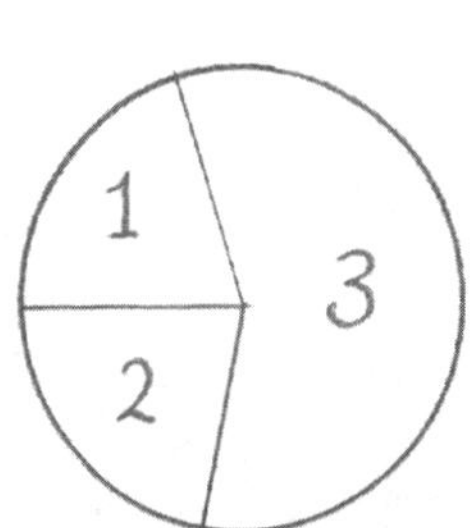

spinner 2 ○

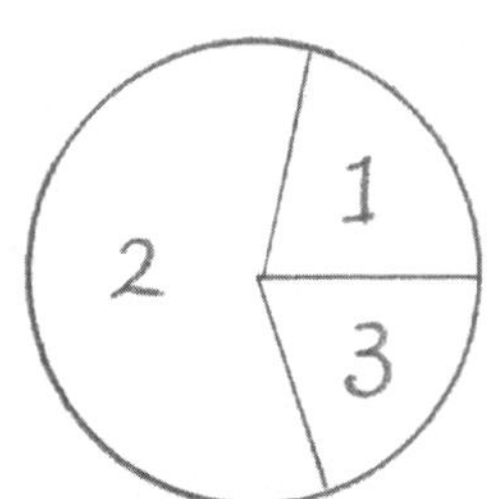

spinner 3 ○

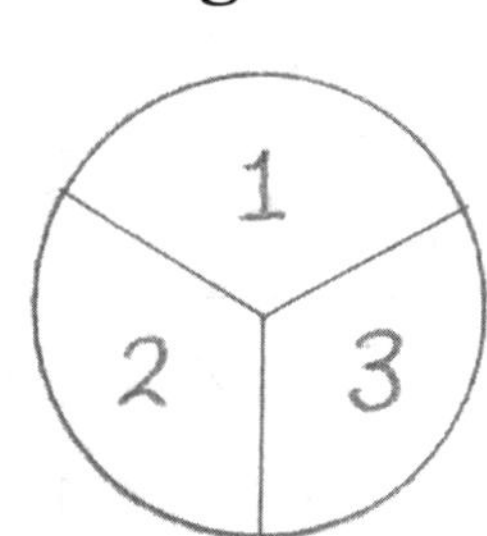

spinner 4 ○

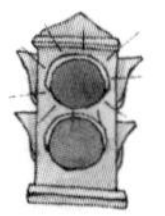

Lesson 2 Review

SAMPLE A **Directions:** A train left the station at 9:30. It arrived in Sharon Hill twenty minutes later. Which clock shows the time the train arrived?

○ ○ ○ ○

1 **Four planes are on the ground at the airport. Two more planes land. How many planes are on the ground all together?**

○ 8
○ 6
○ 7
○ 2

2 **Find the calendar that has thirty-one days.**

June

S	M	T	W	T	F	S
				1	2	3
4	5	6	7	8	9	10
11	12	13	14	15	16	17
18	19	20	21	22	23	24
25	26	27	28	29	30	

June ○

September

S	M	T	W	T	F	S
					1	2
3	4	5	6	7	8	9
10	11	12	13	14	15	16
17	18	19	20	21	22	23
24	25	26	27	28	29	30

September ○

October

S	M	T	W	T	F	S
1	2	3	4	5	6	7
8	9	10	11	12	13	14
15	16	17	18	19	20	21
22	23	24	25	26	27	28
29	30	31				

October ○

November

S	M	T	W	T	F	S
			1	2	3	4
5	6	7	8	9	10	11
12	13	14	15	16	17	18
19	20	21	22	23	24	25
26	27	28	29	30		

November ○

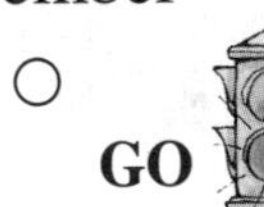

GO

Name ______________________

Sunfish

Catfish

Bluegill

Bass

Kinds of Fish

1 2 3 4 5 6 7 8

Number of Fish

GO

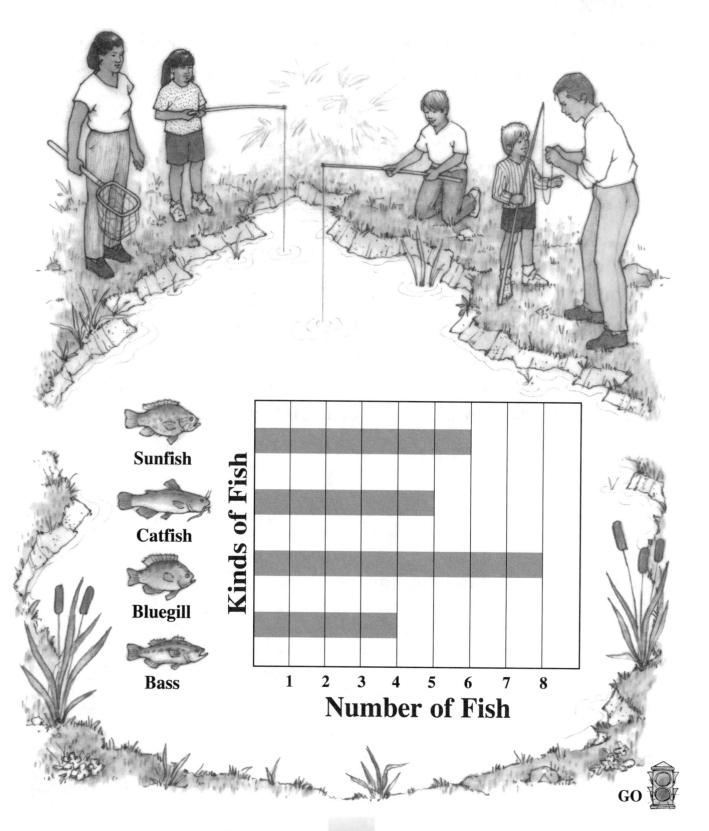

3 **Look at the graph. What kind of fish are there fewest of in the pond?**

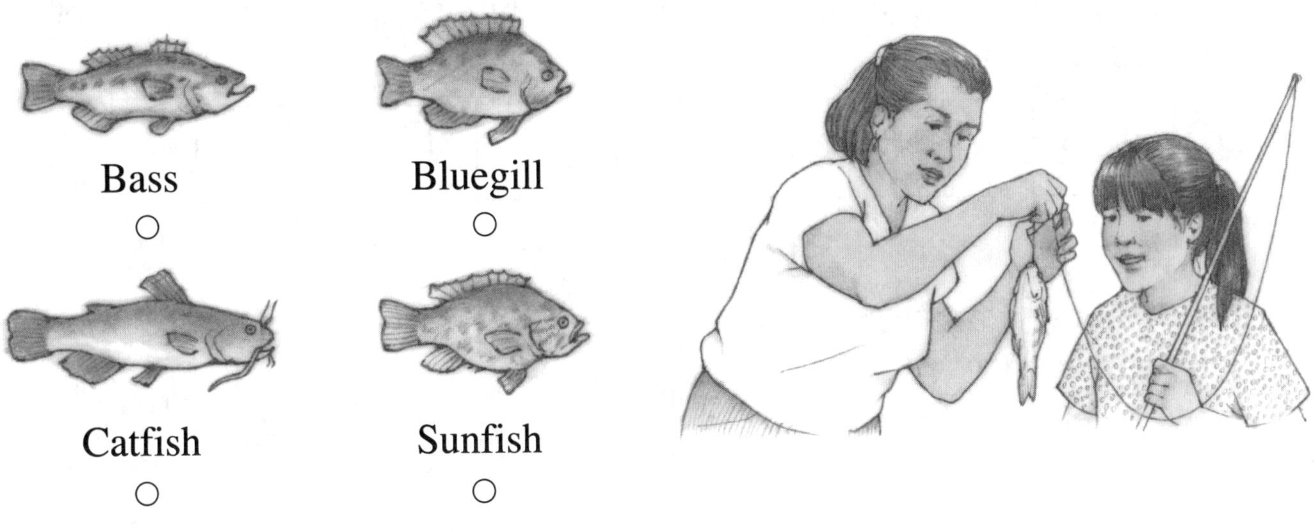

Bass ○
Bluegill ○
Catfish ○
Sunfish ○

---

4 **The average weight of the sunfish in the pond is 10 grams. How much do the sunfish in the pond weigh all together?**

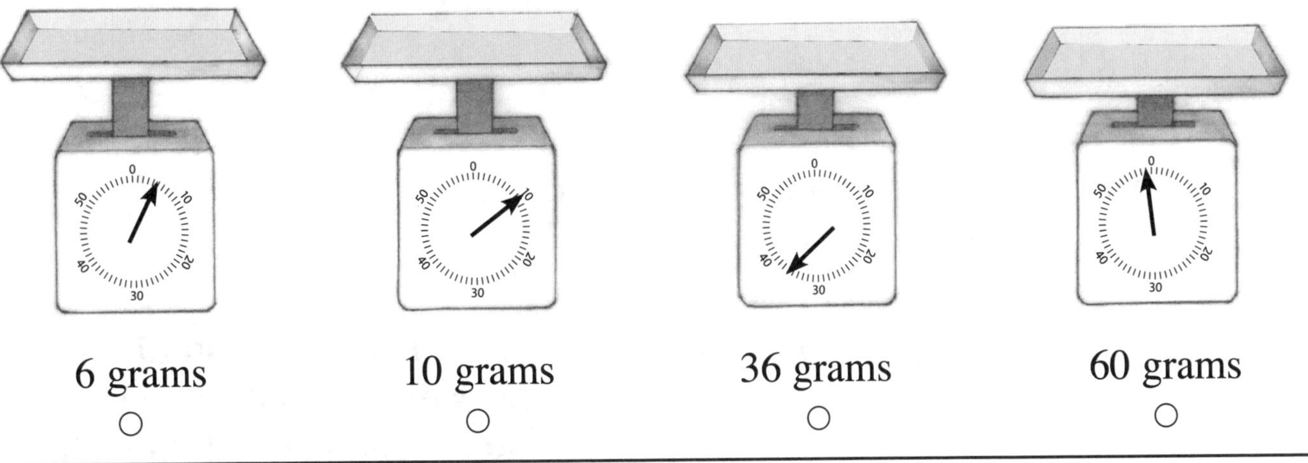

6 grams ○
10 grams ○
36 grams ○
60 grams ○

---

5 **Nadia counted eight of this kind of fish in the pond. What kind of fish did she count?**

Bass ○

Bluegill ○

Catfish ○

Sunfish ○

STOP

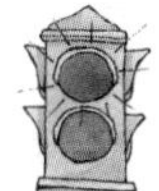

Name ____________________

Mathematics Final Test

Directions: If you are counting by ones, beginning with 42, find the empty box where 48 should be.

SAMPLE **A**

42	43	44				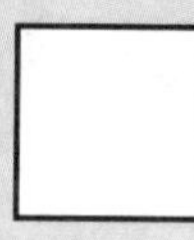
			○	○	○	○

1 **How many cm long is the ear of corn? (from stalk to silk)**

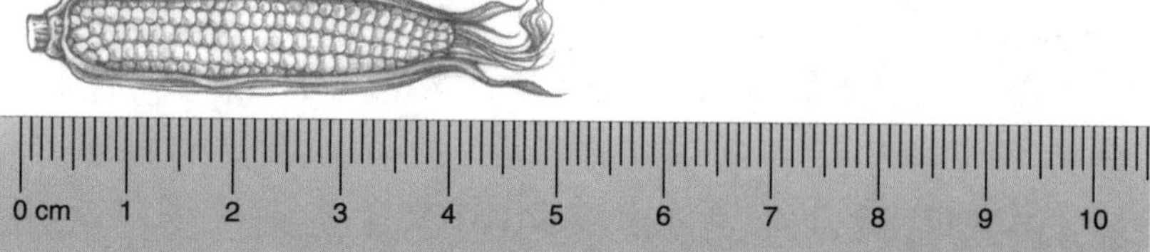

○ 10 cm ○ 9 cm ○ 7 cm ○ 5 cm

2 **Find the group of shapes that shows just one square.**

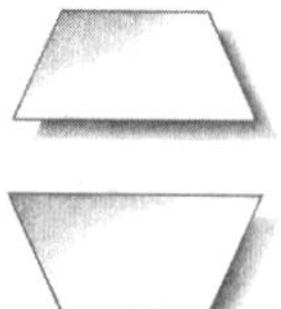

Pair 1 ○

Pair 2 ○

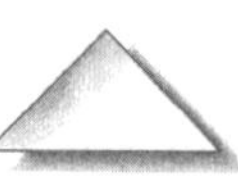

Pair 3 ○

Pair 4 ○

3

1 2 3 4 5 6 7 8 9 10

42

93 98 99

Rudy is hanging numbered keys on a board. Which numbered key should go in the box that is circled?

○ 77

○ 88

○ 89

○ 98

GO 

Name ______________________

4 **Which coin can be removed from the second group so both groups have the same amount of money?**

○

○

○

○

---

5 **Find the fraction that tells what part of the set is circles.**

○ $\frac{5}{8}$

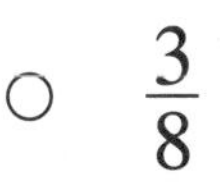

○ $\frac{3}{8}$

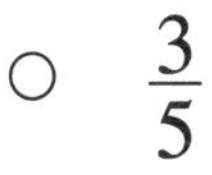

○ $\frac{3}{5}$

○ — $\frac{1}{5}$

GO

Name ____________________

6 **Which number should the missing address be?**

427	421	437	434
○	○	○	○

---

7 **Toshi made a shape on his geoboard. Paula wants to make the same shape. What will her geoboard look like?**

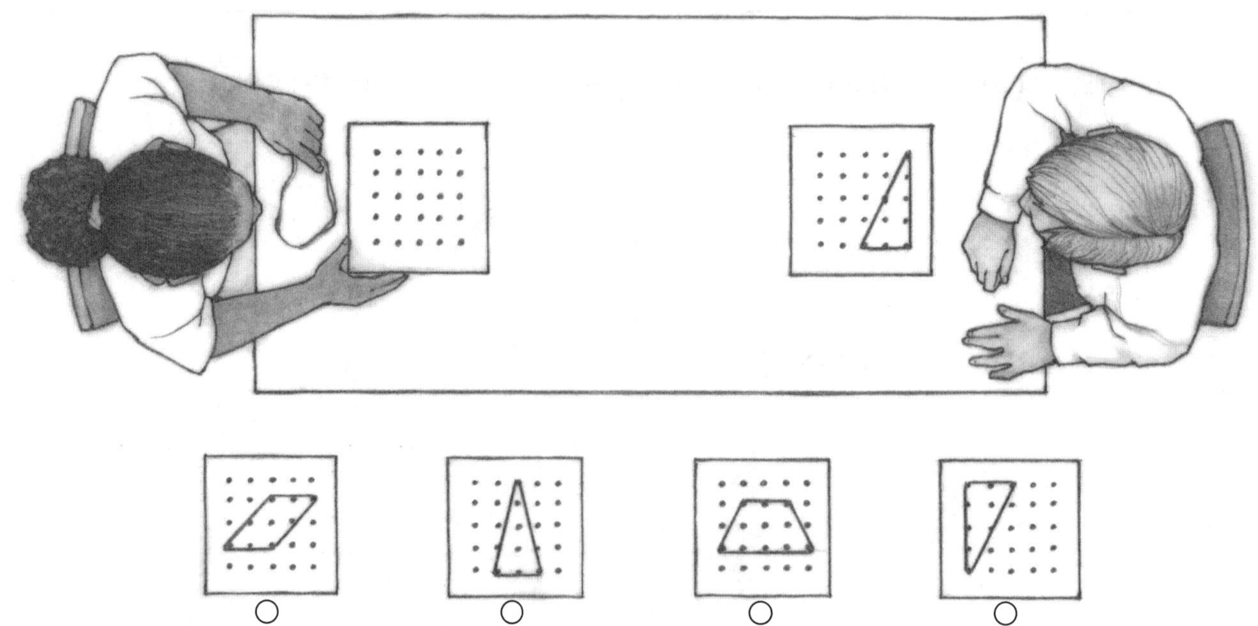

○ ○ ○ ○

GO

Name ____________________

8 **Elle saw that some t-shirts on a clothes line formed a pattern. If the pattern continued, which pair of the t-shirts would come next?**

○ ○ ○ ○

9

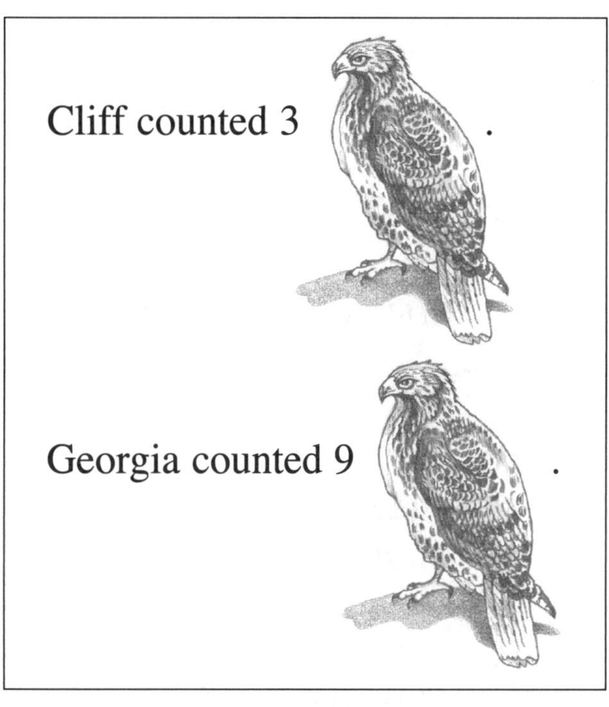

Cliff counted 3 .
Georgia counted 9 .

Cliff counted 3 hawks on bird watch day. Georgia counted 9 hawks. Which number sentence could be used to find how many hawks they counted in all?

$9 - 3 = \square$	$3 + \square = 9$	$3 + 9 = \square$	$9 - \square = 3$
○	○	○	○

STOP 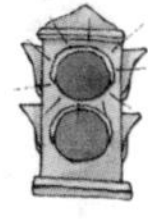

Name ______________________

Test Practice Answer Key

Page 324
1. 40 cents
2. 14 books
3. 33
4. 64

Page 326
1. bus
2. 15
3. train

Page 328
A. last picture

Page 329
1. 360
2. Shape 4
3. 2 + 2 + 2 + 2 =

Page 330
4. measuring cup
5. 85 cents

Page 331
6. Beth
7. 7 15 10 18
8. box
9. 9

Page 332
10. 12
11. spinner 2

Page 333
A. third picture
1. 6
2. October

Page 335
3. Bass
4. 60 grams
5. Bluegill

Page 336
A. last box
1. 5 cm
2. Pair 4
3. 88

Page 337
4. second picture (dime)
5. 5/8

Page 338
6. 427
7. last picture

Page 339
8. first pair
9. 3 + 9 =

Name ____________________

Grade 2 Record Your Scores

After you have completed and checked each test, record your scores below. Do not count your answers for the sample questions.

Practice Test

Mathematics Skills
Number of Questions: 11 Number Correct ____________

Review

Number of Questions: 5 Number Correct ____________

Final Test

Mathematics
Number of Questions: 9 Number Correct ____________

This page was left intentionally blank.

Tangram Activities

Directions: Have an adult carefully cut apart the seven pattern pieces on this page. Then, follow the directions on each of the tangram activity pages following.

Tangram Template

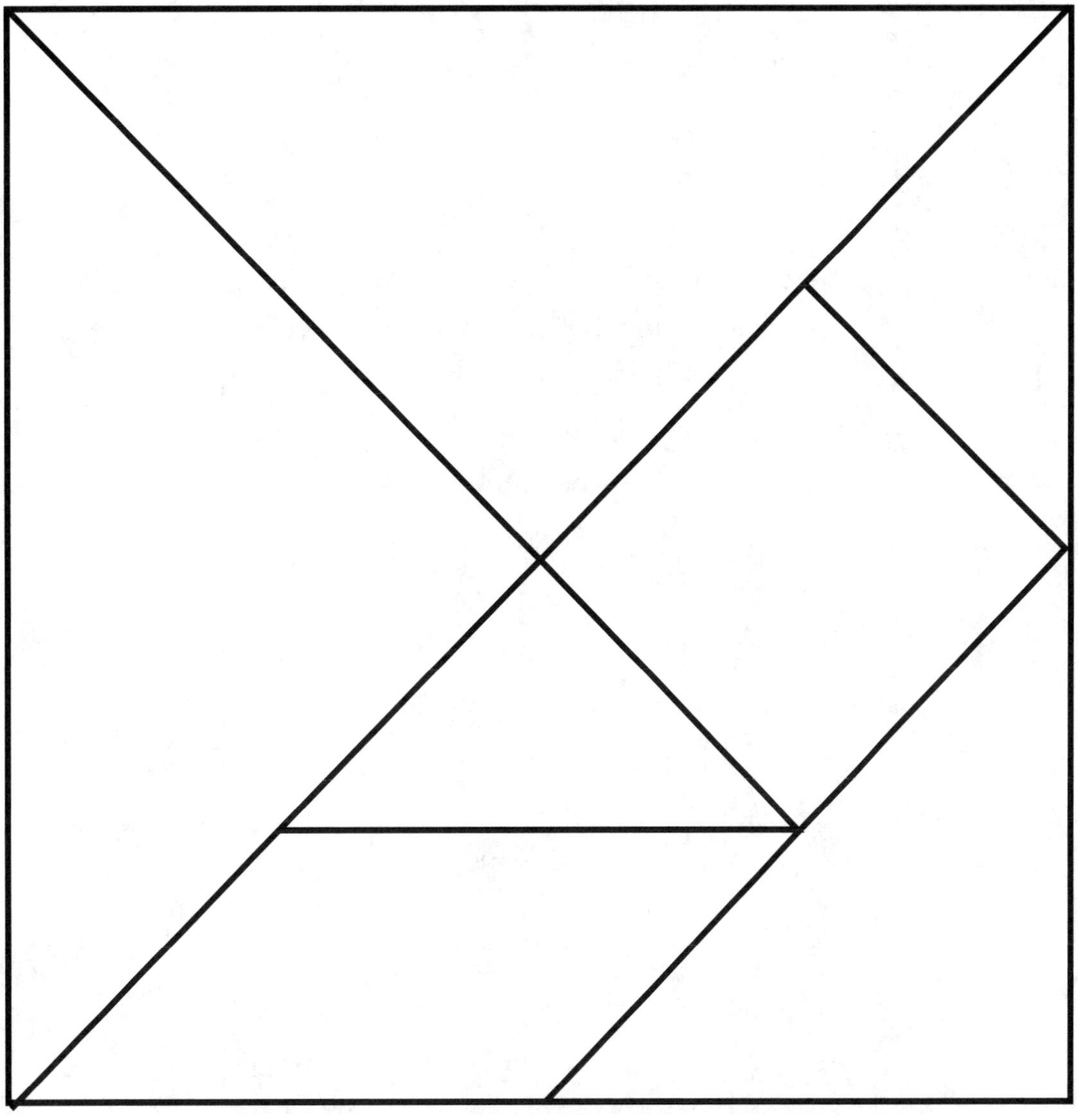

This page was left intentionally blank for cutting activity on previous page.

Name ____________________

Match the shapes using the pattern pieces from page 343.

Name ____________________

Match the shapes using the pattern pieces from page 343.

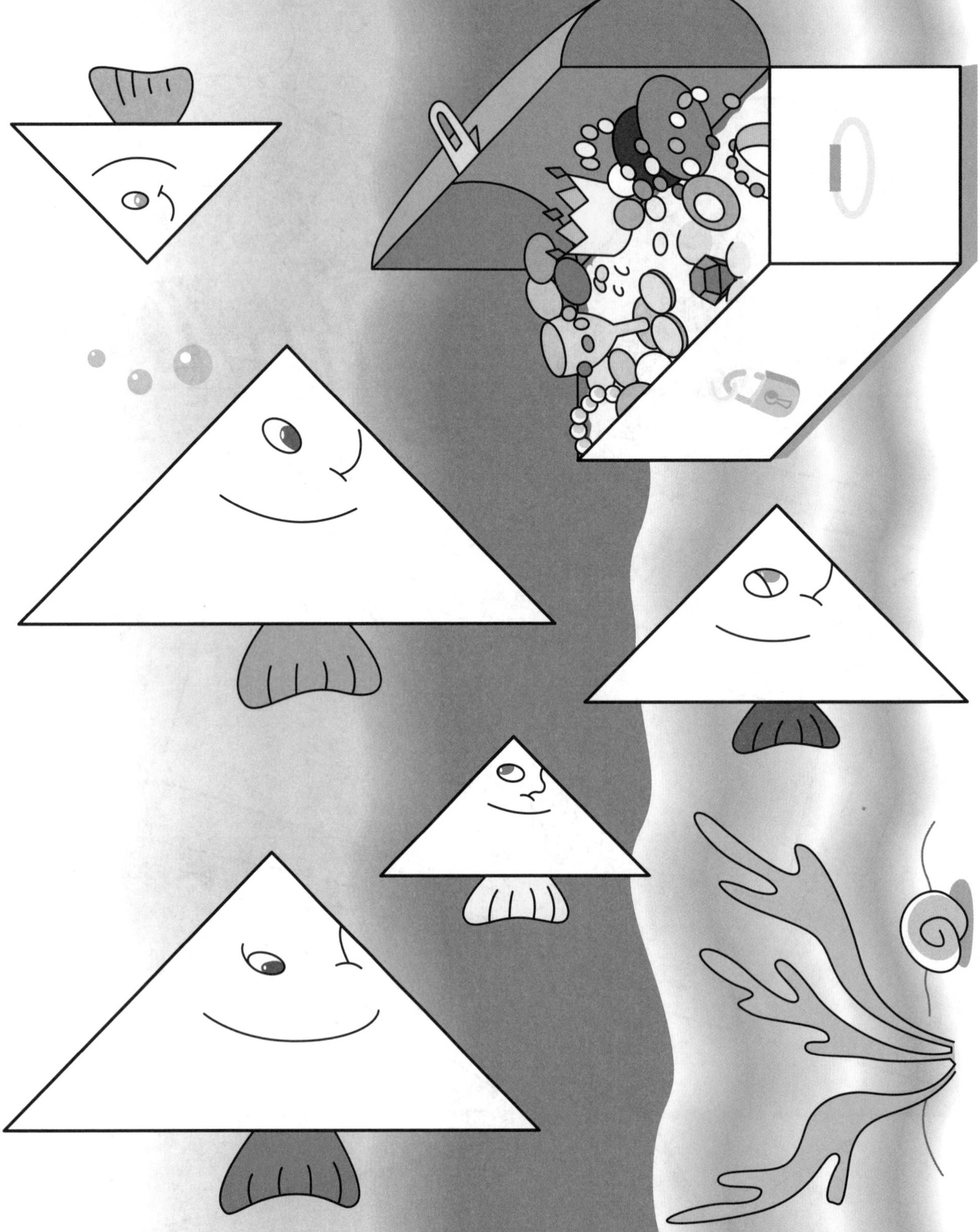

Name ____________________

Match the shapes using the pattern pieces from page 343.

Match the shapes using the pattern pieces from page 343.

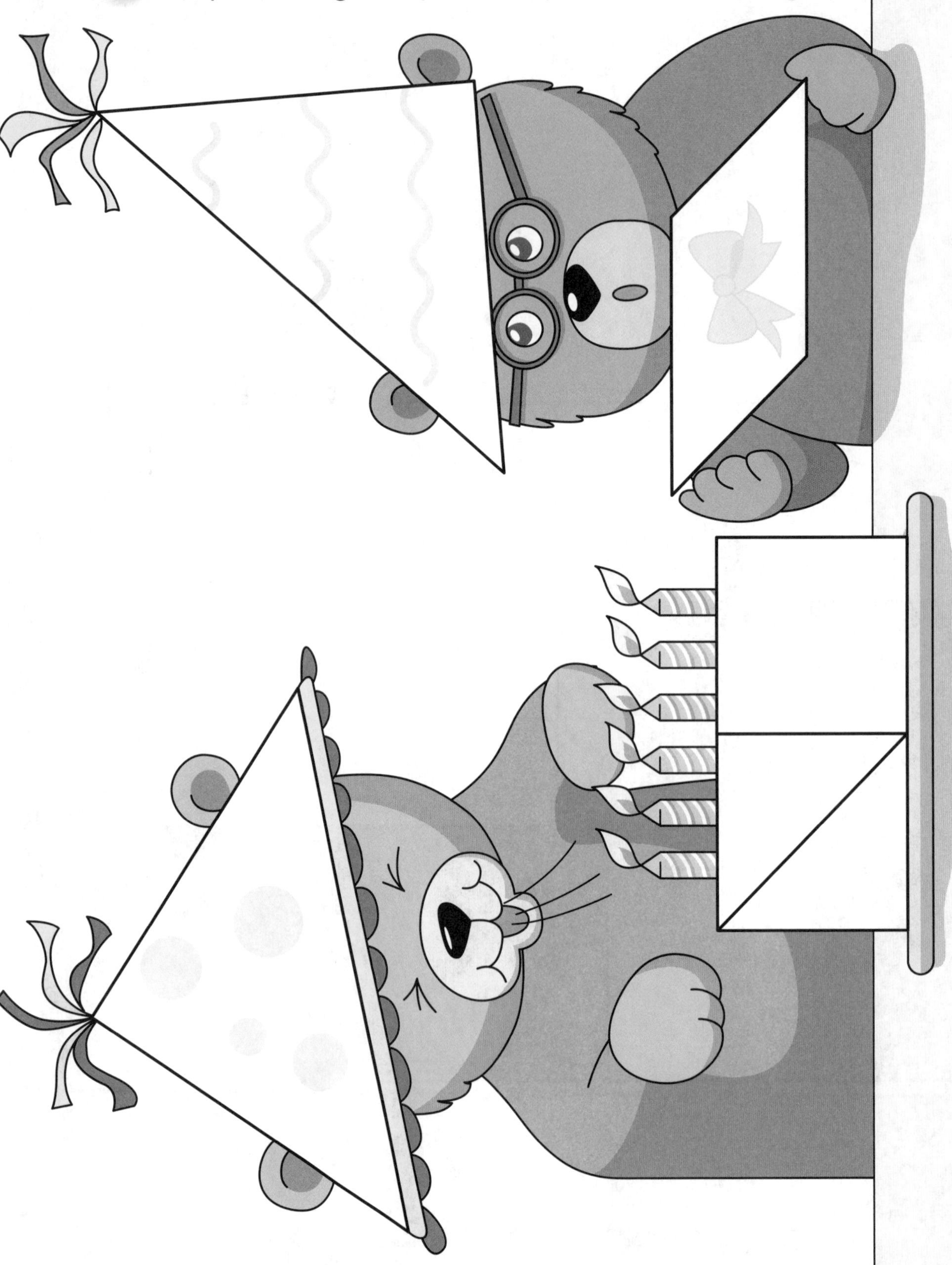

Name ____________________

Match the shapes using the pattern pieces from page 343.

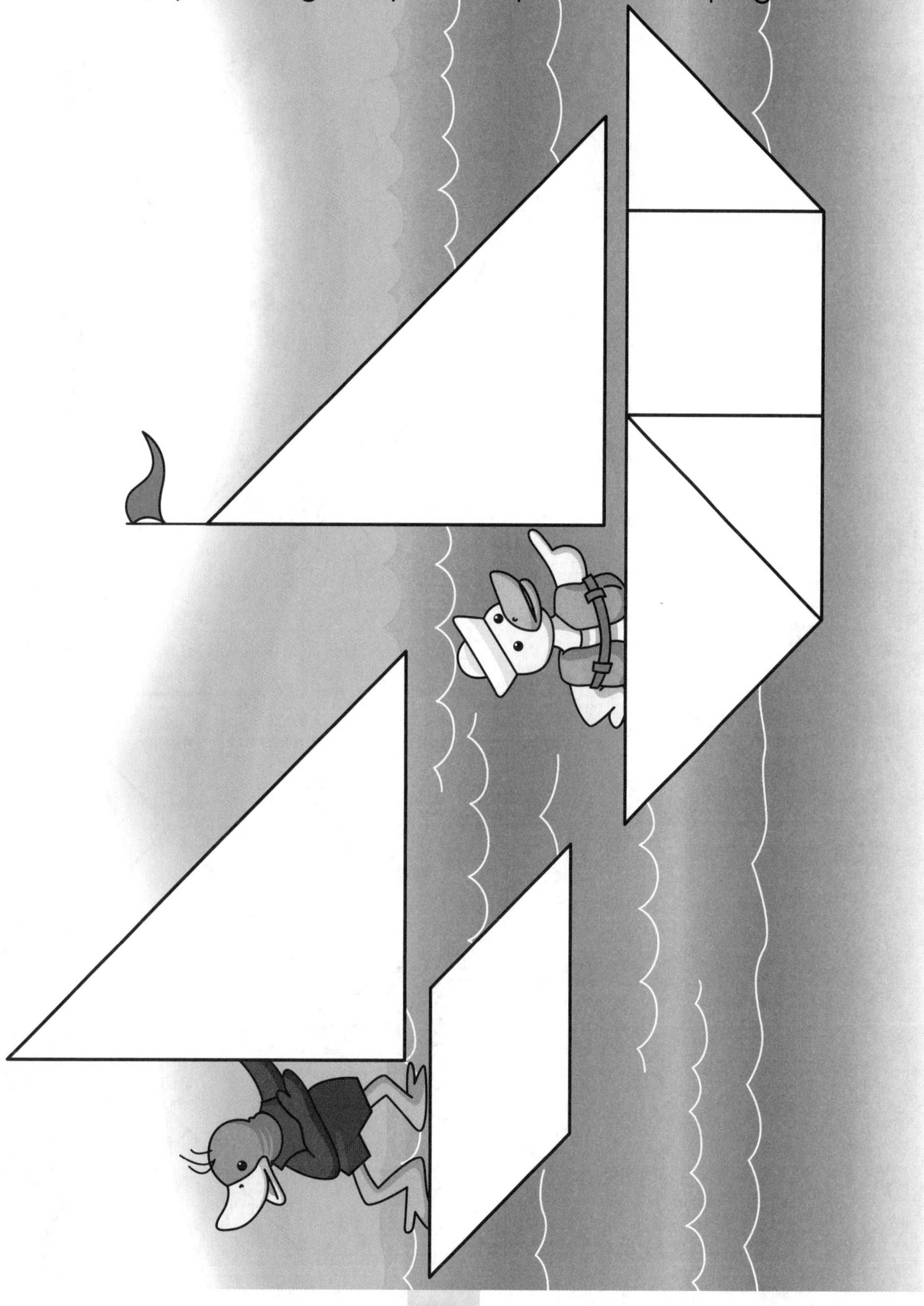

Name ____________________

Match the shapes using the pattern pieces from page 343.

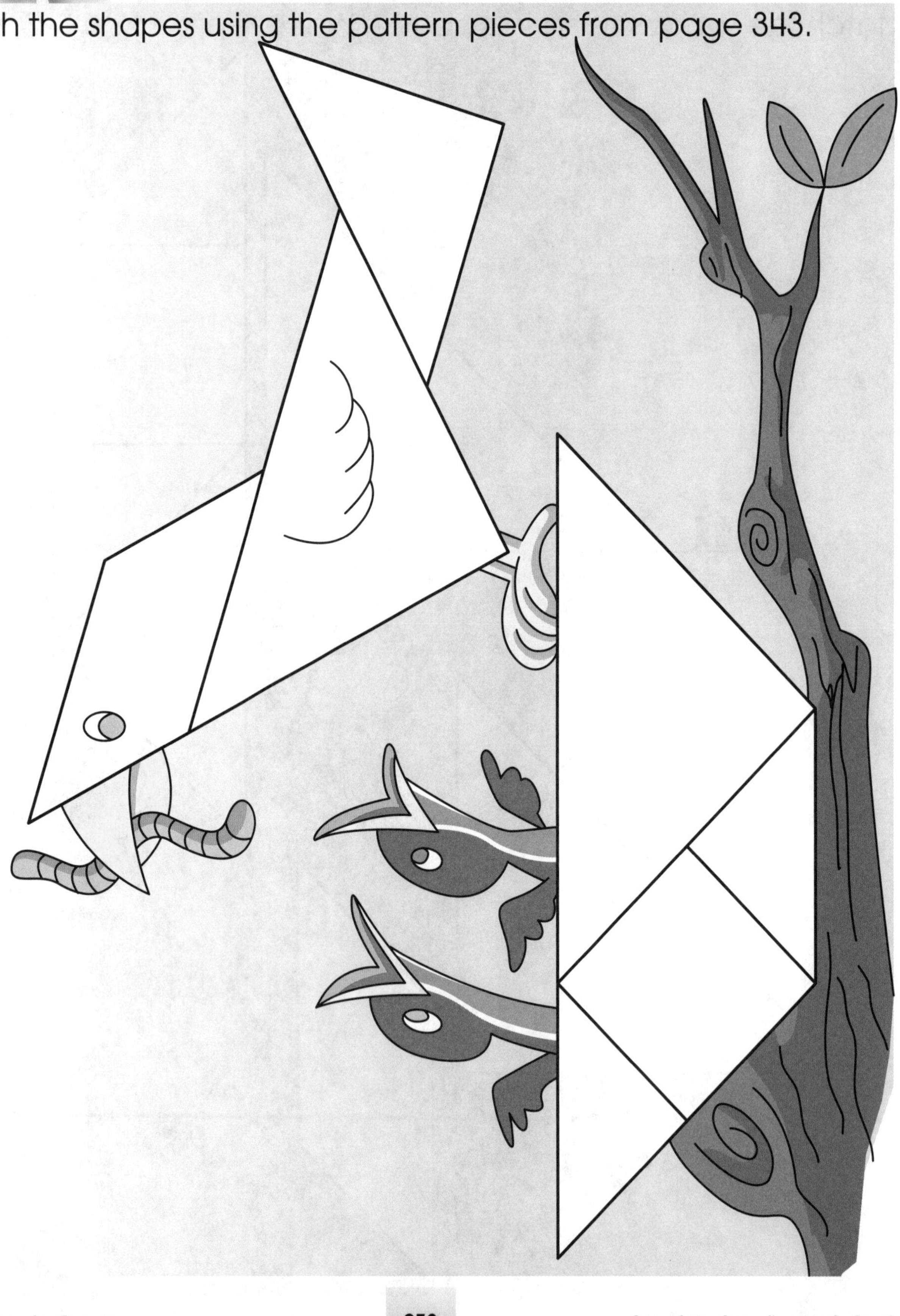

Name ____________________

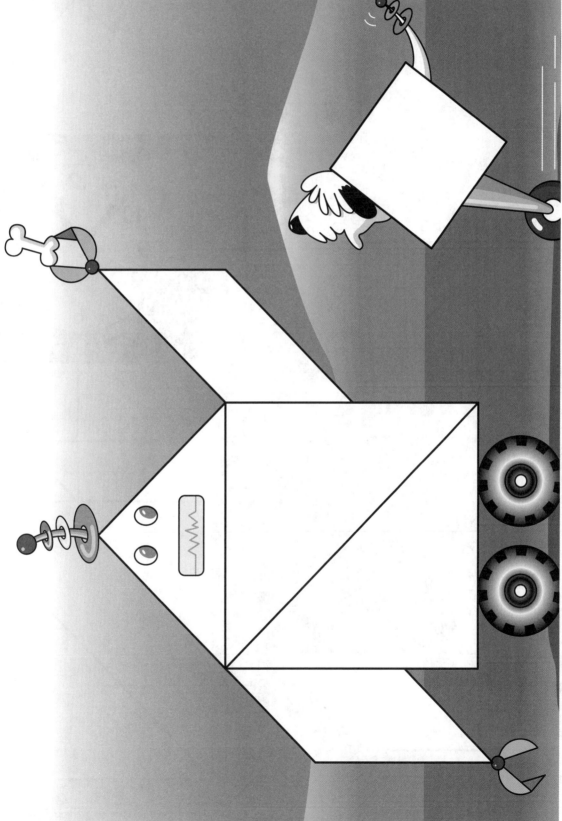

Match the shapes using the pattern pieces from page 343.

Name ____________________

Match the shapes using the pattern pieces from page 343.